SHETLAND SANCTUARY

by the same author

★

IN THE HIGH GRAMPIANS
A NATURALIST ON LINDISFARNE
I WENT A'SHEPHERDING
LUNDY: ISLE OF PUFFINS
AT THE TURN OF THE TIDE

★

published by Lindsay Drummond

SHETLAND SANCTUARY

Birds on the Isle of Noss

by

RICHARD PERRY

FABER AND FABER LIMITED
24 Russell Square
London

*First published in mcmxlviii
by Faber and Faber Limited
24 Russell Square London W.C.1
Printed in Great Britain by
Latimer Trend & Co Ltd Plymouth*
All rights reserved

In Gratitude to
my Wife
whose unselfish co-operation made an
expedition of such length possible
and
To the Memory
of
John Elder (Donnie) Jamieson
ob
16 : 4 : 48

CONTENTS

Part I
LIFE ON A SHETLAND ISLAND

Part II
A STUDY OF A BREEDING COLONY OF GREAT SKUAS
(*Stercorarius skua skua*)

Part III
A STUDY OF A BREEDING COLONY OF ARCTIC SKUAS
(*Stercorarius parasiticus*)

9

CONTENTS

Part IV

A STUDY OF A BREEDING COLONY OF GANNETS
(*Sula bassana*)

Part V

FRAGMENTARY AND INCIDENTAL STUDIES

Part VI

A SHORT HISTORY OF NOSS BIRDS

POSTSCRIPT—1948

APPENDICES

ILLUSTRATIONS

ILLUSTRATIONS

MAPS

PREFACE

My debt to my wife I have already acknowledged.

Hardly less is that which I owe to G. T. Kay, without whose indefatigable efforts on my behalf, extending over a period of three years, it is difficult to conceive how this expedition could have materialized from the dream stages. The fact that he himself was deeply interested in the objects of the expedition makes me hope that I have not imposed upon his kindness too greatly.

If my wife and he were primarily responsible for enabling the expedition to get under way at all, the fact remains that any success I may have had is entirely due to George and Laurence Sutherland, and in particular to the latter, who for five months ferried me to and fro across Noss Sound, at all hours of the day and in all atrocious weathers; and who, in affording me the hospitality of Gungstie throughout that time, did me innumerable kindnesses. Had Laurence not been Laurence—always good-humoured and unselfish, always efficient, always reliable—I do not like to think what difficulties and unpleasantnesses I might have had to overcome and to endure throughout that long stay on Noss: but, thank God, his grin was as cheery on his last day as ferryman as on the first.

Nor must I forget that to Margaret and Donnie Jamieson and Thomasina and Willie Laurensen is due the fact that at the very last moment the latter were able to provide accommodation for my wife and son on Bressay. They proved the merriest companions my wife has known for many a long day.

My thanks are also due to Norman O. M. Cameron, the laird of Noss and Bressay, and to the Royal Society for the Protection of Birds, who have preserved Noss as a Bird Sanctuary for many years, and but for whose guardianship there might very possibly have been no great skuas for me to study.

With regard to the actual account of the expedition I have to thank James Fisher, G. T. Kay, R. F. Moore, George Russell,

15

Laurence Sutherland, L. S. V. Venables and G. K. Yeates for reading portions or the whole of various drafts of the MS. Their criticisms have saved me very many errors, while their knowledge of Shetland and of Noss and its birds has been put freely at my disposal—as has also that of James Jamieson, the former R.S.P.B. Watcher on Noss, and his daughter Jessie Laurensen, whose information was largely responsible for my being able to write a concluding chapter on the history of Noss birds. I have, however, exercised the right to reject criticisms with which I was not in agreement and to express my own opinions.

I am especially grateful to Emily C. H. Milne for permission to include on pages 265–7, her poem *Kin Doo Mind?* One does not need to be acquainted with the Shetland dialect to be deeply moved by her marvellous use of the simple vernacular.

Finally, I am indebted for my illustrations to C. A. Gibson-Hill, G. T. Kay, James Monk and John Taubman, who took special photographs for me, and also to James Fisher, H. N. Southern and W. W. Nicholas for other essential photographs; and to E. S. Reid Tait for advising me on the derivations of Shetland place-names.

As usual, the Scottish Students' Library has generously supplied me with innumerable reference books, and the Editors of *Aberdeen Press and Journal, Britannia and Eve, Country Life, Country Living, Everybody's, Field, Life and Letters, National Review, Nature Lover, Scotland's Magazine, Scots Magazine, Scotsman* and *Scottish Field*, have allowed me to make use of material that has previously appeared in their journals in one form or another.

With regard to the actual text, I have set down in Part I my impressions of Shetland and her people; but no part of the British Isles is more diverse climatically, geographically and sociologically than Shetland: so the reader should bear in mind that these are predominantly the impressions of one man, in one part of Shetland, during one half of one particular year. For a better understanding of every aspect of Shetland I recommend him to a remarkable Study—Andrew C. O'Dell's *The Historical Geography of the Shetland Islands.*

RICHARD PERRY

Drumguish

1948

16

Part I

LIFE ON A SHETLAND ISLAND

I

SHETLAND HO!

I first took the road to Noss in September 1945.

The way there had been long and tortuous. Six eventful years had passed since that spring and summer when my wife and I had lived for five months in the old lighthouse-keeper's cottage on the very top of Lundy—that isle of puffins guarding the approaches to the Bristol Channel. Of our adventures there I have told in an earlier book. Suffice it to say that we undertook that expedition—if I may thus describe it—mainly in order that I might fulfil an ambition to make a long-term study of the thousands of sea-birds nesting on the island's cliffs and sidings, and more especially of razorbills, guillemots, puffins and kitti-wakes. A few naturalists had watched these species for varying periods of the breeding season, but none had devoted an entire season to their study and I was curious to find out what would be the result of such a study.

To the majority of my fellow-men the idea of any man squat-ting on a cliff day after day for twenty weeks, watching and taking down notes on the behaviour of a group of sea-birds, must, I suppose, seem an extremely odd proceeding: yet the fascination of such work is, in fact, appreciated by thousands of people in the British Isles, whose inhabitants have always been distinguished from those of the rest of Europe by their interest in one form or another of natural history. For me those five months on Lundy remained an unforgettable experience through-out the years of war that followed: while for my wife there was the memory of a unique and exciting, though gruelling, depar-ture from the more normal trend of life.

It was inevitable, therefore, that somewhere about Christmas 1944, when living in the Scottish Highlands, we should be think-ing of the possibilities of undertaking another expedition of this kind; for in the meantime we had, as I have related in other books, followed a no less unconventional life on farms in various parts of the Highlands and Islands, and also in East Anglia, not forgetting a spell as a coastguard on the Holy Island of Lindisfarne, off Northumberland. Despite the rigorous nature of these experiences our wanderlust, together with an insatiable curiosity about the lives of those who dwelt in the remoter parts of the British Isles, had been whetted rather than blunted.

As my study for this new expedition I wanted, again, a bird that nested in big communities—partly because there was a much wider range of behaviour to be observed in a community, partly because the behaviour of the individual tended to be more interesting and diverse in the stimulating environment of a social group of its fellows, partly because I should have a choice of subjects in the event of accidents befalling the particular birds or group I was watching, and certainly because I enjoyed watching social communities, whether of birds or deer, dragonflies, seals or fish. The breeding ground of the species selected must also be easily accessible and easily observable at close range, and the subject nesting preferably above ground. The ubiquitous gull conformed to these requirements, but I had not found any species of gull particularly interesting in its behaviour, and the family had already been extensively and intensively studied by both British and European naturalists—not that that was necessarily a bar to further research, for no one observer could exhaust either the possible angles of approach to his subject or the latter's variations in behaviour.

There was, however, one ideal subject, the gannet, better known in Scotland as the solan. An attempt had been made in recent years to estimate the world population of gannets, whose breeding grounds lay on the eastern and western shores of the Atlantic, and in 1939 their numbers were adjudged to be of the order of some 83,000 breeding pairs. Despite this census, however, and the fact that a book of 550 pages had been written about the gannet as far back as 1913, no naturalist had ever watched the inhabitants of a gannetry for any length of time and there were gaps in our knowledge of their breeding behaviour. The question was which gannetry should I study? There were ten big gannetries in the British Isles. Six of them—on Grassholm, the Little Skellig, the Bull Rock, St. Kilda, Sula Sgeir and Sule Stack—could be ruled out forthwith as inaccessible, having regard to the long-term study I had in mind. There remained those on Ailsa Craig off the coast of Ayrshire, the Bass Rock off Berwickshire, and Hermaness and Noss in Shetland. Various difficulties of access and suitability knocked out three of these four, leaving Noss as the only possible, though not necessarily practicable, choice. When, however, I learnt that not only the gannet, but the great skua, the arctic skua, and the black guillemot or tystie, also nested on Noss, I knew that the obstacles to my selecting this gannetry would have to be very great before I would give up the project, for very little was known of the breeding history of the two skuas, and both they and the tystie would be new to me as breeding birds.

The great skua, the famous Bonxie, nested, indeed, only in one or two parts of Orkney, outside Shetland; while the arctic skua nested sparsely in the Outer Hebrides and one or two districts of Sutherland and Caithness. The bonxie's main breeding grounds lay in Iceland, Faeroe, and possibly Greenland: the arctic skua's in the high north of both Western and Eastern hemispheres. According to the latest censuses I might expect to find on Noss any number from 1,800 to 4,000 pairs of gannets, 80 to 100 pairs of bonxies, and 25 pairs of arctic skuas.

Noss was also the breeding ground of great numbers of fulmars, guillemots, razorbills, puffins, and eider ducks, all of which I wished to watch again, not to mention such interesting small birds as the Shetland wren, the Shetland starling, the rock-pigeon, and the Faeroe snipe. Moreover Shetland, 100 miles from the Scottish mainland and only 180 miles from both Norway and Faeroe, was a land where we might expect to find the inhabitants living markedly different lives from those in other parts of the British Isles, and where we might see new methods of agriculture and fishing. It seemed hardly credible that a part of the British Isles could be almost 150 miles nearer to Iceland than to London and on approximately the same north parallel as, say, Okhotosk in Kamchatka, the Kenai Peninsula in the Gulf of Alaska, or Cape Farewell at the southern tip of Greenland;

while on studying a large-scale map I was astonished to discover that Shetland—the *Hjaltland* of the eighth-century Norse settlers—with its 3 big islands and more than 100 smaller islands, stretched more than seventy miles from north to south and had a maximum breadth of twenty-five miles; yet, so sea-worn was its coast, no part of any of the islands was farther than three miles from the sea.

From my correspondent in Shetland, G. T. Kay, I learnt that Noss, a small island on the east side, was only inhabited for a few months during the lambing season by the farming tenants, the brothers Sutherland, whose farm was on the adjacent island of Bressay; and that while accommodation could probably be found for me on Noss, it was unlikely that my wife and son could be included, so that if I wished to bring them I should have to find lodgings for them on Bressay. My original intention had been to undertake the expedition in the spring of 1945, but as it proved impossible to arrange these details by correspondence, and as in any case Shetland was still at that time a prohibited area, I decided to postpone it until the following spring, but to make a preliminary tour of inspection in the autumn of 1945.

And so it came about that on the evening of September 3rd—the hottest day in the Highlands that summer—I took ship from Aberdeen, and early the next morning caught my first glimpse of Shetland when the mists sundered, revealing the craggy Viking frame of the Fair Isle, that wonderful metropolis of migratory birds twenty-eight miles south of Shetland. Two hours later the *St. Magnus* began to pitch and roll in the tumultuous roost of tides off Sumburgh Head, the gigantic toe of Shetland proper. Then, for another couple of hours we steamed steadily up the long leg of Mainland, before there loomed out of the sea, almost directly ahead, the hazy outlines of two steep-sided, cone-shaped headlands—our first intimation that we were opening up the Sound of Bressay. The west cone was the Ward Hill of Bressay: the east cone Noss Head.

Lying roughly parallel to Mainland for six miles from north to south, but almost meeting it at its north end, the hilly island of Bressay was responsible for the magnificent harbour, some two miles long and three-quarters of a mile wide, of Shetland's port and present capital Lerwick.

Lerwick was my first surprise in Shetland, which I had pictured as a sparsely populated and very desolate land of poor crofters and fishermen. But here, to all appearances, was a flourishing seaport, with a one-and-a-half-mile frontage of piers and wharves crammed with shipping, while the grey-stone, blue-slated dwellings and offices of its six thousand inhabitants rose steeply, tier on tier, to the very crest of the hill high above the waterfront. Standing on the pier with Theo Kay, waiting for the ferry-launch which was to take me across the Sound to Bressay, I could see, framed in a dip in the high hills at the south end of that Island, the straight rick-shaped crest of Noss Head. My companion pointed out to me the road to Noss, which wound steeply uphill from the Hoversta mail-pier, almost opposite Lerwick, on to the moorland roof of Bressay.

Kay had arranged for me to stay with John and Margaret Jamieson at their summer home in Hoversta. As the Sutherlands had finished herding the lambs way back in August, and would not be visiting Noss again for some days, I had leisure in which to get acquainted with Bressay, which was more like the picture I had conjured up of Shetland.

Though its average west to east breadth was only just over two miles, I found it a formidable island on account of its moorland backbone—rising to a height of over 700 feet on the conical apex of the Ward Hill—and the boggy and peat-hag ridden nature of its hinterland, the precipitous cliffs of its south and east coasts, and the deeply penetrating voes and long straggling nesses of its north coast. Hoversta lay in a little bay, sheltered from the north and east winds and open to the southern sun that shone uninterruptedly for a week that glorious September. It might be described as the metropolis of Bressay, with its little post office and stores and, on the hill behind, the big dairy farm. Far up on the moors, as much as three miles from Hoversta, I would meet the women of Bressay trundling their hand-barrows, piled high with goods, along the roads and green tracks to and from the metropolis and the pier, where the ferry-launch landed its cargo of freight and passengers from Lerwick.

The bulk of the island's 450 inhabitants lived in communities, scattered croftings, or little townships of ten or a dozen croft-houses huddled together, with perhaps a burial ground and the ruins of a tiny chapel in their midst. The communities were strung along a four-mile stretch of the west coast from Kirka-bister in the south, through Ham to Hoversta, then north to Heogan and over the moors and lochs beyond Heogan to the townships of Beosetter and ultimately Gunnista, where the Sutherlands lived. On the east side of the moorland backbone above Hoversta, however, on the road to Noss, there were only three or four remote and lonely croftings and the partly ruined township of Old Brough, the oldest inhabited township on the island.

On the one side of the road to Noss, the twelve-acre cornfields of the dairy farm. On the other side the sparsely placed croft-houses, some of undressed grey stone and neatly straw-thatched roofs weighted with stones roped up parallel with the eaves: others whitewashed, with tarred-felt roofing, the commonest type in Shetland. Down the steep of the hill from each croft-house stretched long narrow strips, divided by open drains, of cultivated or once cultivated land, where men and women were working at hay or corn, much as they had done for generations —for not only was the scythe being used for the corn but here and there I saw, for the first time in Britain, a woman reaping with a sickle, laying at each cut five handfuls of oat-stalks. The scene was a pleasing one of communal activity. Some crofters were binding and stooking their corn. Others were still busy with their hay, putting up little rectangular ricks with beauti-fully steepled tops, which they covered with old fishing-nets and weighted down with stones, against the Shetland 'bree'. Everywhere I met ponies leading home little loads of hay or peats in tiny carts, all painted red and blue.

To my great disappointment no pure-bred Shetland ponies, or Shelties, were to be found on Bressay—or, for that matter, many anywhere in Shetland, though there were one or two stud farms in Unst, the most northerly island. Though some of the ponies on Bressay were very small, none approached the diminutive stature of the true Sheltie, being crossed for working purposes with Highland ponies or garrons. Most were of the traditionally favoured black-dun colour and of immense girth, with flowing

manes and tails: but here and there I came across bay or golden
ponies or skewbald ones—black with white belts, or brown and
white, or golden and cream. Despite their out-crossing, however,
they retained the dominant characteristics of the sheltie—inde-
pendence and impatience. Wary little beasts, they would not
stand to the stranger, and their impatience when in harness was
very marked.

Day after day the sun shone down from dawn to dusk on
the lone-placed croftings of this spacious north land, ripening the
quivering plots of slender-stalked greyish-green Shetland oats to
pale gold. And there was no wind. The reek of peat-smoke
hung over all the island. Day and night the plaintive maaing of
lambs, awaiting shipment in the *St. Magnus* to Aberdeen, was
carried on the light airs across the Sound from Lerwick and, four
times in every hour, the mellow chimes of the townhall clock
high on the hill above the waterfront.

After sunset a galaxy of lights shone out from Lerwick and
were reflected in the black pool of the Sound along the waterfront in shimmering yellow, green and red streaks. Southwards,
a brilliant incandescent glare from the Kirkabister lighthouse
came and went upon the sea. To the north, the hidden sun was
betrayed by a long bar of luminous green above the hills of Mainland. Peace and quiet on earth. The friendliness of lights in the
sea's calm night. Lamps twinkling from lonely croft-houses on
the steep hill-side. The sound of a fiddle. These were the things
that Bressay seamen would remember in night-watches on the
Seven Seas, drawing them back to Shetland. I, too, should
remember them on the hills of Scotland and in the green lanes of
England, and I was tempted to settle for a while in these islands
of the sea and take a crofting holiday from my work as naturalist
and writer.

II

THE GRANDEUR OF NOSS

Naturally, my first step out of Hoversta took me along the road to Noss. Once on top of the hill and past the gate and grating which prevented the stock from straying off the Scattald—that portion of moor and hill on which the crofters had the rights of grazing their sheep—the road bore away eastwards towards the straight crest of Noss Head, which just topped a fold in the high ground between the Hill of the Ander on the one hand and the eastern escarpment of the Ward Hill on the other. Sweeping down through desolate moors, the long switchback road, passing between the reedless lochs of Setter and Brough, climbed again to the dip between the Ander and the Ward, past Old Brough with its huddle of ancient croft-houses clustered about the trackway that wound in and out of them.

Then, when I had breasted the hill above Brough and rounded the small lochan of Ullins Water, there rose up before me, startlingly close, the Island of Noss—the Nose or Rocky Point—in shape a high-crowned sombrero with a double brim abutting on to the rocky shore of a narrow Sound immediately below me. From its green voe-bitten brim, half a mile in breadth, the island mounted steeply seawards in what seemed a single vast concave sweep to its narrowing hay-rick crown, which much resembled the 'barn' of Cairn Toul in the Cairngorm Hills.

White solans plunged into the crystal waters of the Sound and down into the chalk-green and milk-blue deeps above the white sand. Droves of periscopic-necked shags and cormorants fished in the dark purple shadows of the reefs. Strings of shrilly piping tysties and families of eider duck swam out from little clefts, or geos, in the jagged inclined rocks edging the Sound. Flocks of curlew and ringed plover, and turnstones, redshanks and oyster-catchers rose from the white beaches of the Noss voes. Little

26

flights of rock-pigeons clipped across the narrow waters from Bressay to Noss. Rock-pipits and twites flitted about the rocky brow-edge.

Noss made more instant appeal to me than any other island I had seen. On the Bressay shore green braes, shaved like lawns by white-faced Cheviot sheep, swept down to the Sound from the almost sheer siding of the 450-foot Ander—aptly named the Penthouse Hill. Laid out on the dyke-strewn braes were the roofless grey ruins of the deserted croft-houses of Norther House and Noss-Sound. And on the Noss shore stood waiting, as yet unapproachable, on its long green ness the grey and yellow-lichened, blue-slated homestead of Gungstie—the *Stadir*, or dwelling, of Gunnar or perhaps Gunnhildar. Rising behind it, a gentle hill of green pasture swept back to a wide flat of moor-land and the ultimate steep of Noss Head.

Lying in the heather on the Ander, with wheatears and dark-plumaged Shetland wrens stuttering from the dyke at my feet, I determined then and there that Gungstie was the home—or one home!—for which I had been searching this past twelve years. Its spacious surroundings, its aspect of untrammelled grandeur, of peace and tranquillity, of standing at the threshold of the hourly changing pageant of Nature, was supreme—this grey storm-fast home which, for four centuries and more, had stood firm against the Shetland 'bree' and against the great seas that rolled through the Sound and sometimes swept over the Ness itself, some twelve feet above. I saw this sturdy home as a retreat, not only in summer, but at any season when I felt in need of solitude—not from my family, for that was loneliness, but from the daily distractions of twentieth-century civilization. I saw the book-lined study within and the great fire of driftwood. Only in such an environment could be achieved that calmness of mind and detachment from contemporary human affairs essential to the construction of a work that got down to the bedrock of life: cutting away from those hypocritical artificialities inseparable from any form of urban or industrial civilization, and from the desperate conditions of modern society in which absolute truth was unknown.

And then, when I was tired of writing, and my immediate

inspiration was spent I had only to step to my door to be in immediate contact with the sea, stretching away to a landless horizon from the perpendicular cliffs of the Bard Head of Bressay in the south-west. In the Sound, at my very door, going about their daily business would be those birds and beasts appropriate to the season. What a contrast to the desolate moors and hills of the Highlands, which were almost devoid of all forms of life except deer, sheep and rabbits for eight months in the twelve! Here, surely, in this strong homestead of Gungstie could be found that perfect serenity difficult to acquire in the everyday world.

Such were my immediate reactions to a first vision of Noss, and I wrote home in such glowing terms that my wife took alarm and wired: *Am not going to live on Noss!*

That the island had been inhabited from the earliest times was evident. Below me, on the edge of the Sound immediately opposite Gungstie, was a grassy tumulus, once a Pictish broch, and there was another a little farther along the Sound. These circular defence towers, with staircases in their massive walls, controlled the seaways approaches to all the coasts of Shetland and were ascribed to the Celtic period between, say, 500 B.C. and A.D. 600. Old Brough, and many other Burghs and Broughs, bore witness to the number of these stations or *brochs* that formerly existed in Shetland. It was possible that these grass-covered mounds on the shores of the Sound might be ascribed to the yet earlier Bronze Age for, when one was excavated at the beginning of the nineteenth century, cavities (twelve feet long, six feet broad and five feet deep) were found in it more suggestive of a burial site than a broch.

Historians, in tracing the voyages of St. Brendan, an Irish priest of the sixth century, had noted that on one voyage he arrived at *an uninhabited rock frequented by myriads of sea-fowl . . . and filled with birds of snow-white plumage*, and had concluded that this rock was Noss. There did not seem to me, however, to be any sound reasons, either topographical or ornithological, for drawing such a conclusion. On the other hand, there was definite evidence of Irish priestly immigration to Noss, for those green pastures above the homestead of Gungstie lay on the Hill of Papilgeo, which was *papilsgjo*, the Priest's (Irish) geo or creek; while in the deserted township and Irish priestly centre of Cullingsburgh, on the north side of the Ander on Bressay, an inscribed Ogham Stone had been found which commemorated the daughter and grandson of Naddodd, a Viking of Faeroe, who discovered Iceland in 861. Noss was also mentioned in Snorre's *Edda* and in a deed of partition after Hans Sigurdssøn in 1490, while Scatt Records located five Norse settlements on the coastal green in the south-west portion of the island.

The Noup, the great sea-cliff of Noss Head, was known to mariners, perhaps Dutch, as Hang-lip at least as early as the beginning of the sixteenth century: just as the Ward Hill of Bressay was a *Wart*, a hill on which bonfires had been lit as beacon-marks for sailors, or as warning of invasion, since Pictish days. By the end of the sixteenth century the Hollanders had as many as two thousand herring-busses lying at one time in Bressay Sound (which they knew as Grotta Bay), so that a man might almost walk across their decks from Bressay to Lerwick. A tombstone in the Cullingsburgh burial ground records the death in 1636 of a commander in the Dutch East India Fleet.

The first detailed reference to Noss, however, did not occur until 1633, when Robert Montieth described the island as being grass for the most part, 'stored with Bestial', though with considerable cornland. He made no mention of its inhabitants but referred to a little church or chapel, fourteen feet in length, built by 'shipwrakt' persons at some unknown date.

In the summer of 1700 the Rev. John Brand found one family living on the island, but in 1733 two or three families were cultivating sixty marks of arable land, which might have been thirty or sixty acres, and in 1774 the island was reported as being well-covered with verdure and well-cultivated, the corn being very forward. By this date only the walls of the Votive Chapel in front of Gungstie were standing, though the burial ground was in use until the middle of the next century.

For the first thirty years or more of the nineteenth century the tenant of the 'neat farmhouse' was a farmer named Copland, whose son, born in Gungstie, was to become the 'most learned of modern physicians and author of a dictionary of medicine'.

Very fertile, with moss on the low ground and long grass on the sides and hill affording fine pasturage for milch-cows, Noss at this time produced the best milk and butter in Shetland, though a superabundance of rabbits worked havoc among the corn. With the rent of the island standing at £40 per annum, including all rights in the fishing—an exceptional clause in a Shetland lease—and with the wages of farm servants only £5 a year, old Copland made a lot of money during his tenancy of Noss and his daughter married a whaling-skipper. By 1853, however, the rent had been raised to £70 per annum.

During the eighteenth and nineteenth centuries Shetland crofters were forced by the landlords, as a condition of tenure, to deliver up large quantities of fish. To obtain these they had to row thirty or forty miles out to the 'banks' in their *sixerns*— six-oared boats with 18-foot keels—twice a week during the season May to August. In order to shorten the rowing distance stone bothies were set up at strategic places, often otherwise un-inhabited, in which these 'haaf' fishers lived during the summer. During Copland's tenancy one such haaf-station ('haaf' being old Norse for *haf*, ocean) was located on Noss—with another on the Bressay shore—to which fishermen from Quarf and other Mainland parishes resorted, paying a few shillings rent for their 'huts'.

The year 1839 might be said to inaugurate the modern history of Noss. In that year, exactly one hundred years before the Sutherlands took over the tenancy of the island, their great-grandmother left her home at Norther House on the Bressay side of the Sound. Noss had been a cattle farm in her day, with twenty-four inhabitants, and she herself had worked on the farm, on which four pairs of oxen were employed for ploughing—as they still are in one or two of the remoter parts of Shetland, such as the Fair Isle. According to James Catton, however, who was a Wesleyan missionary in Shetland for three years, Gungstie was the only house still standing on the island in 1838. Yet in 1861, when the island was entirely laid down to pasture, yielding rich crops of grass, and Gungstie was occupied by a shepherd, there were fourteen inhabitants; and in 1870, when the Marquis of Londonderry took over Noss as a stud farm for Shetland ponies, which he exported to his Seaham coal-pits, there were again twenty-four inhabitants. By keeping the stallions on Noss and the mares in Maryfield Farm on Bressay the Marquis was able to breed the Sheltie along scientific lines for the first time: his ideal pony being between thirty-four and forty-two inches in stature with 'as much weight as possible and as near to the ground as it can be got'.

Though this venture continued until 1899 the island's population had declined to its eighteenth-century level of a single family by 1881, and at this level it remained for the next fifty-eight years. In 1904, James Jamieson took up what was to be a thirty-six-year residence in Gungstie as shepherd to the Maryfield flock of black-faced sheep, and he and his daughters were probably the first inhabitants of Noss to take an intelligent interest in the island's birds. Finally, in 1939, the black-faced flock was sold and the Sutherlands put in 450 Shetland sheep. As they occupied Gungstie only during the spring and summer Noss was now, for the first time for centuries, an uninhabited island for three-quarters of the year.

The present absence of any permanent dwellers on Noss accounted for the fact that I had to wait a week after my first vision of the island before being able to get in with George and Laurence Sutherland, who were taking out a second lot of lambs for the Lerwick mart. The experience quickly initiated me into the difficulties to be overcome by anyone contemplating making a home on Noss or even working on the island for a season as a naturalist. Of these difficulties I had been well and often warned by Theo Kay and others, but had tended to discount them, wrongly in this case, as the product of local inertia. The main difficulty lay in getting a boat into and out of Noss, for the Sound, which was a quarter of a mile in length and no more than 200 yards at its greatest breadth, was open to the sea at either end, and along the whole length of the rocky Bressay shore there was not a geo, nor the smallest cove, in which a boat could be beached above high-tide mark, much less moored off. There was no evidence that anyone had ever attempted to lay a permanent slipway or mooring, for the good reason that the embarking place on the Bressay shore changed from day to day according to the airt of the wind and the height of the tide, and there were days when the swell, piling up at either north or south entrance, ultimately broke in when the tide was favourable and rolled right through the Sound. When this happened, no boat could cross to Noss. The Jamieson family, of whom the daughters handled an oar as expertly as their father, had experienced winters when they were Noss-bound for periods of ten days, and on one occasion three weeks, at a stretch. If, then, a man wished to go out of Noss into Bressay for any longer period than the few hours of low-water between tides, but had no companion to return with the boat and haul it up on the Noss side, his only alternative was to drag the boat ashore over the boulders on the Bressay side and manhandle it fifteen or twenty yards up a steep and slippery rock-slide to the safety of the brow-edge. Only a man of exceptional physique and knack could perform this feat with the heavy Shetland four-oared boat, and there was no doubt that it would prove a feat beyond my strength, for despite its clean shapely lines the high-stemmed *fourern* was broad-thwarted and very solidly built.

Here, then, was a first and formidable obstacle to be overcome before an expedition to Noss could be launched. Should it not prove feasible for my family to spend the spring and summer in Gungstie, as the Sutherlands had intimated, then I should be entirely dependent on the daily goodwill of Laurence, the younger brother, for getting me in and out of Noss, for he would be living alone in Gungstie from April until August. Both the brothers—George fair-haired and blue-eyed, and Laurence, dark-haired and brown-eyed—were young men of fine physique, like many Shetland men, and to Laurence, at any rate, portage to and fro across the Sound presented no insuperable difficulties.

The brothers had not been into Noss for a week or two, and the boat was lashed down to heavy stones and chained to a stake in a cleft of the brow-edge. Manhandling her down a rock-slide and over a boulder-beach exposed at low water, we pushed off across the Sound, grazing and bumping over reefs and boulders and, when clear of the big beds of heavy tangle-weed, which impeded the long thin-bladed oars, pulled diagonally across a strong current. With a reef, the Longa, stretching out into mid-Sound from the Bressay shore and a shoal, the Taing of Flit-Sand, almost meeting it from the Noss side, it was hard to believe that there was in existence a more awkward or in-hospitable shore.

Nor were there any sheltered inlets on the Noss side either, but more beds of tangle and a shelving reef, which permitted a boat to get well into a steep bank of rock and loam, in the face of which a ship's ladder of herring-boxes had been built. On top of the bank, it was true, there was an old windlass; but we did not make use of it, dragging the boat up instead over rollers laid across a passage-way in the rock, and hauling it a little way up the bank clear of the tide.

So narrow was the Ness at this point that the long south frontage of Gungstie almost straddled it from a little bay—the Nesti Voe—on the one side over to the Sound on the other. It seemed a fine solidly built and commodious dwelling, this homestead of Gunnar, with covered yards and a paddock behind it, dating no doubt from the era of the pony farm some seventy-five years earlier. But a rude shock awaited me when we went into the house. Storms had displaced a portion of the roof-ridge and shattered a chimney, and the interior of the house was saturated with damp. Paper was peeling from the walls in great bulges and plaster from ceilings lay thick on the floor; hearths were choked with masses of rubble fallen from the chimneys. The Sutherlands had match-boarded one of the two living-rooms throughout, rendering it tolerably habitable; but it was clear at a glance that the house could not provide fit permanent quarters for a woman or a child. Although the Sutherlands had warned me of this, before ever I set out for Shetland, it was a bitter disappointment, for the general lay-out and aspect of the house had about it that air of adventure and trueness to natural background essential to the capturing of the right spirit for the type of expedition I had in mind: while, from the naturalist's point of view, it was no less essential that, whether at work in the field or not, one should always be on the spot at all hours of the twenty-four.

On my left hand, as we entered, steep winding stairs mounted

c　　　　　　33

to two bedrooms and a central recess where bags of flour and meal and other bulky foods were stored. Adjacent to the stairs a narrow passage led to what in the Jamiesons' time had been the visitor's sitting-room. On my right hand was what had originally been the living-room, before the house was enlarged, and was now the workshop and depository for those innumerable items inseparable from the occupation of sheep-farmer, fisherman, and islandman, ranging from a workbench crammed with every imaginable tool, to drums of paraffin, old fishing-nets and coils of ropes, blocks of candle-wax washed up on the shore, etc., to great wool-bags on which the collies slept when Laurence was in residence—in short, a treasure-trove to make an adventurous schoolboy whoop with delight.

Immediately beyond the outer door was the entrance to the present living-room. Long, low and narrow, with only one tiny window affording light from a small yard at the back of the house, my impression was of being in a ship's saloon—the more so as from a seat at the table under the window one looked out of the open doors over the ness and the Nesti Voe to the sea and the Bard Head; and, as in a ship, the room was crammed with furniture—several chairs, a couch along the wall opposite the table, a dresser and an H.M.V. gramophone surmounted by a portable radio at the east end; and at the west end the inevitable peat-burning stove, introduced into Shetland from America about thirty years ago and still in universal use throughout the islands. The quarters were as snug as I could have wished for, had the house been in better repair. However, if I could have the use of one of the two bedrooms for myself, I might be able to find accommodation for my family on Bressay, and go in and out of Noss as I pleased—or, rather, as Laurence pleased. There did not seem to be any other alternative. Camping was out of the question. Living conditions in a tent were not compatible with long hours of work in the field and intensive note-recording when off-duty—certainly not for a period of months in a climate as inclement as that of Shetland. These expeditions demanded every available hour of a naturalist's time and every ounce of his mental and physical energy. I stopped work in the field only when I was exhausted. Once home, and the remaining hours, after a meal and a wash and a shave, were mainly taken up with recording in permanent form the day's field-notes, before turning in for a sleep and another day in the field. I could not afford to waste time and, much more precious, nervous and physical energy, tinkering with stoves or getting up in the middle of the night to tighten guy-ropes.

So much for portage and housing difficulties. There remained the question of whether the island would provide suitable field conditions. Leaving the brothers to gather their sheep off the hill and down to the *crö*, the stone-walled handling-pens on the shores of Booth's Voe, a few hundred yards east of Gungstie, I hastened up a 'green road' over the Hill of Papilgeo to a stone dyke—or, rather, wall, for it was of exceptional height and thickness—that stretched right across the narrow 'ankle' of the island from the geo of the North Croo to the Stinking Geos at the head of the Voe of the Mels, where the haaf fishermen had 'lodged' in their stone booths, and where until the latter half of of the last century there had been one of the little Shetland water-mills in which corn was ground. This hill-dyke divided the in-bye grazing and former cultivated land of the foot of the island from that extensive moor, tilted from north-east to south-west, which ultimately swept up against a central bulwark of bluffs ranging right across the breadth of the island. From these bluffs—the Maiden's Paps—Noss Head rose very steeply, culminating in the tremendous overhang of the Noup. For an island with maximum axes of only one and a quarter miles by three-quarters of a mile the area of ground to be covered seemed, at first sight, impossibly vast—as was always the case with new country—and in the few hours at my disposal a trek round the coast-line appeared my most satisfactory plan; so like, no doubt, many others before me I chose the line of least resistance along the lower-lying south coast: more particularly because I was aware that there was just one place on the south side of the Noup from which the gannets could be watched at close range.

From the hill-dyke an old sled-road—now a deeply rutted and boggy track gone back to the wild—skirted the edge of the moor to the old, though still green pastures of Setter. There the 'road' ended and I had then to climb steadily round the cliff-edge dyke, which had fenced off all the high ground on the island from the precipitous cliffs and deep geos for the past hundred years.

When halfway to the top of the island I had my first sight of the famous Cradle Holm of Noss—an enormous table-block of cliff, more than 160 feet high, sundered from the island by an L-shaped chasm. On the upper edge of the Holm, where the chasm was only sixty-five feet across, was still to be seen the stump of a stake, to which ropes for a cradle had been attached. According to tradition it was about the year 1600 that a cragsman from one of the fowling families on the remote Atlantic island of Foula undertook to scale the sheer and in places overhanging cliff and fix two stakes on the Holm, round which ropes might be slung across the chasm. This incredible feat he successfully accomplished, but refusing to take advantage of the cradle, began to climb down the way he had come and fell to his death. For 250 years thereafter the cradle was slung in June and dismounted in November, most years, for the purpose of fattening a dozen sheep and possibly a cow on the Holm's lush grazing and also to obtain the eggs and young of large numbers of gulls and eider ducks which nested on its flat top. (The Nossmen were also accustomed to go down the Noup on ropes for eggs.) In 1864, however, that same cautious tenant of Gungstie, who had built the dyke around the cliffs, caused the cradle to be permanently dismounted.

The Cradle Holm lay only a little below the south corner of a large inverted L-shaped bay known, probably from the sharp bend it made round the Noup of Noss, as Rumble Wick—that is *Onghul* Wick, the bay of the Fish-hook. From its southern corner a small promontory projected twelve or fifteen feet from the cliff-top, and from it I found that I could look down and across to the adjacent cliff-face, on which several hundred pairs of gannets were still in residence, the nearest only ten or twenty yards distant. From this point of vantage I could also see most of the thousands of gannets occupying the ledges along the 400-yard back wall of the Wick and, at a great distance, not far short of half a mile, those on the south face of the Noup, which rose like a pyramid 592 feet sheer from the sea. As a spectacle, both

of cliff scenery and of bird-life, it was tremendous, but for my
particular purposes conditions were not ideal. I should have
liked more gannets at close range, and as the cliff beneath the
promontory fell away sheer for some 250 feet I foresaw much
trouble from strong up-currents of wind. But, considering the
inaccessibility of most gannetries, these conditions could hardly
be bettered; so, after only a short stay at Rumble Wick, I continued on my tour of inspection, climbing up the almost vertical
steep of the Head to the summit of the Noup and across its
straight crest, which was less than 100 yards in length and sliced
off so cleanly on the seaward side that no part of the cliff was
visible beneath: just a 200-yard drop to the sea. The descent on
the north side of the Head, where more thousands of gannets
were sitting up on the north face of the Noup, was even steeper
than that of the south side, falling away sharply to a deeply
indented coastline of many holms, geos, and skerries.

By this time the day was drawing on and, as little was to be
gained by continuing on round the coast, now that I had in-
spected the gannetries, I left the cliff-dyke and struck inwards to
the Maiden's Paps, in search of skuas; but I was not able to form
any opinion as to what working conditions would be like in their
case. There were only about a score of bonxies present—fourteen sitting together in one place on the Paps—and only once
did a pair of arctic skuas pass over my head.

For the rest, my first impressions of an island and its birds
were, as always, vague and general, with the details telescoped
one into the other—rock-pipits everywhere; a shag with two
grey juveniles still in the nest deep down in the dark recesses of a
geo; hundreds of fulmars dotted about cliffs and sidings, which
were luxuriant with scentless mayweed and giant angelica;
occasional hooded-crows and once a raven; starlings, twites and
a wren at the homestead; and, dominant, the gannets, and the
final impression that it was going to be a difficult island to work.

By the time I had made my way from the Maiden's Paps over
very rough and boggy moor to Gungstie, evening was coming
on and it was time we were out of Noss. Solans were plunging
one after another into the voes out of a wind-swept blue sky, and
spray from surfing combers was throwing a mist upon the Bres-

say shore. The weather was breaking up. The swell, that had been piling up at the south end of the Sound all day, was now beginning to run on into it in dangerous-looking rollers—one, two, three, one after the other. These made the *fourern's* passage across to the Bressay shore too hazardous to be repeated a seventh or eighth time, loaded down, as it was, to the gunwales with its cargo of two men and a score of lambs. So, letting go the remainder of the lambs, which were penned at the edge of the Sound with flakes and hurdles tied to iron stakes cemented in the rocks, we got out of Noss while the going was good. Landing far down at the north end of the Bressay shore, we dragged the boat up the cliff to the brow-edge and lashed her down to big stones, against the equinoctial gales now threatening—for the brothers would only be going into Noss three or four times more before the turn of the year. Whether I should be going into Noss again in the spring of the next year was, as yet, only a matter for speculation.

III

BRESSAY FOLK

The inhabitants of Bressay were predominantly crofters, their dwellings were small, and there was a housing shortage. Thus, though I scoured the island from end to end during my autumn visit, I had eventually to leave Shetland without being able to make any arrangements for accommodation in the spring. Throughout the winter, however, I was in touch with Theo Kay in Lerwick and the Jamiesons and Sutherlands on Bressay, but as the months went by it began to look as if I should have to resign myself to leaving my family behind, while I went off on my own to live with Laurence Sutherland on Noss. In the latter event I should have to knock a couple of months or more off my expedition, arriving on Noss about the middle of May and leaving late in July.

Then, in February, Margaret Jamieson wrote to say that she had been able to find us two rooms in a house belonging to Willie and Thomasina Laurensen in Heogan, which it will be remembered was a community at the north end of the island, about as far from Noss as it was possible to live on Bressay. I had made only one visit to that end of the island, and all I could recall of Heogan was that there was a derelict fish-manure factory there and that it was the terminus of the Hoversta road.

However, the expedition was now definitely on, and I arranged to arrive in Shetland at the end of March or early in April—a date that would coincide with the return of the earliest bonxies to Noss and would be well in advance of that of the arctic skuas; and I should hope to stay on until the first young gannets left the cliffs late in August or early in September, though my wife, having heard various reports of the Shetland climate, thought that June or July might see her back home again. In any case I should spend most of my time on Noss, with a bed in Gungstie whenever I wanted one. I should not, of course, be able to cover the full breeding season of the gannets, for they began visiting the nesting cliffs late in January or early in February and did not finally quit them until some time in October: but comparatively few of them would have laid eggs before the end of March. My plan would be to make my main study the gannet, with secondary studies of the bonxie and the arctic skua, and allot any time I could spare from these studies to the tystie, and if possible to the fledging of the young guillemots and puffins. Only one point troubled me. The Norwegians, stationed in Shetland during the war, had bought up all the available small boats, and I had not been able to obtain a light one, which I could manhandle myself. This meant that I should be entirely dependent on Laurence Sutherland and, as he would not be settling permanently in Noss until about April 22nd, I might only be able to get into the island once or twice before that date. However, I might still get hold of a boat on my arrival in Shetland, for nowhere in the British Isles was there a more sea-conscious people and one whose happiest hours, men, women and children alike, were those afloat in *fourern* or yacht, launch or fishing-smack.

With these plans and hopes in mind we locked the doors of our house in the Grampians at 6 a.m. on April 2nd and set out for Inverness on a morning straight from summer: but when our plane landed at Sumburgh Head six hours later, after a brief halt in Orkney, we found ourselves in the cold grey north and had said good-bye to summer. From Sumburgh we motored the twenty odd miles up the long leg of Mainland to Lerwick. At a casual and no doubt travel-jaundiced glance from the car's rear seat—in which I was jammed with luggage and our two dogs, who had accompanied us to so many remote places in the British Isles—Mainland conformed to my earlier conception of Shetland and appeared an unutterably desolate land: as wild and savage as that of the Outer Hebrides, with bleak moorlands and steep hills terribly mutilated by centuries of peat-scalping. It seemed an almost unpeopled land, until we began the long winding descent into Lerwick and looked down on the magnificent harbour of Bressay Sound.

The homestead of Gungstie

There rose up before

The Cradle Holm and Noss Head

Island of Noss

Rumble Wick and the Noup of Noss

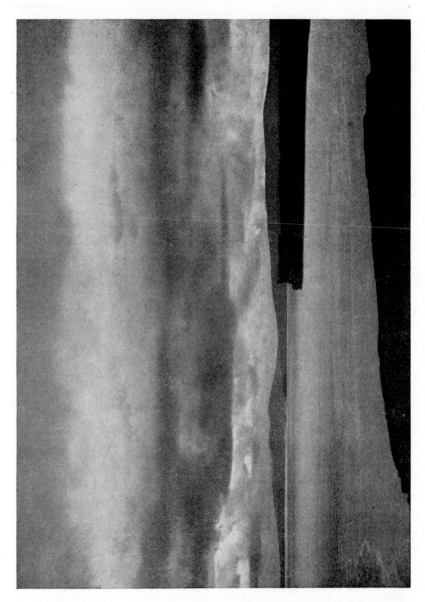

The Bard Head and the hills of Mainland

After a meal with the Jamiesons in their Lerwick flat—complete with every modern electrical appliance—I stood once again on the pier, waiting for the Bressay ferry. But this afternoon, instead of crossing direct to Hoversta, the ferry-launch took us away north up the Sound and disembarked us on the high pier of the fish-manure factory at Heogan—though 'disembark' was perhaps hardly the right term, for it entailed climbing from the launch's cabin-roof, dog under arm, up an iron ladder on the side of the pier's piles, and then hauling up our chests, bicycles, and equipment with ropes.

Thomasina was on the pier to meet us. Weather-beaten but startlingly blue-eyed, laughing, yet a little apprehensive as to what manner of folk she might be taking into her house; clad in sou'wester and oilskin, knee-booted; she, we were to find, personified Shetland. She had brought down the inevitable hand-barrow to the pier, and on this we trundled some of our goods and chattels half a mile up the road from the factory to a two-storied stone house in South Heogan on Cruester Hill high above the Sound.

It was rather an odd house, inasmuch as the two ground-floor rooms in the front were not connected with the upstairs rooms, which were served by a door at the back. The ground floor, facing north, was ours for as long as we cared to make it our home, and called for little comment, except perhaps to note that at one end of the living-room was the inevitable peat-burning stove and at the other end, in a recess which had evidently at one time been a box-bed with doors or curtains, an excruciatingly short bed. By the time we had unpacked some of our stuff, made up a bed for my son on a couch in the other room, and had a meal, a Shetland 'bree' had begun to blow, and we were saying that this expedition was going to be as rigorous as any of our previous experiences; while my wife was quite sure that the end of June would be long enough for her.

There was a little garden, sheltered from the north wind by a dense hedge of stunted elder and willow, in front of the house, and it was a pleasant surprise to find there daffodils with full golden trumpets, though in our garden at home the trumpets were only just coming down to half-mast, despite the spring-like weather we had enjoyed since the middle of February. But, although honeysuckle climbed up our wall, we found it difficult to conjure up a picture of a bleaker inhabited scene than that spread out before our window at breakfast the next morning: yet no scene could have been more expressive of Shetland, land of fishing boats and croftings, whaling stations and guano factories. There seemed nothing incongruous in the tall chimney-stack rearing up from the huge, gaunt and rusted, corrugated-iron shed of the abandoned fish-factory down in the hollow of Heogan at the edge of the Sound, though scattered about the boggy yellow sweep of hillside half encircling it were a dozen thatched or felt-roofed houses, each with its strip of crofting land.

At first sight it seemed a miracle that there was any soil to cultivate in Heogan. Not here the green and pleasant places of the deserted, or partially deserted, townships on the east and south sides of the island. There the old inhabitants had cultivated their strips, which radiated out from the township, on the run-rig system, each family harvesting its various scattered strips for one year only, balloting for a new set of strips the next year. But they did not cultivate the natural soil. At the time of our arrival Bressay, and for that matter the greater part of Shetland, was a spongy morass of waterlogged peat-hags, *sphagna* and other bog-mosses, brine-stunted heather, rushes and sorrel; and I was continually struck by the similarity between the herbage-floor of the Grampian highlands above 3,000 feet and that of Bressay at sea-level, with its star-moss and thrift, its crowberry and creeping-azalea, and clumps of moss-campion. A dominant feature of the Shetland scene was the vast area of hill and moorland not only flayed of all vegetation down to the peat but scalped down to the very gravel. Much of the Ward Hill, for example, was naked peat. This denudation of the topsoil was not solely due to centuries of peat-cutting and subsequent erosion. No, the cultivated land of the old townships was *made* soil, scalped by the crofters from the surrounding moor and hillside and brought down to the rigs in straw *kishies* on their own backs or in net *maeshies* by their ponies. But not only did they denude the hills of their soil, they also flayed them of their turf, which they used as bedding

for the cattle, which were never outside the byre from November until May. With this bedding and with straw they made a
midden, adding the resulting inky-blue compost, together with
tang and sand from the shore, to the foreign soil on the rigs. A
time came, however, in the 'forties of the last century, when their
Scottish landlords, who had already oppressed the common folk
of Shetland to a degree of serfdom unparalleled even in the Highlands and Islands of Scotland, cast covetous eyes on the intensively cultivated run-rigs—which were at the same time unpro-
ductive because no family cultivated the same rigs for more than
one year at a time—and evicted their miserable tenants, in order
to graze big flocks of sheep. Some of those evicted died, more
emigrated, a few began all over again and hacked out new croftings in such places as Heogan on the wind-swept, almost soil-
less west side of Bressay. In the words of a lament written in
1875:

> That place, which once was hallow'd ground,
>   Is covered by a shapeless mound—
> Sheep desecration reigns around,
>   The black-face dwelleth there.
>
> The poor who cannot get away
>   For sympathy need not pray—
> 'A few fat lambs will better pay
>   'We can no quarter give.
>
> 'To yonder heath so bleak and bare,
>   'Where sheep can't feed you must repair,
> 'Our pasture ground we cannot spare,
>   'Whether you die or live.'

Now, in these opening days of April, *voar*—as the spring
cultivation was known in Shetland—was just beginning in
Heogan, and the leys of rye-grass were already surprisingly
green. I had not expected to find Shetland greener than Spey-
side, with luxurious grass bottoms to the deep drains on either
side of the roads and even a spray or two of gorse in flower on
the road-banks. Nowhere was this greenness more striking than,

when standing on the Hill of Cruester, 165 feet above the Sound, one looked across to the dark Irish-green pastures of the Knab, with the grey buildings of Lerwick rising from waterfront to hilltop and the long rounded backbone of Mainland stretching north and south as far as the eye could reach, concealing all that lay to the west.

Some crofters were only just beginning to delve their land, turning it over with the only practicable tool in ground so water-logged that open drains every few yards were essential to cultivation—the spade. This Shetland spade, however, was not the common garden-spade but, like their peat-spade, a handleless, long-hafted instrument with a foot-rest projecting from the shaft and a thin narrow blade; and their method of using this spade was a new one to me. Working as a team, Willie and Thomasina and, on other crofts, three beshawled old maids or two old men, with a granny between them, were to be seen 'delling' with their spades, prodding over a single great clod of earth with a combined heave, then stepping back or moving sideways and prodding up another clod, turning over the long narrow quarter-acre strips of beautiful crumbling tilth very neatly and at surprising speed.

There were no ponies in Heogan and on one croft near the factory, which had already been dug, a girl, having broadcast her oat-seed, was now dragging a little hand-harrow over it— a rectangular wooden frame, measuring some four feet by two feet, with iron teeth on the long sides of the frame. She was watched with interest by numbers of gulls standing on the factory roof and sitting on the adjacent hillside.

Other crofters were putting in their potatoes and, when we took a walk over the moors to Gunnista the day after our arrival, we found the Sutherlands planting out their cabbage seedlings. Almost the first man-made feature that had aroused my curiosity as I had steamed up the coast of Mainland the previous autumn, other of course than the peat-stacks shored up with huge stone slabs, were hundreds of little square, sometimes round, stone-walled enclosures dotted about hill and dale, often on the moors at some distance from the nearest habitation. At first sight I took these mysterious enclosures to be small sheepfolds or *crös*. On closer inspection they proved to be even more puzzling than I had supposed, for some of them lacked any apparent gate or other form of access, short of climbing their dykes. And it was not until I chanced upon one that had been cultivated that I discovered that the ubiquitous enclosures were the famous 'plantie-crubs', kroos or cots of Shetland, in which cabbage seedlings were raised from seed broadcast in May or June. For the best part of a year the little green and purple seedlings were left in the crubs, until in the following March or April they were planted out on the crofting strips or in other crubs, to be used ultimately as winter feed for the cattle or, being able to stand the frost, as spring feed for the lambing ewes. Some of the mature plants, however, were retained for seeding purposes, being uprooted and replanted in May and the seed shaken from the pods in the autumn. The mature plant could only be wintered on one or two of the islands, and Bressay, being the most favoured of these, exported thousands of seedlings to Mainland every spring.

In no part of Britain did winter-keep for livestock present a more formidable problem than in Shetland, where there was, to all intents and purposes, no bite of grass or sedge from November to May. Milk was very scarce when we arrived at Heogan, and though we were able to get some every day from the Hoversta dairy farm, we noticed that the crofters were diluting their tea with tinned milk. As no cows were to be seen in Heogan we presumed that none of the crofters had one, until we realized that the cattle were still winter-stalled and that it would be well on into April or even May before they would be tethered out around the croftings. There was of course, nothing for them to eat outside during the winter, except tangle on the seashore, and no shelter for them on these northern islands, which were treeless, except for dense thickets of elder, willow and sycamore around some of the croft-houses and steadings and one or two experimental plantations of both conifers and deciduous trees in the limestone dales of Mainland. All the same, I suspected that the main reason for following this traditional Scandinavian custom of keeping the cattle stalled for more than half the year was in order to conserve the dung, which was so precious in Shetland. To me, however, the practice seemed unnecessarily barbarous, for I could not but believe that an hour or two's exercise on fine days would have contributed to their health. Moreover in these days of concrete floors and drains, instead of cobbled byres, the most valuable constituent of the manure, the urine, was lost, whether the cattle were stalled or not.

It was true that to-day, thanks to the introduction of turnips, cabbages, oil-cake and seeds-hay, the cattle no longer had to be *lifted* out of the byre in the spring, as was often the case in the old days, to be revived by a drench of boiled docken-roots. In those days, too, the little shelties were also wintered out in the deepest snow and hardest frost without a wisp of hay throughout the winter. No wonder those that survived had founded a breed unrivalled for hardiness and endurance. Nevertheless, if the cattle could now *walk* out of the byre in the spring, many were so thin that it seemed a miracle that their legs could hold them up—though, in this respect, it was only fair to remember that the Shetland breed of cattle had evolved, like the Shetland sheep, on slender lines and those of Foula, in particular, were noted for their razor-backs. It was not surprising that Shetland cattle had an almost 100 per cent clean bill of health from tubercular infection, for it was clear that no seriously infected cow could stand up to the hardships of a Shetland winter.

I was disappointed to find that the original pocket-sized crofter's cow—said to be a pale-faced, chocolate-brown, polled breed—no longer existed in the pure state, for most of the Shetland stock had been crossed with shorthorns and black-polled bulls were now in almost universal use; but there were some interesting little blue and brownish-grey cows, with white faces, black muzzles and white horns, to be seen in the byres, and the white face appeared to be the hallmark of the breed.

I had long wanted to make the acquaintance of the native Shetland sheep, that queer crittur partly responsible for the new prosperity of the Shetlanders and not to be confused with the larger Black-faced sheep, Cheviots, and Scotch-cross sheep introduced by the landlords. I did not have to wait for an introduction. Willie and Thomasina had been living in our part of the house up to the time of our arrival and, like the other crofters, Thomasina had been feeding her sheep on potatoes, cabbages and a little corn and oil-nuts, for there was nothing for them to eat on the croftings and scattald except tangle and a little moss; and one of the first things we learnt in Shetland was to keep our outer door shut, if we did not wish to find the sheep eating our potatoes and the hens anything edible on shelves within flying reach.

Bressay, like most of Shetland, was grossly overstocked with sheep. When we wandered along the shore round Heogan or across the scattald to Beosetter we would see black-shawled women peeping from behind the curtains of their little windows, fearful that we would violate the sanctity of their small plots of ground that represented to them fifty years or more of sweat and toil, or that our dogs would harry their precious dozen or score of ewes now ready to drop their lambs; while one or two old men would come to their doors and shake their fists at us, muttering imprecations. However, we were not the sole objects of their wrath, for even the farm shepherd, whose black-faced sheep ran on the moors above Heogan, was exposed to their invective should he pass through the township with his collies. But far from our dogs disturbing the Heogan sheep, it was the latter's outrageously house-tame behaviour that troubled our dogs, accustomed to the wild black-faces of the Highlands!

This particular object of fanaticism on Bressay, the Shetland sheep was, however, very nearly worth its weight in gold, for though the major industries in Shetland were still fishing and agriculture, the hand-knitting of the magnificent Fair Isle-patterned hosiery now exceeded them in revenue. With few exceptions every woman, young and old alike, knitted. Using a sheath and three needles instead of four, their output was amazing and a revelation even to my wife, who was herself a fast knitter. With a bigger American demand for hand-knitted garments than they could meet, prices were fantastically high for tourists and £5 a week lay within the grasp of every knitter. The crofters' wool came off the backs of that dozen or score bags of skin and bone on four legs, which somehow or other they had kept alive through the winter: each crofter receiving back, carded and spun, for her own use half the weight of wool despatched to the Scottish mills.

Never was there an uglier object of value: but in its ugliness lay its value, for the starvation diet responsible for its lean and angular long-legged body was also responsible for the fine and silky quality of its wool—so fine that a lace-shawl, eighteen feet square, could be drawn through a wedding ring. Thomasina's score of ewes were of the dominant white variety, hornless like most of the breed: but on the other Heogan croftings representatives of all the colours included in the breed were to be seen. Next in numbers to the white was the *moorit*, which was a uniform golden-chestnut or fawn as it was termed in Shetland, with a small round woolly head and protuberant yellow eyes. Much fewer in numbers were the dark-brown or black; the *sheila*, a grizzled black sheep in which every black hair had a white tip; and here and there a parti-coloured *catmuggit*, with perhaps a cream-coloured back and a dark-brown chest with a white collar, a black face with white blaze, nose and nape, and white socks! Because some of the arable strips were not fenced and because grazing was so precious the crofters habitually tethered out their sheep in pairs, when they were not on the scattald, and this resulted in such amusing combinations as a white-faced black ewe tethered with a chocolate-coloured *moorit*, or a white ewe tethered with a dark-brown one. Add to this the fact that some crofters tied coloured wools or tapes in the 'bits' punched or cut in the sheep's ears, and that others, instead of using paint or keel, sewed red or black squares of cloth on their sheep's rumps, and the cumulative effect was sufficiently curious!

Though every croft had its own ram, these were usually sold after the tupping season as they tended to grow too wild and strong to submit to tethering: but there was one left in Heogan, tethered near the factory on what would have been waste land anywhere else in Britain, but for which in Shetland an annual rent was paid. A shaggy, treacle-coloured fellow with curly black horns, he afforded us some amusement whenever we passed him on our way to the well.

An interesting fact about the *moorit* sheep was that their wool became both paler in colour and coarser in texture if they were pastured for any length of time on green ground instead of black ground or heather. Thus, while a big flock of fawn *moorits* ran on the high heather moors above the Bard Head and the Mills of the Ord on Bressay, the Sutherlands found that three years on the predominantly green island of Noss took the colour out of the fawn *moorits*, while the *sheilas* tended to become more and more grizzled. They were thus obliged to run most of their *moorits* on the scattald at Gunnista. On the other hand the coloured sheep stood up to a hard winter better than the white ones and were the more successful mothers. One had only to clip a dark ewe to be amazed at the warmth and the thickness of the pile on the underside of its fleece, in comparison with that of a white ewe. In order to obtain good-sized wedder lambs, however, the Sutherlands were accustomed to run a pure-bred Cheviot ram and a Cheviot × Shetland ram in Noss for a month with a quarter of their stock, before turning out their twelve Shetland rams. The latter were all white, lightly built and long-legged animals with curling yellow horns somewhat similar to those of a black-face ram. Nevertheless the *moorit*, black and *sheila* strains persisted, no matter what the colour of the ewe, and every lambing brought its valuable quota of hardy coloured lambs. The percentage of twins was much higher than in the case of the black-face, which did not thrive in Shetland on either green or black ground, and the Noss flock usually produced a 90 or 100 per cent crop of lambs at marking time. Here and there on Bressay we saw an early lamb. Though puny and sickly looking at birth, with a vivid redness about mouth and nostrils, and some no bigger than long-legged cats in body, they throve and grew more quickly than the cross-lambs.

I had read much about the wild nature of Shetland sheep and the impracticability of working them with collies: but I found that these statements were based on faulty observation. Though some of the crofters had collies, few of them were even half-trained. Consequently, when a crofter wished to single out his own puckle of sheep from the township's couple of hundred grazing on the scattald, he was to be seen, as likely as not, chasing over the hill with two or three companions in pursuit of now one sheep, now another. Naturally, then, when a shepherd came along with his trained collies and attempted to round up these township sheep, they either scattered in all directions, being all independent lots and the majority hand-fed and scornful of dogs, or moved towards the dogs in a bunch snorting and stamping their feet, before bounding off a little way in no determinate direction. But where, as on Noss, the sheep lived an almost wild existence during the winter and were regularly worked with dogs and gathered in the same direction each time in the summer, there, as I had seen, they ran together as smoothly as a flock of black-faces at the first sight of the shepherd and his dogs and hastened down to the in-bye pastures. A man could have driven them with voice and whistle alone.

I have mentioned our reception at the hands of a few of the older generation of crofters. Had this been the universal attitude of the Bressay folk towards us my wife would indeed have been back in the Highlands long before midsummer; but, happily for us, it was the laughing Thomasina and her shy and courteous sailor-husband: the ever-hospitable Jamiesons; the kindly joking Willie Manson of Maryfield Farm; the inexhaustibly good-natured Sutherlands; the irrepressible John Smith (now, as I write, in South Georgia with four hundred other Shetland whaling-men)—to recall only those we knew best—who were more truly representative of the people of Bressay. Never had we met such an infectious laugh as Thomasina's—or, for that matter, of Ruby our neighbour—and nowhere had we enjoyed the company of a merrier or more good-natured folk, once the ice of initial suspicion had been broken. Ever laughing and practical-joking, whether at the peats or on the hill, in dance hall or post office, the Shetlanders' zest for living seemed immense, and not for a long time had we lived among such a strong and healthy people. There was a bloom on the girls' cheeks, a deep-sea tan on the men, and a nut-brown weathering on the faces of the older women and a vigorous intelligence in their clear blue eyes that contrasted oddly with the sober colours and old-fashioned lines of their head-shawls and hobbled skirts, but was in full accord with their intense curiosity as to our business. Meeting them on the hill, *kishies* of peats on backs, they would not scruple to ask us the most searching questions in that abrupt straightforward manner of the Shetlander, with blunt rapid speech containing many 'thee's' and 'thou's', the substitution of 'd' for 'th', and a somewhat Welsh intonation.

I have rather stressed the dominance of the older generation on Bressay, and among Heogan's twenty-five or thirty inhabitants there were in fact only two young men, one child, and one baby. The truth was that Shetland was still predominantly a land of fishermen, sailors and whaling-men, with a big proportion of the menfolk away at sea for two or three years at a time. During the war, indeed, some of the Bressay whaling men had been down in the Antarctic for several years at a stretch. Thus, much of the work about the croftings was done by the women and old folk. Even so, *vigour* seemed to me the key-word in any description of the people of Shetland, now that they had been released from the serfdom of their ancestors, and *vigorous* was the adjective descriptive of their agriculture. Shetland was the only part of North Britain in which I could remember seeing drains and dykes in good order. The neat flat-coursed sandstone dykes, with a top-course of uprights, were a constant pleasure to the eye: while the intensive cultivation of the croftings astounded me. In how many districts of the Scottish Highlands, for example, would I have found crofters raising crops not only of oats and potatoes, but also of cabbages and seeds-hay?—over and above garden produce and the flowers that every Shetlander grew, often in little stone-walled 'crubs' far removed from the township: cultivated bluebells, rose-root, and lady's-mantle growing side by side with lupins, bachelor's buttons, tiger-lilies and michaelmas daisies, and they in turn beside American mimulus and grotesque Australian daisies. Yet the soil of Shetland was infinitely less potentially fertile than that of most parts of the Highlands and Islands.

I marvelled at the transformation that had taken place in the people of Shetland during the twentieth century. From being the most wretchedly oppressed people in Britain they had become, I supposed, richer than any other fishing or crofting community. From haddock and herring fishing in home waters, from service in the whaling fleets, the Merchant Navy, and the Royal Navy, and from Fair Isle hosiery, a relatively immense capital had poured into Shetland this past decade—though the two wars had exacted a fearful toll of her young men. And if the Shetlanders were keen to add to their new-found wealth and kept the prices high for tourists, many of them spent freely and generously and were not afraid to put out their wealth in new fishing-boats and other projects requiring considerable capital. Though they still had their critical problems connected with agriculture and fishing and with the depopulation of their rural areas, complementary to centralization on the port of Lerwick, we were conscious every day of living among a virile and progressive people. Though the climate was a cruel one for the agriculturalist I could not think but that we were going to witness in the near future a revolution of life in these northern islands, with more and more young men quitting the Merchant Service to settle permanently in Shetland, to fish in home waters and open up some of those considerable areas of crofting land that had gone out of cultivation during the two wars.

IV

FRUSTRATIONS OF A NATURALIST

To be successful, a bird-watching expedition or, for that matter, any kind of expedition required good fortune and good weather. It seemed that we were not going to enjoy either for I was not, after all, able to obtain possession of a boat. Moreover, Shetland had not enjoyed the fine weather in March that we had had on Spey-side and the Sutherlands were consequently behind-hand with the *voar* at Gunnista and could not promise a day in Noss until the second week in April. However, until then, I could at least prospect Noss Sound, see what was doing off Noss, and get the feel of the island and its birds.

So, on the second day after our arrival, I was on the road to Noss once more. Seven months had passed since my last visit, and this time I had more than four miles of Bressay to traverse from north-west to south-east—down the steep Hill of Cruester, along the edge of Bressay Sound to Hoversta, and then up the hill out of Hoversta on to the roof of Bressay. It was a calm sunny morning and the notes of a blackbird whistling in Lerwick carried clearly over the glassy waters of the Sound, together with the cooing of eider ducks and the bass laughing of great black-backed gulls—the Swaabie in Shetland. Other blackbirds were whistling thinly and tunelessly, like ring-ousels, from such varied stations as the fish-factory, a plantie-crub down by the shore, the thorn-hedge at Maryfield Farm, and the Hoversta post office, but no hen blackbirds had yet arrived on Bressay.

Little flocks of twites twittered in chorus from fencing-wires. Pairs of corn-buntings wheezed from the telegraph-wires and flew down heavily on to the ploughed land. While plentiful all along the cultivated west-central strip of Bressay, the corn-bunting eschewed the remoter townships and croftings, not penetrating even to Heogan. Grey crows watched me pass, unalarmed, from telegraph-poles, and a raven hovered inquisitively only a few feet above my head—for the birds of Shetland evinced less fear of man than those of any other place known to me. Flocks of rock-pigeons were feeding on the arable fields of the dairy farm, while other small flights swept low over the island, Noss-wards. Swarms of up to three hundred glossy black, straw-billed, Shetland starlings whirled over the pastures and sang and chattered from telegraph-wires and, amusingly, from chinks in the stone dykes. Their strong, whirring, trilled chatter, resonant as that of the twites, distinguished them immediately from the common starling, and their alarm-notes were so harsh that they recalled the heron's grating cry. They also employed another note indistinguishable from the hasty and elusive whistle of the flighting wheatear. Together with those of wheatears and wrens their songs were to be heard from the remotest deserted townships.

Lapwings were tumbling over the bogs and the pastures of the old townships. Mallard, teal, pintail and golden-eye duck swam on the lochs. Up on the desolate moorland roof a few raggedly blacked golden-plover whistled mournfully and a jack merlin mounted after a singing lark, but then sheered off to play with its mate. An immature glaucous gull veered low over the Loch of Setter below Old Brough.

Three ponies were sucking up the wind-blown froth at the edge of the loch. They had been out-wintering and their coats of brownish hair were several inches long; but they were not shaggy, for each hair was separate and glossy, like those of a long-haired goat. This hair covered every part of their bodies, with long fringes from cheeks and legs and tails, which were so long that several inches of their ends swept the ground.

And then, Noss! Once again I stood on the green tumulus and gazed at the promised land across that narrow Sound of limpid amethyst and peacock-blue waters banded with dark purple. Sentinel on its green ness the lonely house seemed waiting for men to step forth and go about their day's shepherding or fishing. Knowing so much of its history I found myself waiting expectantly for a figure to appear at the green door and, shading his eyes, look across to see who was waiting on the

Bressay shore. Apparent confirmation of its being inhabited was lent by the cats, which I could see examining the rabbit-buries, one after another, in the sandy warrens above Gungstie; by the sheep around the homestead, especially the *sheilas*, at which my collie barked as they stood out so darkly against the Hill of Papilgeo; and by the two old out-wintering ponies, which I could pick up through my binoculars on the old grazing at Setter. Though a chill haar, infiltrating from the southern sea, caused Noss Head to appear very distant and colourless, spring's green cast was discernible in the old plough-rigs on the otherwise wintry yellow sweep of Papilgeo.

There was little evidence, however, that the island stood at the threshold of a new breeding season. Off the promontory of the Feadda Ness far up the south coast there was the just perceptible whiteness of fulmars and kittiwakes sweeping to and from the cliffs. From time to time solans rounded the ness and disappeared, bound for Rumble Wick and the Noup. What would be happening at the gannetries now? I was thankful that there were no reports yet of any skuas having been seen in Shetland waters, for James Jamieson had known the bonxie to return to Noss as early as April 2nd. All the same it was exasperating beyond measure to be less than 200 yards from my objective, yet as effectually barred from it as if the Sound had been the Atlantic Ocean.

The Sound itself would have made an interesting seasonal study, for through it was a constant traffic of birds and beasts. Its brow-edges were littered with the shells of limpets and razorfish upon which common gulls, swaabies, and herring-gulls feasted. From time to time a pair of the latter would yodel antiphonally. Shetland was above all, the land of gulls. Sitting in Kay's study in Lerwick, all windows closed against the 'bree', my curiosity had been aroused by a faint and apparently familiar conversational murmur that seemed to fill the room. It was the herring-gulls talking on top of the chimney. At Heogan a one-legged herring-gull was accustomed to stand on top of the peat-house or sat tamely on a green hillock in front of the house waiting for scraps. There were thousands of herring-gulls nesting on the Bressay cliffs and skerries, and there would be a great yodelling of gulls over the Sound of Bressay in the early morning, at that hour when masses of singing larks mounted into the teeth of a gale and up into the low cloud.

From Gungstie, and from the dykes and stone walls of the old houses on the Bressay shore, dark-brown barred, rufous wrens chittered and advertised their presence with brief shrill whistles. To attempt regional comparisons of the songs of birds was a somewhat unsatisfactory procedure, for the volume and quality of a bird's song was so dependent on seasonal and breeding factors and the relative density of population: but the Shetland wren's song could be described as a distinctly articulated twittering of lisped notes, high-pitched and penetrating, though tuneless, with the ultimate rattling trill neither so prolonged nor so emphatic as that of the English wren's. On Bressay wrens were very catholic in their solitary distribution, lisping their thin sweet whistles impartially from the top of the highest cliffs or hundreds of feet down the sidings, from the edge of a loch or of a stony sea-beach, from the fish-factory and especially from dykes in the townships, and even from that vast and desolate amphitheatre of heather and peat-hags under the Ward Hill, where twelve-inch icicles still hung from the hag-banks. For long periods at dawn they were to be heard answering one another with continuous song, phrase after phrase.

Small flights of starlings were continually crossing the Sound to and from Gungstie, where they clustered on the chimney-stacks and roof-ridge with herring-gulls, chattering merrily. Pairs of fulmars sat about the turfy dome of the old corn-drying kiln at the back of Gungstie, on the square chimney-stacks and copings of the old houses on the Bressay shore, and on the grassy banks, over which they swept noiselessly, hovering inquisitively a few feet above my head. Others gyrated in little flocks on the waters of the Sound, where drakes kaaloos (long-tailed duck) blowing their musical hunting-horns—*caw-caa-calloo, caw-caa-calloo*—dived with a sudden opening of wings like the unfolding of a flower's pointed sepals. A solitary tystie was also diving at long intervals with a barely perceptible splutter of wings, emerging perhaps with a small crab after a submergence of up to forty seconds. It dismembered the crab by shaking it vigorously and pecking at it on the water, diving to recapture it after each de-legging, swallowing the legs but not the body. From time to time twenty or thirty gannets would converge on the northern approaches to the Sound, when they perceived one of their kind to hover and plunge, and join in the fishing.

The Sound was a favourite short-cut and fishing ground, not only for birds, but also for beasts. Pairs of brown-hided por-poises cart-wheeled through, one always leading the other by a head, and two grey seals were fishing. One of the latter swal-lowed down three large flat-fish in the space of two minutes, crunching them with a backward chuck of its head and bolting them whole, while another gripped a monstrous angler-fish, whose grisly toothed gape was wider than its captor's head. The activities of the seals attracted shags, cormorants, gulls and ful-mars, the latter sweeping low above the water, dipping in their webbed feet, and snipping up fragments of fish chopped off by the seals.

When two days after this preview of Noss in spring I made my way to the Sound *via* the Sand Vatn—a wild loch set in that amphitheatre of remote moors between the Bard Head and the Ward Hill—I was much relieved to find that no bonxies had yet arrived there, for I had found a colony of them on the heights around the loch the previous September. But in the early after-noon, when I was just preparing to leave the Sound and return homewards over the Ander, there was an alarum from a flock of oystercatchers mounting high over the Sound from the Noss side and a pair of rock-pigeons dashed along the brow-edge with a flash of dark green. A minute or two later, two large brown birds, with silvery Y's glinting on their wings, came out of Noss through a milling crowd of gannets and gulls and bore away in the direction of Grimsetter Loch, midway between Noss and the Bard, veering high and low in their passage over the sea. A little later a third bonxie came out on the same line of flight. They might only have returned to Noss that morning from their Atlantic wanderings: but their presence, though more or less in-evitable, was a bitter blow to me, and I was deeply chagrined to see how my plans were going awry.

Worse was to come. In the late afternoon it began to blow a whole gale out of the north with squalls of rain and hail, and the grey-blue waters of the Sound were lashed into a smother of white-caps and blown spray. The gale—the strongest since the Old Year—blew without a minute's cessation until the morning of the 10th, when the Sutherlands had hoped to get into Noss for the day. It was only just possible to walk against the wind in any exposed place and the Bressay ferry—a converted German lifeboat—bucketed through the swell to Lerwick as if it had been crossing the harbour bar of Lindisfarne. No doubt we had experienced other days as cold on that island and also on Lundy, but the only comparable cold of which I had any present memory was that on the high tops of the Cairngorms, and for the first time since the New Year full winter clothing was a necessity. I struggled the four miles and more over the wind-swept moors from Heogan to the Sound—though there was not the slightest possibility of being able to get into Noss—and I had to admit that it was a beautiful, though gruelling experience to come over the hill of storm-wracked Bressay on this arctic day to the comparative shelter of the south side of the green Ander with its placidly grazing white-faced sheep, and look down on the gorgeously coloured, sun-illumined Sound. Snowy surf broke in foaming crests on the brown reefs of the Cols Ness at the north end of the Sound and disintegrated in curdling smothers of milky whey. The deep pool of white sand in mid-Sound blazed like a green jewel in its purple bed of barrier reefs. Grey skirting-curtains of successive squalls blotted out intermittently the dark-blue northern sea.

For some time the interior of Noss appeared to be birdless, but after a while I perceived two bonxies flighting close together high over the hill above Setter, and subsequently a third. There could be no doubt that they were taking up their nesting-territories on the island, and it was no solace to me that their numbers still seemed very few, that an occasional one could be seen harrying a swaabie over Bressay, or that four or five could now be watched bathing in the Sand Vatn. Such observations could only be of a general nature and it was the particular observations of individual pairs that I had set my heart on.

Though the gale abated during the night to a light breeze
another opportunity had been lost, while seven days of well-
nigh continuous gales and strong winds had put the Sutherlands
behind again with their *voar*-work at Gunnista, and the earliest
date they could now promise was the 19th. Nor did these northerly arctic winds, always in my teeth in the long grind back
from the Sound to our eyrie on Cruester Hill, in any way soothe
that ever-growing canker of bitterness within me at the ill luck
that was keeping me out of Noss. As day followed day I worked
myself up into a state of high nervous tension. In any case the
calm on the 10th was only a lull, for it began to blow strongly
again on the 11th and the next night I turned in to bed early in
a state of nervous exhaustion, with in addition a lacerated throat
and aching from head to feet with rheumatism. My wife was
already in bed with the same complaint.

In the morning we awoke to another day's rain, low cloud
and damp. The excessive humidity was a distressing feature that
caused more discomfort than the bitter winds. To wake up
morning after morning to walls running with water and concrete and linoleumed floors exuding moisture; to put on clothes
damp to the skin; to be aware that it would be impossible to set
foot outside the door without rubber boots; to know that the
well for all water was a quarter of a mile distant, that driftwood
must be sought for along the shore of Bressay Sound and humped
home on one's back or one's wife's back, and that coal must be
barrowed up in hundredweight sacks from the Heogan pier; to
be aware that it was nine miles to Noss Sound and back in the
teeth of a gale, with a probable soaking into the bargain; and to
realize, worst of all, that when I reached the Sound I could do
no more than gaze across at the island and make the best of a bad
job by taking note of those birds fishing in the Sound of or those
bonxies at the Sand Vatn—to be aware of all these things on
awakening to a new day was to saddle the expedition with as
bad a beginning as I had pictured only in hours of deepest depres-
sion. Add to this chapter of woe the severest bout of feverish
ague I had ever experienced, so that for some hours I tortured
myself with despair that I had contracted some illness that might
lead to the abrupt ending of an expedition that I had looked

forward to for so long and by which I had set so much store, and it will be understood that at the end of our second week on Bressay the said expedition seemed to be in real danger of foundering.

However, as I was no worse by the 15th, I took heart again, though I was too weak to stroll more than a couple of miles on a rare fine day; and by the 17th was sufficiently recovered from my malignant ague to struggle over to the Sound against a stiff and still arctic wind—for all my energies were now bent on getting myself hardened up again in readiness for the 19th. I took what comfort I could from the fact that during a stay of two and a half hours only one bonxie came out of Noss with that characteristically low veering flight, now down to the water, now up again; and, as previously, I was apprised of its presence, long before sighting it, by the mounting up from their feeding places of twittering oystercatchers and after them hoodies, starlings (of whom as many as eighty were massed on the Gungstie roof), and some common gulls from a small colony on the Big Ness south of Gungstie. I had never yet seen more than four bonxies in the air over Noss, but how many were there on the ground of that wild expanse of moor and hill? There lay the rub! However, the damage was done now: for even if we got into Noss on the 19th I was not fit enough to put in a full day's work. I could only pick up what threads were left from this disastrous fortnight's wreckage and concentrate on making a good job of the months to come.

The next day I lay out at the Sound for more than four hours, continuing the process of hardening, though I was wracked with ague again: for it was bitterly cold despite the brilliant sunshine. Once again no birds were to be seen milling off the cliffs and only one bonxie went into Noss, soared to some hundreds of feet, and came out again in the direction of Grimsetter, causing the customary alarm among oystercatchers and rock-pigeons.

The weather deteriorated again the next day, and when I got over to the Sound at 8.30 a.m.[1] on the 19th it was to find a swell running into it, with a shift of the wind into the south. I knew that I was only foxing myself if I made believe that it would be

[1] G.M.T. is used throughout.

possible to force an entry into Noss in such conditions, but hoping against hope that the Sutherlands might consider it possible I sheltered from that dreadful dank cold wind in the lee of the *broch*, a prey to bitter despair, burning with fever one minute, breaking into a cold sweat the next. I felt that the coming week would determine whether the expedition was going to prove a ghastly failure or a belated success. If the latter outcome was still possible, then I must find a way to shake off the weakening ague and regain my physical strength and mental equilibrium.

Yet another new date was fixed—this time the 22nd. Throughout the 20th and 21st it blew a gale out of the west, with torrential squalls of rain and that same fearful dank air, and mocking intervals of sun-blue seas and clear brown islands. By this time I had given up all hope of being able to catch up on the three weeks that had been lost, but had gained some peace of mind by coming to the resolve to visit Noss again the next April, if I felt subsequently that any vital work had been missed, and stay by myself on the island for the requisite three or four weeks.

During the night of the 21st the gale abated: but it was with little hope of success that I arrived at the Sound at 9 a.m. the next morning, with low cloud wreathing the Ander and Noss Head. When, after an hour's wait, heavy rain began to fall and there was still no sign of the Sutherlands, I resigned myself to yet another setback: but half an hour later I saw the most heartening sight I had seen in Shetland, when two black-and-white collies appeared round the shoulder of the Ander and immediately after them the burly figure of Laurence Sutherland.

Though the wind had dropped to a light breeze I could hardly have picked a less promising day to go into Noss: but it was in exultant mood that I helped Laurence to unlash the boat and launch her down the rock-slide and over the boulders.

And so it was that, after rescuing a sheep stranded by the flowing tide on a skerry below the Big Ness, I set foot on the promised land at long last, three weeks after our arrival in Shetland.

For several weeks no human being had landed on Noss. Pairs of herring-gulls were pecking about on the rocks near the landing steps. A curlew protested noisily at our intrusion. The cus-

tomary fulmar was sitting on the corn-kiln. Little flocks of
twites were singing in the plantie-crub at the back of the house.
A small flock of turnstones, accompanied by the inevitable
purple sandpiper, were feeding on the white sand beach of the
Nesti Voe and there were eiders and mergansers on the Voe itself.

Leaving Laurence to put things shipshape at the homestead, I
hastened up the green road to the moors to find, as I had feared,
some scores of bonxies present. Everywhere I saw great dark
fowl standing watchful in ones or twos on heather ridges, or
sitting confidently on green mounds in the surrounding heather
or bent, glowering like bulldogs, preening, or sleeping with
heads turned back. I made no attempt to count them; but they
covered an enormous acreage of the island, from the middle of
the moor outside the hill-dyke, over the Maiden's Paps, and up
on to the boggy flats of the Hill of Setter, high above the Cradle
Holm and Rumble Wick.

All the way up to Rumble Wick—where I found two-thirds
of the gannets in the selected gannetry already sitting on nests—
I was subjected to a ceaseless barrage of barking protest from
hundreds of herring-gulls nesting on the cliffs and, when I
reached the Cradle Holm, by the deep cries of several scores of
swaabies and the first summer-homing lesser black-backed gulls
on the steepy grassy siding opposite the Holm. Though arctic
skuas, puffins and arctic terns had yet to return to the island, and
though tens of thousands of cliff-birds had yet to take up permanent residence on the breeding ledges, hundreds of guillemots and kittiwakes were occupying ledges on the face of the
Holm; rock-pigeons dashed out of the geos, in which tysties
were sitting up on cliff-platforms; and deep down in the chasms
shags perched erect on well-built nest-drums. One with a nest
under a boulder near the top of the cliff on the landward side
snapped at me, snake-like, flashing its yellow 'buccal lantern',
and brayed hideously, *i-āg*. Hooded crows were already building at various places round the coast, favouring especially the
extreme points of holms projecting seawards between twin geos;
and oystercatchers, which also favoured the points of these green
tongues, had full clutches of eggs.

By 4 p.m. I had completed my first day's preparatory survey

of the island's birds, my only consolations being that there were
still a number of pairs of gannets, very close to my O.P., which
had not yet begun nest-building; that bonxies, though no doubt
paired and in territories, did not appear to be doing anything very
much except sit and stand about, permitting me to pass un-
molested through their nesting grounds; and that no arctic
skuas were present.

An hour later we went out of Noss, with the intention of getting down to serious work on the 25th, when Laurence would
finally be settling into Gungstie for the next four months. As
it happened nothing was lost by this further delay, for during the
night as fierce a westerly gale as any we had thus far experienced
blew up and continued all the next day without abate.

By the appointed day, however, the gale had subsided to a
southerly breeze and it was a summer's afternoon, with a pale-
blue sea and infinite visibility, when we assembled at the Sound.
We were a full party, for besides Laurence and myself there
were his brother George and my wife and son, who were coming in for the day—not to mention five dogs and a cow and four
stirks which we cornered, after a good deal of roping and wrest-
ling, and with much swearing, in a little cove of white sand exposed at low-water, and swam them across one by one, with
Laurence kneeling in the stern of the boat holding their halters.

Going straight up the moor through the bonxie grounds on
this occasion, the island seemed absolutely silent, with the noisy
gulls restricted to the coastal strip and the bonxies themselves
still showing little sign of activity. After we had had a picnic
tea on the O.P. at Rumble Wick and my family had gone down
again to Gungstie, with the intention of crossing over to Bressay
with George Sutherland, I settled down to my first leisured
study of the gannets.

Here at last, then, after an interval of seven years I was free to
study that tumultuous kaleidoscopic spectacle that had few
parallels in the world of Nature—the breeding cliffs of vast
numbers of colonial-nesting sea-fowl. Once again I found it a
spectacle not only intensely fascinating, but of infinite biological
possibilities, had one the mental acumen to interpret correctly
what the eye saw and to analyse correctly what the notebook

recorded—two operations not necessarily synonymous, for the human mind had always to be on guard against prejudice (inconscious, if not conscious) formed by previous thought or knowledge, or supposed knowledge.

For four or five months to come my presence at the cliffs would be restricted only by the limitations of my powers of physical and mental endurance, which in their turn would be influenced to some extent by the one factor I could not control, the weather. For the rest I, by my wife's self-sacrificing co-operation, had attained for this not inconsiderable span of human existence, to a personal freedom from all *extra*-ornithological responsibilities perhaps unique in this year 1946. There was indeed good cause for the sudden change to a mood of intense exhilaration and profound gratitude at my lot in life.

The scene was one of great animation and ceaseless tumult.

From the long west wall of the Wick and more faintly from its east wall, the Noup, rose to my eyrie, crescending and diminishing, but never totally subsiding, a raucous medley of diverse harsh and musical cries, from thousands of individuals of several different species of sea-birds, blended into one harmonious din, one pattern of sound, from which only now and again could one detach the separate components—the squeaky, braying, *wick-gewer, wick-gewer* of kittiwakes, the prolonged and humourous *woo-orr-rr--gg* and other familiar protests of guillemots, the intermittent cawing of fulmars and, dominant, the harsh grating rise and fall of the gannets' interminable *gūrrah, gūrrah, gūrrah*. And ever in the background was the hollow booming of the sea, surging to and fro in the high-arched caverns and geo-cracks in the wall of cliff, an intermittent moaning which at first I attributed to seals.

With the exception of the great west slab of the Noup, where only fulmars and a few herring-gulls nested among the whorled blue-green clumps of rose-root and masses of soaking scurvy-grass, there were tens of thousands of sea-birds, most conspicuously gannets, nesting all round the inverted L of the Wick from Geordie's Holes at its south corner to the extreme east end of the Noup itself. The mauve and red sandstone face of the Noup was shaded a dull green and yellow with thrift and lichen; tarred with black overflows of rain-water, spilling over the cliff from the drains cut across the green Head above; and whitewashed over its middle two-thirds with a cream distemper of guano and liquid excrement, voided by endless rows of gannets and kitti-wakes and tens of thousands of guillemots huddled together on long ledges and broad cornice-platforms.

From the dyke, only a foot or two back from the cliff-edge, starlings whistled cheerily and couples of twites twittered sweetly, while wrens whirred in and out of its crevices or perched in song on the extreme edge of a crag 400 feet above the sea. Hooded crows cawed harshly from the holms. Rock-pipits dived over the cliff, down to the reefs far below, on which rock-pigeons alighted from time to time and where pairs of swaabies prowled around. On one broad reef, stained with orange, brown, and green weed, a pack of eider drakes were sleeping in the sun, while other fleets rocked gently on the waters of the Wick, where tysties waited off the cliffs in ones and twos.

From time to time a solitary bonxie, or a pair, sailed out over the Wick, turned, and flapped away along the cliff-wall, emit-ting a buzzing *keg-keg*. At their passing snowy clouds of kitti-wakes would 'shoal' off the cliffs, eddy round, and swoop up to their ledges again. In the chasm of the Wick weaved hundreds of gannets, fulmars and kittiwakes, while the dark oily-blue waters below, which were spangled with white hieroglyphics traced by chains of guillemots, continually erupted in glaucous-green fountains thrown up by the shallow dives of gannets plunging obliquely, as a preliminary to bathing.

Evening drew on and by 8 p.m. there were very few birds on the wing. From the dizzy heights of the Noup the sea grew dark and cold, its relentless swell cruel and unutterably lonely. My will alone held me back from that fatal step into space from the edge of the cliff. Seven years' exile from sea-cliffs had left me defenceless against the lure of heights, and I was glad to go down through the bonxie grounds in the fading light three-quarters of an hour later to the friendly cooing of eiders in the Sound and the piping of oystercatchers around Gungstie, and enter what was to be my true home in Shetland for most of five months to come.

V

THE DAYS OF A NATURALIST

Your chances, during the months that followed, of landing on Noss unannounced would have been slight, with the Sound as a barrier and either Laurence's dogs or mine ever on the alert, should you have taken us on the blind side and dropped anchor in Booth's Voe. (Though a man named Booth was tenant of Gungstie in 1844 the name of this Voe could also have been derived from a settlement of haaf-fishermen's *booths*, as their summer huts or bothies were designated.) Should you have succeeded in stealing a march on us you would probably have found Gungstie deserted, for it was only during spells of heavy rain and in the evening that Laurence and I were normally to be found at home, though the former was usually near at hand, working in his plantie-crubs or in the *crö*. If I had not had an all-night sitting on the cliffs I usually put in from five to nine hours in the field during the morning and afternoon, and then went out again in the late evening.

Should you have found us at home the likelihood is that we should have been having a meal, cooked on stove or primus: potatoes and mutton, perhaps—the latter mainly salted—or fresh or salt herrings, dried or fresh piltocks (the young of the coal-fish which swarmed in incalculable numbers in Shetland waters), salted haddock, oatmeal or pan-bannocks. Centuries of living on salt foods had apparently endowed the Shetlander with a craving for them: possibly this was due to a deficiency of mineral salts in the soil. At all events he did not suffer in health from this excess of salt in his diet, though he seldom ate green vegetables or fruit, while fish was his chief delight. Not only did Laurence and other Bressay men prefer herrings any day for their main meal to roast meat, but they found them more sustaining for heavy work.

You might perhaps have found my wife frying bacon and eggs for us, after a night's piltock fishing with Laurence in Booth's Voe or a row round the north coast of the island to rescue sheep marooned on skerries or fallen into geos. We picked up one lamb miraculously safe and unharmed on a reef at the base of a sheer cliff with a 100-foot drop, though its dam floated, a swollen carcass, on the surge alongside the reef. But seldom indeed were both wind and swell light enough to permit the passage of a *fourern* outside the Sound, and one morning towards the end of June I had to wait for two hours on the Bressay shore before a southerly swell had ebbed sufficiently for Laurence to cross from Noss; and on the last day of the month the Sound was impassable—for the first time in Laurence's experience at that season—and it blew a fresh breeze to a moderate gale, without a minute's cessation for ninety-six hours.

The vile weather—once the cold dry May was out the rainfall was much in excess of the normal thereafter, with a monthly average of more than four inches—was one of the reasons for my wife's comparatively infrequent visits to Noss; that and the gruelling pull from Heogan with small son Brent on the back of her bicycle, and the fact that she soon began to enjoy herself with the merry Bressay folk. What with crossing to Lerwick once or twice a week for the rations and good things that filled the Lerwick shops, fetching milk and mail from Hoversta, the various chores at Heogan, dancing into the small hours of the morning, bottle-feeding some of Thomasina's lambs, *rooing* the sheep—which did not, as sometimes supposed, imply plucking out the wool by the roots, for there was a natural rise of the fleece from the skin—and working at the peat-bank, life was pretty full for her.

Laurence had two peat-banks on Noss in the corrie of Punds-geo at the north end of the Maiden's Paps. His method of cutting peats was novel to me, for the Shetland *tuskar* had no foot-rest and was pressed down into the peat with a left-handed grip of its long handle; and instead of a companion lifting the slab of peat off the blade of the *tuskar*, the cutter himself raised the twelve-inch or eighteen-inch slab and laid it on the bank above in one motion with his cut—a difficult operation for the novice, very neatly expressed in this nineteenth-century verse:

> *Drive da tuskar deep,*
> *Lift them, wan by wan,*
> *Lay them gently on da bank,*
> *Hael[1] noo, in[2] ye can.*
> *Raiz dem to der feet,*
> *Right afore da sun,*
> *Twa or tree tagether put,*
> *Wan can't stand alon.*

As he cut, so he piled the slabs one on top of two, tier on tier, forming a breastwork of peats full of air-holes. During May, all Bressay, right to the top of the Ward Hill, even ground formerly under cultivation, together with many square miles of moor on the roof of Shetland above Lerwick, erupted in dark-brown weals and semicircular embattlements of raised peats, drying before being stacked and carted home. In some parts of Shetland the peat-banks were far removed from the nearest township or crofting and were brought down from the hill to the roadside on overhead wires, on the backs of ponies, and even by boat.

Had you dropped in at Gungstie towards bedtime you would probably have found Laurence lying his long length on the couch, smoking a cigarette, while I puffed at my pipe on a chair near the stove in the opposite corner, from which I could look out to sea through the open doors, writing up my notes in permanent form, drawing up my plan of action for the next day and, at the same time, holding an intermittent duologue with Laurence on sheep-farming and crofting, life in the old townships, fishing, birds, and life in general. The folk of Shetland, like those of all island communities, had been accustomed to make their own laws, and a rough climate and hard living conditions had made them as virile as the Bedouin of the desert. The strong woman of Noss, who went in for smuggling and had her own novel method of manhandling snooping excise-men, was still remembered on Bressay: but tales of the inhabitants, though true and often extremely funny were, alas, unprintable in any form of literature except the realistic novel.

[1] Whole.   [2] If.

Were it a sunny evening, then we might have been found sitting on the long bench outside the house—though, on such rare evenings, I was more often away for a night on the cliffs—while Laurence cleaned his catch of piltocks and I wrestled with the inevitable notes, what time the twin-lambs played among the gravestones in the burial ground at our feet and chased one another around the old fish-drying bothie on the end of the ness. Three or four stone slabs, on which were incised coats-of-arms and skull-and-crossbones, and two or three green mounds, so pathetically small as to suggest children's graves, were now the only visible remains of this old burial ground.

Though the May sun might shine for fourteen hours out of the twenty-four on the wondrous green lawns of the Ander across the Sound there would be an arctic chill in the fresh easterly breeze: but the long southern frontage of Gungstie, drawing and reflecting the sun's full heat, sheltered us from the dank fog skirting the Head and Rumble Wick; and it would be very peaceful, with the English buzz and murmur of flies clustering on the warm wall and about the fish-guts on the flagged path beneath—residues from the piltocks strung up to cure on a line along the wall. Bachelor starlings twitter from the roof-ridge. Noss's one cock sparrow chirps mellowly. A wren trills intermittently from a post in the burial ground and twites twitter from the fencing-wires on the brow-edge of the Nesti Voe, but prelude and *finale* of the rock-pipit's *diminuendo* of notes are lost in the throppling of the Sound. A blackbird's leisurely whistles carry clearly across the Sound from the deserted croft-house of *Houllmastouri on the crest of the Bressay road, while a wheatear on the Gungstie chimney mimics a partridge (of which there were none in Shetland) and from time to time utters a perfect likeness of a shepherd's whistle, deceiving my collie more than once, causing him to rush to the edge of the Sound and bark at an imaginary shepherd on the Ander. Then it flies down from the roof and 'dances' before its mate perched on the plantie-crub wall. Spreading and shutting the white feathers of its tail, it flight-leaps from side to side between two points a yard apart in the corner of the crub, without pause at either point, in perpetual motion.

Fulmars sit side by side with the starlings on the roof-ridge and plane to and fro, with a soft cooing note, over the ness, low along the brow-edge of the Sound, and in sweeping circles over the Nesti Voe. From the voe comes a great din of 'bagpipes' from a flock of kaaloo, seventy strong, now packing before leaving for their northern breeding grounds. The red-billed terns, nesting on the rocks at the end of the ness, mob their querulous-voiced neighbour common gulls, with a prolonged and vicious chatter, resembling the clattering of castanets, and beat buoyantly up and down the Sound, with harsh caws and a high-pitched screeching. Cooing eider ducks and shags bathe vigorously, with loud smacks of threshing wings, in the lucent blue-green waters, and a pair of red-throated divers fish the racing tide, with wailing *ayoo* and wild and melancholy *ow-oo-ow*, *ow-oo-ow*.

The interminable quacking *uck-uck-uck* of the 'rain geese' speeding in arrowy flight across the sky above Heogan and the Sound of Bressay, with a powerful swishing of straight pinions audible from a great height, at all hours of the day, but especially morning and evening, was one of the sounds that would always recall Shetland to me. There were two pairs of non-breeding divers on Bressay, one on the Sand Vatn and the other on the lochs of Beosetter north of Heogan: but I seldom found time to watch them on the lochs. They resembled in flight some giant grey auk with unexpectedly long and rigid wings, and when they alighted one saw the smooth grey head, the speckled ashy-black back, and that wine-red stain on the throat. When I appeared over the skyline of the Sand Vatn hills one morning the male abandoned his mate, but returned half an hour later in the company of a cormorant. When he was still some way distant his mate greeted him, stretching out her neck along the water and uttering a single wail; while he, 'throwing up' and jinking once or twice, squared his paddles and alighted on rounded belly some distance from her, skidding along the water with a hiss of churned wake. Then they gradually swam together and, when joined, dived together once, slipping under barely noticeably and surfacing again some yards apart. Attracted by my dogs they passed close by me and hung about inquisitively for some time, before gradually swimming farther away and settling down in the water to sleep. On a bonxie appearing, however, both awoke and swam farther out into the loch.

Soon after nine o'clock the sun would pass behind the towering pent-house of the Ander, plunging Gungstie into cool shadow, and larks began their vesper song over the bonxie grounds, which were otherwise quiet. On the summit of the Noup, however, there was warmth in the sun's rays for another hour or so, and from its commanding height one could, on a fair evening, make out the hump, long arrête and twin peaks of Foula—the only peaks in Shetland—due west over Grimsetter Loch and the white croft-house of Gorie, lonely home of Jessie Laurensen (daughter of James Jamieson of Noss), whose husband had only just returned from South Georgia after an absence of six years. Free of cloud for once, Foula's wild St. Kildan contours appear impressively, almost incredibly, close; for as the raven flew, the Sneug of Foula and the Noup of Noss were thirty-five miles apart. To the south-west the gentler arrête and craig of the Fair Isle, fifty miles distant, are only faintly visible. To the north, far beyond the central cone of the long island of Whalsay and the easterly projecting Out Skerries, and beyond the big island of Fetlar north again of Whalsay, rises the big hill of Saxavord in Unst and, west of north, Rona's Hill, Shetland's 1,475-foot giant.

At dusk peewits begin to tumble over the moor and snipe 'drum' over the Maiden's Paps and the Head. Though distinguished by the title of Faeroe snipe, there were no specific distinctions in their plumage at a casual glance, except perhaps the brilliant colouring of their orange-chestnut tails; nor in their behaviour, with that characteristic mounting to drum after every shower of rain and on moonlight nights.

There is still bright light in the red north at eleven o'clock, and at midnight, when an orange first-quarter moon is setting behind the hills beyond Gorie and the half-imagined cloud-cap on Foula, the *Simmer Dim* is at its full. The Cradle Holm lies in deep shadow, however, and to climb up from the Cradle to Rumble Wick and the Noup is to pass from sunset into sunrise, for there is a pale pink glimmer all along the eastern horizon off

the Noup and it is light enough to write up notes without straining the eyes. It is a rare experience to be able to sit on the summit
of the Noup at midnight, with my legs swinging over the sea,
and enjoy a warm on-cliff breeze. For an hour or so round about
midnight all is quiet on the Head, except for the occasional
twitter of a hovering wheatear, the infrequent yodel of a herring-
gull, the shrill pipe of an oystercatcher, and the sullen surge and
roar of the sea. For companionship there is only the friendly
beam from the No Ness lighthouse and the dim shape of a
haddock-boat lying to its seine-nets off the Voe of the Mels.
From time to time a gannet or a fulmar sweeps across the void
of the Wick and bonxies are continually going to and fro
Rumble Wick and the Hill of Setter. Through the night there
are intermittent outbursts from the gannets and kittiwakes sleeping on the cliffs and an occasional sleepy *oo–oo* from a guillemot.

Half an hour after midnight fire kindles and flows along the
wind-stretched clouds above the Out Skerries and at 12.55 a.m.
larks begin to twitter abruptly over the Head and the bonxie
grounds. By 1.50 a.m. wrens are already trilling in answer to
their mates' bat-like twittering and broken liquid ripples. The
fire burns ever brighter and more golden and the great north
pile of the Noup glows a warm dull red. Sheep begin to leave
the bonxie grounds to graze on the green holms and *saeters*. At
2.10 a.m. rock-pipits are tinkling and by 2.30 a.m. wheatears
are again in song. At 2.45 a.m. a golden sun lips the sea a little
to the east of the Out Skerries and rises with incredible rapidity,
to the wild crying of arctic skuas: but it is another hour before
the quartet of twites begin to twitter from the cliff-dyke, when
the sun is shining full upon the southern half of Rumble Wick,
and it is four o'clock before the starlings waken.

Back at Gungstie the green of the island is full of the piping
of oystercatchers and the sporadic cries of wakening gulls,
while the feral cats are running about the sandy warrens at the
head of the Nesti Voe; but eiders are still asleep on their roosting
skerries. Far down beyond the Bard a yellowish beam is still
flashing from the No Ness lighthouse.

Standing at the door of the silent homestead gazing out to
sea, I am conscious, as on a dawn fishing, of the cold relentless

surge of the soulless ocean and the fresh cool rush of the dawn wind. Grim and impregnable seems the black mountain wall and cone of the Ward towering up on the other side of the Sound. This is the hour that belongs to all life except man. He seems hardly to be noticed in this hushed dawn world. The sound of an oystercatcher's wings (which will be inaudible at a later hour) as it takes off into flight from the beach, evokes a flood of memories of dawn on other islands.

The transition in June from winter to cool summer—if it could be called that, for there was little noticeable rise in temperature and full winter clothing was still the order of the day— was marked by that vintage weather that Edmund Selous's account of his travails in *The Bird Watcher in the Shetlands* had led me to expect, though up to this time we had not experienced it ourselves. But now for the first time the foghorn boomed hour after hour from the lighthouse at Kirkabister round the corner of the Bard Head, while the Noup and at intervals all Noss was wreathed in mist. From the cliff-top, the void of Rumble Wick became a warm and airless abyss of fog-vapour, in which ghostly figures of gannets and kittiwakes wafted and veered around. The Noup would be invisible and the mist so thick that I could only peer dimly through it to those gannets thirty yards distant from my O.P. At other times, however, when the remainder of the island was swathed in thick damp fog, the Noup would be clear, and there would be the extraordinary spectacle of clouds and shafts of white 'steam' pouring across the Head and vertically down the entire length of the Noup's south face, like spray from a Niagara Fall, then billowing up westwards over the Rumble Wick cliffs, while the late afternoon sun, shining behind me in the west, cast my shadow on a shaft of rainbow-mist laid out on the sea.

Had you visited Gungstie during the month of May, you would have found our company increased by one, in the person of an old shepherd, who came over from Mainland to help Laurence with the lambing. A hardy soul, he was accustomed to take off his boots and socks on the coldest evening and sit with his bare feet on the damp stone-flags flooring the living-room, puffing at his shag and occasionally wheezing with laughter at some joke in his broad Lerwegian dialect, which I found extremely difficult to interpret. Though Laurence was up at three or four o'clock every morning during the lambing it was usually eleven o'clock and sometimes nearer midnight before we turned into bed, for before night fell all the ewes and lambs had to be gathered into the paddock at the back of the house, and those ewes with new or weakly lambs penned in various outhouses—a lengthy and often complicated operation, apportioning the right lamb or twin-lambs to the right ewe. If any small lamb were left out at night on the Hill of Papilgeo, its liquidation by a swaabie was a certainty; and in their first lambing season on Noss the Sutherlands had found it necessary to shoot seven swaabies at the paddock, before the latter were finally deterred from attempting to get at the lambs in the early morning. The bonxie, however, had never been known to attack a lamb or ewe on Noss, in the experience of either James Jamieson or the Sutherlands; nor, for that matter, was there any *bona fide* evidence that such attacks had ever occurred anywhere in Shetland. On the contrary from time immemorial the crofters on such breeding grounds as Foula had welcomed the bonxie for the pertinacity it showed in driving away the sea eagle, the raven and the swaabie, all of which caused losses among lambs and cast ewes.

It was some years since ravens had nested on the Noup, though three or four pairs nested on the Bressay cliffs and a pair of old birds often came into Noss, but were driven off to one coast or the other, first by the common gulls on the Big Ness, then by relays of lapwings and oystercatchers at the hill-dyke, and finally by the lightning attacks of the arctic skuas which, mounting from their breeding grounds on the moor, swiftly overtook the ravens, no matter what their height, and stooped on them from above, when the latter rolled over on to their backs, characteristically, to evade them.

A day or two after our arrival in Heogan I had been astonished to find a pair of ravens constructing a nest of dry tangle on a ledge of sandstone just below the top of a grassy headland only a score of feet high, a few hundred yards from the nearest crofthouse. I could, if I had wished, have walked down into the nest (as someone else subsequently did); and sitting on the nest with her head into the cliff the hen-bird would be unaware of my coming until I stood looking down on her from a distance of six feet. Before the latter began incubating, a fulmar was accustomed to sit on the nest during her periods of absence, while a couple of shags roosted on another ledge below. After a complete cup of moss and sheep's wool had been built into the tangle-stalks, four peacock-green eggs, with very little additional brown marking, were laid and subsequently robbed by one of the crofters who had sheep on the scattald.

By the end of May all but half a dozen of the ewes had dropped their lambs, the old shepherd had returned to Lerwick, and Laurence himself found time to go out of Noss occasionally and give his brother a hand with the work at Gunnista. Thus in the months that followed you might have found me alone on Noss for two or three days at a time, with the boat pulled up on the Bressay shore, and an unwonted stillness around Gungstie: but only on one day during those occasional periods of solitude would you have caught me not working. That was the day when bruised and battered from many falls on the island's tussocky 'nigger-heads' my spirit faltered, after weeks of battling with storm and cold and of driving myself relentlessly in my work. Shrinking from setting out immediately on the normal seven- or eight-hour round, during which I would be subject to the ceaseless attacks of mobbing bonxies and arctic skuas, I stretched myself out instead exhausted on the grass in front of the house —it was a hot summer's morning for once—and abandoned myself to the full enjoyment of an isolated break in that ceaseless round of duty-*cum*-pleasure, which was the lot of a professional field-naturalist. I might lie back and snooze if I wished, record a casual note without having to put any strain on the mind, or jot down pleasant idle impressions of the island, without having continually to plan and organize, and to concentrate on 150 pairs of skuas and some 200 pairs of gannets, and to register almost from minute to minute some detail of behaviour or distribution of this species or that, this individual or that. Had I not heard from time to time the *kek-kek-kek* of a flighting bonxie I would not have known that skuas nested on the island, and there were moments when I devoutly wished that they did not. Before I had landed on Noss in April I had not envisaged for one moment that I would have to record details of the nesting of each of 150 pairs of skuas: the gannet was to have been my main study. By my obstinacy I had let myself in for an almost superhuman task. Before I returned to Gungstie that particular night I had twenty-two pairs of bonxies to check for chicks hatching and four pairs of chicks to find and ring, besides at least twelve pairs of bonxies and thirteen pairs of arctic skuas to check for clutches of eggs—all to an incessant running the gauntlet of their painful mobbing and almost minutely recourse to two notebooks for details of nest-location, probable date of hatching, etc., and to recording fresh data in these; while carrying throughout a heavy rucksack of food and equipment.

And all to what end? Months of labour in analysing and resolving non-consecutive field-notes into sequential and coherent book form and intelligible appendices, followed by more months of working on the manuscript and correcting the proofs, and no doubt the frustration of inevitable delays in publication. My reward? A possibly unique study of animal existence, but sadly imperfect, as all a naturalist's work must be because of the limitations of human intellect and physique, which demanded intervals of rest and sleep; whereas the subjects demanded a full twenty-four hours' concentration day after day during the crowded weeks of the breeding season; inevitably imperfect because, no matter what experiments human ingenuity might devise, the human intellect could not penetrate the animal's ego nor determine the true origins of an animal's reactions to any natural or artificial situation. And, final reward, a permanent record and a memory of one aspect of the sometimes fascinating, sometimes wearying hours that together made up the naturalist's life, with its ever fresh and exciting avenues of exploration: coupled with the writer's life of rare moments of exultation and hours and days of jaded reaction when the expedition was over, the book written and in print, and not to be looked at without nausea for a year or more after publication—the inevitable corollary to intensive and protracted physical and mental effort.

All these things I jotted down by way of mental relief. There was a limit to the amount of note-taking and statistical recording a naturalist could stand, before his spirit rebelled at what was, for the hour, an intolerable bondage—but then I had been out at three o'clock on a cold morning the previous day; it was less than twenty-four hours since I had gone out of Noss after thirty hours in; and after weeks of desiccating cold one's spirit did not take kindly to a return to such arctic conditions, following upon a few days' comparative warmth. But, now, a fine day allowed me to lie and ruminate and indulge in the despicable vice of self-pity. I had thirty-six hours of solitude before me and only my dogs to demand *extra* ornithological attention, additional to the ever-pressing demands of a too cormorant-like digestion.

Perhaps I was provoked nostalgically by the ceaseless and very English wheezing and 'shrilling' cries of two fledgeling starlings running over the burial ground, one after each parent, with threatening importunity; by the summery buzz of a passing moss-carder bee—or, rather, the splendid Shetland sub-species of this golden bee of the moors, which was the only one on Noss, though the Shetland variety of the small heath-bee occurred on Bressay—on her way to the lousewort or the azure star-flowers of the vernal squill, which mingled on the upper parts of the cliffs and geos with luxuriant clumps of bird's-foot trefoil and misty pink thrift, with the universal white and less plentiful red campion, and magnificent bushes of yellow-disked rose-root.

A cat was basking in the sun, close beside a pair of heedless oystercatchers, on the green braes beyond the Nesti. Cats had been running wild on the island for at least fifty years and no doubt for very much longer than that. Though toms had been turned down from time to time all the cats at present on Noss were feral and did not approach the house when men were about, though the rabbit-warrens close at hand were their main stronghold and only occasionally did I see individuals along the cliff-dyke as high as the Noup. There had not, however, been any reversion to tabby colouring: black-and-white, tortoiseshell, and ginger were their colours. Late in July I had found one feeding seven black and ginger kittens with rabbits on the lower part of the Head, where they had their lair beneath the brow-edge of an old peat-bank; and there were two more litters of three and six kittens respectively in the sandy warrens at Gungstie, where the rabbits paid no apparent heed to their strange neighbours. Despite these fair-sized litters the community—the only one of predatory mammals on the island, though there were hedgehogs on Bressay—could not be said to thrive on a diet of rabbits and no doubt some eggs and young birds, for their condition was poor and the total number of adults probably did not exceed ten. No doubt they were originally turned out to keep down the rats, with which the island was infested at the end of the nineteenth century, though it had now been entirely free of them for many years past. Possibly they were also turned out to keep down the rabbits, but the latter had since been extensively farmed and domestic stock had been released, to which albino and black individuals still bore witness. During their first winter on Noss the Sutherlands had trapped one thousand couples; but there were now only some scores left.

From time to time a Norwegian shark-boat or whaler would come into my field of view from behind the Bard Head. All through the spring and summer—for the first time since the war —these Norwegian boats had been bomb-harpooning the lesser rorqual, the smallest of the finner whales, and baiting sharks on flexible steel lines. For weeks past the swaabies had been feasting on a bloated mass of whale's intestines washed up on the rocks below the Cols Ness. If the yodelling and wailing of gulls and the braying of rain-geese were two sounds that would always recall Shetland to me, a third was the even *chug-chug-chug-chug*, minute after minute, of the whalers' diesel engines hammering out their implacable rhythm. On calm summer evenings this lulling thropple from the whale-boats, continually chugging in and out of the Sound of Bressay, would gradually beat its way into my consciousness like some tribal drumming in the forest, as gradually fading away again. A score of them at a time might be seen tied up alongside the Lerwick wharves and one would occasionally put into the Heogan pier with a cargo of stores for the fish-factory, which had opened up again in June, under Norwegian management, for the Shetland herring season—to the great discomfort of all the inhabitants of Heogan, for the stench that poured forth from the factory chimney, when processing got under way, was nauseous beyond all conception and perceptible at a distance of six miles. We could only take heart with the poet who had written:

> Banish care, good folks at Olna, though you're
> > skeenfished[1] with the smell,
> And rotten 'crang'[2] pollutes your lovely voes;
> Though they've ruined your whelks and mussels,
> Spoilt your stomachs too, as well,
> > You, thro' time, will dis-remember all your woes.
> > > I. NICHOLSON, Hentilagets.

The factory's reopening, however, was much appreciated by the gulls, and once the herring-boats began unloading into the factory pits—toiling all night sometimes to unload a heavy shot of 200 crans, 200,000 'silver darlings'—a great white block of gulls, 1,500 or 2,000 strong, would mass all day on the hillside overlooking the factory, their snowy breasts contrasting with the greyish-white swamp of cotton-grass on the lower slopes of the hill.

Built of wood and copper-bottomed, with davits for dinghy and a top-heavy superstructure housing the crew of five in the stern, and crow's-nest barrel high on the main mast, the whalers always put me in mind of Noah's-arks or of Mississippi pleasure-steamers. But these wooden arks could ride out an Atlantic gale and their diesel engines were extremely reliable. There were 300 of them fishing off Shetland this summer, mainly for whales. Three or four weeks' fishing sufficed to load them to capacity, when they returned to Norway to unload their catch—Bergen being little farther from Shetland than Aberdeen or Thorshaven in Faeroe, a matter of a day's voyage or so—the whale-meat being sold for human consumption and also for that of silver foxes.

In July three whalers had begun harpooning off the north coast of Noss, and a rorqual would sometimes breach quite close in to the cliffs, leaping perpendicularly out of the sea and falling flat with a thunderous crash, displacing a great fountain of water. When dark 'boiling' fields of mackerel made silver

[1] Nauseated.   [2] Carcase of whale.

79

ripples on the sea with their incessant jumping, a herring-hog—
as the rorqual was known in Shetland—would turn leisurely
cartwheels through the seething mass, in contrast to the quick
wheels of the tiny porpoises which, together with common seals,
would also be among the mackerel. Surfacing two or three
times every minute, with a white foam along his jaws, one
might hear his 'blow' faintly, and a smooth oily patch would
appear on the sea after he had sounded for a period of several
minutes.

It was in July that basking-sharks also began to appear in
Noss waters, and there were days when as many as three would
cruise around Rumble Wick at one time: first two, perhaps,
cruising together, and then all three apart but on the same periphery; while the Voe of the Mels was a favourite resort. For
periods of an hour or more a fifteen-foot basker, or *brigdie*,
would propel his smooth greyish-black bulk in leisurely circles
round and round the Voe, his long and narrow, whitish-tipped
muzzle often breaking the surface. So close would he pass below
the brow-edge of the Voe that I could see the wide-open ivory-
green gape of his gleaming glaucous-white form and the five
black weals of his gill-rakers striping his drab-brown hide, as he
cruised through the clear green waters over patches of white
sand. At a greater distance he presented an extraordinary spectacle with his blackish-grey crinkly-edged sail-fin protruding
as much as two feet out of the water, for this pliable waving
buckler of hide did not jut out vertically from the water, but
keeled over in a supple bend. It bore every appearance of not
belonging to the same creature as the single-fluked tail-fin so
distant from it, which eddied and oscillated from side to side,
without any apparent relation in either its movement or direction to those of the sail, sometimes bending round almost to
meet it in a circle. After twenty minutes of this circular cruising
close round beach and cliffs the shark might cut a big circle
outside the Voe with only the tip of his sail showing above water
for the most part: but would soon come in again, before finally
making another circle right round the Voe and then out, disappearing after perhaps an hour's cruising.

It was late afternoon before I finally got away on my rounds that lazy day. Twice I got up to brew myself coffee and boil up a tin of soup, preparatory to setting out: twice I came out and stretched myself in the sun again; and it was ten o'clock and near sunset when I finally returned from my five-hour round to the silent house, and after a meal and writing up my notes, and a turn round the west side of the house to see if anyone was about on the Bressay shore, climbed the stairs to bed and fell asleep to the eternal rush and surge of the pent sea through the Sound below the towering mass of the Ander.

Part II

A STUDY OF A BREEDING COLONY OF GREAT SKUAS

(Stercorarius skua skua)

I

LIFE ON THE BONXIE GROUNDS

Here, then, was an island of 850 acres, of which 150 acres were pasture west of the hill-dyke and the remainder predominantly boggy peat-moor with a stunted growth of heather and a luxuriant growth of tussock grass. In addition there were perhaps forty acres of cliff-face reaching a maximum height of just under 600 feet. On the steep of the head were extensive fields of *juncus* and, right round the island, a coastal strip of green grazing with, in such places as the North Croo, acres of an extraordinarily dense mat of the silky-haired ribwort-plantain and, on the Cradle Holm where no sheep had been pastured for eighty years, a jungle of sorrel.

With the exception of the two pensioner ponies, sheep were now the only stock outside the hill-dyke, grazing mainly in the coastal strip; and the only cultivated ground was in the plantie-crubs around Gungstie, though formerly oxen had ploughed as high as the Setter slopes above the Cradle Holm, at Setter itself, and on the Hill of Papilgeo: thirty or sixty acres being, as we have seen, under cultivation as far back as 1733.

The island was no longer permanently inhabited of men, sheep were not an influential factor, there was no fowling or egg collecting. Therefore Noss was the purest type of bird sanctuary and its thirty species of breeding birds were externally affected only by the actions of their own kind. It was virgin territory for a naturalist. Could he learn anything new about animal behaviour in as ideal an environment as he could hope to work? What, for instance, was the daily routine of the hundred-odd pairs of bonxies, reported to nest on the island, during their six months residence?

It will be recalled that in the second and third weeks of April I had watched bonxies going in and out of Noss in ones and twos, visiting all parts of Bressay and its Sound, and that on April 22nd I had found scores present on Noss. When I settled down to study their behaviour in detail I observed, from the vantage point of the Maiden's Paps, that each pair or solitary bonxie stood commonly on its own special mound, with per-haps one member of a pair sitting in the heather a few yards off the mound. There was something of the appearance of the golden eagle about these heavy-standing, conical-headed bonxies. There was that same ruddiness about the head, with its shaggy, lanceolate, yellowish mane streaked with brown and white: for there was much white speckling on the heads of some and hoary etching down the necks of most of them, and a greater or lesser degree of whitish and yellowish raying and barring on their mantles; while one or two had thick white rings round their eyes. At a distance and in flight this pale streaking might not be apparent and the bonxie appeared a traditionally dark-plumaged fowl: but in actual fact no two birds were similarly plumaged and there was a wide range of colouring from reddish-brown to biscuit, the paler birds being especially light coloured on breast and shoulders and appearing tawny-white in bright sunlight. Only one or two were devoid of any white markings.

Green oases in the surrounding bog and heather, it was apparent that their mounds had been used year after year, for the trampling feet of their heavy owners, together with guano in the form of excreta, castings and fishbones, had eradicated the heather and coarse herbage, treading out and fertilizing smooth green mounds of grass and moss a few feet or yards in diameter, mainly circular in outline. The determinate factor in their origins had been that, being in the first place slight eminences, they had provided commanding viewpoints and were thus the obvious standing place in a nesting territory. Where a true hill, such as the Maiden's Paps, was available, with a view over all the moor and up the Head, thereon some of those pairs with territories in the hidden corrie above the Paps were to be seen standing more often than on the little mounds within their territories. Physically, the mounds were mainly rest and digestive places, and most bore both long castings and the bleached cast wings and feathers of kittiwakes, while one or two bore little flakes of purple stone picked up around the crumbling dykes. Psychologically, the mounds were the hubs of nesting territories.

In the beginning I could not pass closer than within twenty-five yards of a pair of bonxies on their mound, without disturbing them: but after two or three weeks a pair would remain sitting with no sign of uneasiness, until I had approached to within ten yards of them—seven yards being the minimum range at which one might walk past a mound without its tenant or tenants taking flight.

When flight was ultimately and reluctantly decided upon it was preceded by a heavy hop or two across the mound, or perhaps a waddling run off it, before their heavy torpedo-shaped bodies were launched into the air with quick beats of immensely broad wings. The pair would then circle around me with a feeble buzzing *kek* or *kyuk*. Owl-like, curiously moth-like, were the comparisons that occurred to me as they beat around on unbending pinions; but when they banked, and the eye was arrested by the brilliant white half-moons slanting across their primaries, it was the buzzard that came to mind. When one pair finally took wing it was likely that others in the vicinity would follow their example, until perhaps a score or more were up in the air. In these days, prior to the nesting, the bulk of them would then gradually slip away to sea in overlapping circles. Two of a trio, perhaps, would buffet each other in mid-air, with a squeaky gullish screeching, falling to earth with grappling talons; or one of three would 'float' a little way with wings arched over its back, mane 'hackled' and beak wide open, uttering a quintuple *keeyuk*, to which its two companions would reply with monosyllabic *kek*.

From the Bressay side of the Sound, a day or two after their return to Noss, I had observed two bonxies 'floating' close together over the Hill of Setter. With wings lifted high over their backs they had rocked with the effortless buoyancy of a tumbler-pigeon and the grace of a golden plover joy-flighting; and after a while I remembered that J. Smidt had faithfully portrayed this floating flight in Edmund Selous's book. In this manner, with wings raised three-quarters to the vertical and tips bent outwards, pairs, trios and sometimes solitary birds floated across the island, with that whistling *keeyuk*, which might be preceded by a harsh *gyang-gyang-gyang*, a deeply nasal, almost goose-like honking. This winged display was a feature of the bonxie's aerial life, both over the hinterland of Noss and also over the cliffs and wicks. So also were the prolonged twisting pursuit flights to and fro across the breadth of the island of couples at a considerable height. Then, swift urgent wings hurtled over my head with a roar as of surf breaking on the cliffs, and there would be a tremendous rush of air from others volplaning with swept-back wings from a great height. Less often three or four would soar together over the Noup, straight-winged as ravens, when weather conditions were favourable. (A bonxie and a raven, in flight together, were much of a size, though the former's wings were, unexpectedly, much the narrower.)

These frequent aerial passages over the breeding grounds stimulated those pairs and single birds resting on their mounds to emulation. Rising to their feet they would arch white-blazoned wings so high as almost, perhaps quite, to touch at their backward-curving tips (as some small wading-bird might do), displaying thus the white patterning on the undersides of the primaries; and, throwing up their heads, utter with wide-open beaks (thereby revealing a lavender-white interior) that repetitive *kee-yuk*. Having thus reacted—and three or four solitary bonxies might be displaying at one time on adjacent mounds, possibly not even rising to their feet to do so—a strained bowing of heads and hackling of manes would follow, before they closed their wings and sat down once more in their places.

These were not the only conditions in which this display was employed. An intruder, alighting by a solitary bird on a mound, would be repelled and driven away by a full display with wing and voice. Similarly, three birds would stand together with raised wings, and make short flights thus—when the wing-beat rate was accelerated beyond the normal. At the conclusion of such a flight, one would settle first by one of its companions and then by the other, and two of the three might ultimately fight. This would result in some desultory flying around of those birds on nearby mounds. Most of the bonxies undoubtedly returned in pairs to their breeding grounds, but there must necessarily have been some unmated ones among them, and there were few species of birds of which individuals did not lapse into temporary amorousness from time to time. As the season advanced, however, each mound or mounds became sacrosanct to one pair only.

One would also run with raised wings a few yards off the heather to its mate on the mound and, on a solitary bird being joined by its mate returning from sea, the two would arch their wings and call briefly, before settling down together on their mound. This was the normal greeting between a mated pair. But here is a bird running around its mate standing on the mound: the latter, however, flies away at this demonstration and the demonstrator sits down in its place. My attention is then drawn to another mound bird, which first drives off a second alighting and then, after standing in strained silence with hackles raised for some seconds, again assaults it: whereupon the two, now being off the mound, fight unconvincingly with striking talons. Then both fly round and, alighting on a different mound, fight again, then fly round again and alight in the heather; and now the second bird, probably a female, walks round the male for two or three minutes in an attitude indicative of a desire to mate. With head pointed to the ground and stretched out in the manner of a gull, she makes tentative little runs at the male who, however, pecks at her; and in the end the two settle down a few yards apart in the heather. The hour for the consummation of the mating was not yet due. Perhaps it was overdue, for five minutes after I had retreated from the mound of a pair that had laid their first egg that morning, the female alighted on it, followed two or three minutes later by the male. The latter, after walking round her with head reared up, talking hard, jumped with raised wings to her back, but alighted behind her, whereupon both arched wings and called.

When the female was willing then the male would advance towards her, waving half-spread wings, and balancing on her back the two might mate immediately. After consummation there would be a brief wing-raising display. The consummation, however, was not always as swift as this and might be preceded by much rearing of heads (predominantly by the male) to the accompaniment of a repeated *kek-kek*; nor was it always successful, for a male might jump on and off the female's back five times without consummation. Here, for instance, is one of the pairs that stand commonly on the Maiden's Paps, with a true territorial mound in the corrie above. The two run forward, rearing up side by side, with the male uttering a variant of the *kyuk*. Then the female solicits him with the customary head-pointing and he jumps on and off her back five times before consummation. After this they walk down the side of the hill and drink at a pool, before making over to their true mound by another pool. There they run together with heads bowed and stretched out and the female solicits again. Two days after this the latter laid her first egg.

As soon as I appreciated the significance of the territorial mounds I realized that this habit of a pair making one eminence in their territory a traditional stand, to which they repaired daily —and no doubted tended to do so yearly—would provide un-usually favourable opportunities for numbering each and every pair and following up their subsequent breeding history; though this presumed that the nest would be made somewhere near the mound. The actual pegging-out of the mounds was not, how-ever, such a simple operation in practice as in theory, and there were days of continuous rain (when note-taking was almost im-possible) on which I put in more than seven hours at a stretch at pegging. One pair, for example, might use two or three alter-native mounds permanently; or temporarily during the absence of a neighbouring pair; or, after incubation had begun, tem-porarily during the absence of a nearby bird while its mate was sitting on eggs some distance from its mound. Again, a pair rising from one mound would pitch on another as much as a hundred yards distant: while another pair would sit in the heather with two or three vacant mounds in the vicinity and yet, when ultimately disturbed, alight on some distant mound. Right up to the post-fledging season I was continually checking and re-checking my peg numbers.

Only once was a bonxie ever seen to take any notice of a peg, swooping down on it after I had stuck it in at the edge of the mound; and I took much pleasure in observing a bird here and there sitting close up against its peg. So confident were they, indeed, that a pair would even alight on the mound on which I had left the white peg sack, while I was carrying a few pegs in my hand to other mounds. On the other hand a peculiar mystery was associated with these pegs from the time that I first began putting them in until the very last days of the season, when only a score or two of bonxies were still on the island. Throughout this period the pegs were continually being pulled up and left lying on the mounds or sometimes removed a yard or two off them. I was still finding them out on September 7th. When this tampering first began I took to stamping them in with my boot, leaving only an inch or two protruding. They were then so firmly set that it seemed impossible that even so powerful a bird as a bonxie could pull them up. Nevertheless the practice continued, and though I never observed a bonxie attempting the task, it was incredible that the sheep, which only visited the bonxie grounds sporadically at night, could or would perform such an operation, and no other agency could be imagined— though that a bird should have such a grip in its beak, or such a power of leverage, was hardly credible.

II

ATTACK IN DEFENCE

It was as early in the season as April 10th that one of five bonxies at the Sand Vatn had mobbed my collie slightly: but for the first week on Noss I passed through the bonxie grounds without a suspicion of molestation; and it was not until the morning of the 29th that a bird on the Setter 'flats' high above the Cradle Holm stooped at me from behind. The next evening this same bird zoomed down on me nine times, dropping its feet slightly, though I was sixty yards distant from what I presumed to be its mound. It would either approach me head on, just above the ground, and zoom up with the buoyant lift of a fighter plane a split second before crashing into my face, or swoop down on me from the steep slope of the Head in the background. On the third morning it attacked me when I was one hundred and fifty yards distant, and on the sixth day its mate also mobbed me, though one of the two gave up after three or four attacks. This pair, number 19, laid their first egg on or about April 30th—the earliest on the island.

If the bonxies' taking up of territorial mounds was the initial factor enabling a naturalist to study the individuals of a colony, their subsequent attacks when their mounds were approached provided an index, thereafter, of the precise state of each pair's breeding calendar: for it was customary for the bonxie to begin mobbing a day or two before the first egg was laid. Exceptionally, one might mob intermittently as much as a fortnight before laying, and it was possible that others did not mob until a day or two after laying: but normally, when a bonxie began mobbing eggs might be expected, and 80 per cent of the Noss pairs began mobbing on the actual day of laying or within an interval of three days before laying. Even at this early stage the attacks might be very savage, the aggressor doing everything but actu-

92

ally strike me. The female of one pair, indeed, twice smacked me hard on the right ear before I moved off her mound on the day that she laid her second egg. There was much individual variation in the intensity and severity of the attacks, and where three or four pairs were nesting very closely together a savage pair would so dominate the others that the latter would attack only diffidently or not at all, circling me impotently, uttering a deep nasal *quaa-aa*. As, however, a pair kept religiously to its own mound, once eggs had been laid, they were never to be observed mobbing one another, except occasionally in the air over a breeding area. In this respect the average distance between one occupied mound and the next was fifty-eight yards, with an extreme range of from fifteen yards to one hundred and thirty yards, though, of course, the nearest occupied mound on *one* side might be as much as two hundred yards distant in the next colony; while the average distance between the mounds of the members of the small Bressay colony on the eminences around the Sand Vatn was very much greater.

There was variation, too, in the bonxie's reactions to the various types of intruders on its breeding grounds. The only birds ever mobbed were arctic skuas in adjacent territories, the raven on its infrequent visits to the Noup, and once a fulmar—though the latter was the one species that frequently swept low and unhurried over the breeding grounds.

Dogs were hounded mercilessly from one territory to another with audible swinging smacks on head or back, a black dog receiving severer attention than a yellow one, and the presence of a dog drew off most of the attacks from the accompanying human. A white sheep and her lamb, however, might pass without incident right through a group of bonxies sitting on eggs: but a few minutes later a second pair, also white, would be attacked when the ewe was almost treading on an incubating bonxie. The latter, however, does not trouble to rise from its eggs, merely striking and pecking at the ewe's rump, until she moves away. Even when this same bird has a week-old chick, and two ewes and their lambs approach it and its neighbour, which is incubating addled eggs thirty-two days set, neither mob the sheep, but jumping up and down, with fanning wings half-

93

raised, as when fighting, peck at the ewes' faces or hover with wings still fanning over their rumps, pecking at their fleeces. Neither strike with either feet or wings, though a casual observation of that unusual fanning motion might lead an observer to suppose that they were actually striking with the latter.

Only one who has worked *alone* among nesting bonxies, without companions or dogs, has any conception of the potential severity of their attacks. When two or more persons were on the grounds together the concentrated mobbing of a single person was dissipated. The bonxie was quickly confused and unable to determine upon which intruder to concentrate. Mobbing might never materialize, was much less severe, and was soon abandoned. This was an important consideration to be taken into account by the naturalist, for unless the mobbing was concentrated it was often impossible to determine the mound from which the disturbed pair originated, as they merely circled overhead without, as was customary, attacking the intruder more severely as he drew nearer to nest or mound, and the locating of their eggs was thus a matter of chance. The student of animal behaviour must work alone, if he wished to achieve the maximum results possible. On those very few occasions when I took my dogs with me on to the bonxie grounds I would be struck only once or twice all day.

While the initial attacks, and also the majority, were normally head-on, the bonxie might subsequently attack from the rear and also from the sides, to the accompaniment of a soft *kek-kek* or, in the case of the female, an anguished gullish screech. The latter cry, however, normally signified that I was in the immediate proximity of eggs or young, and coincided with very severe mobbing. In some individuals this screech degenerated into a mere squeak. The actual attempt to strike was clearly and invariably made with a three-quarter swing down of the legs at the moment of the lowest trajectory of the stoop. There was never any question of the wings or beak being used for this purpose, and this was also Selous's experience with both skuas at Hermaness. It was, indeed, extremely doubtful whether the wings of even so powerful a bird as the bonxie could stand up to such usage, but on Noss the question never arose. It was not, however, the spectacular long-range aeronautists that were the severest smackers, but those that hovered almost motionless, with particularly brazen impudence, just above one's head, dropped their legs, and deliberately struck with swinging feet. When kneeling to examine one pair's exceptionally beautiful clutch of golden-stone and golden-brown eggs—huge eggs with rough coarse shells—for example, the female strikes me on the back of the head and, when I stand up, hovers above me most persistently and aggressively, with that hoarse quacking *quark*, still striking at me with her feet. As one would expect, she is a particularly bold individual, returning to her nest, thirty yards from the mound, as I leave the latter—to sit panting, though whether from the physical exertion of mobbing or from nervous excitement I am not prepared to say. Such distress was most marked after periods of mobbing, but on the other hand incubating birds suffered much inconvenience from the heat and, on a humid day with mist on the hill, sat panting on their eggs, with spiky tongue protruding from lower mandible.

This particular pair were more uniformly darkly plumaged than most, and I presumed that they were comparatively young birds. A minority of the bonxies, probably less than one quarter, bore white markings on the head and these I presumed to be the older birds. As I got to know individuals of some pairs it appeared to me that the majority of the females were paler plumaged than their mates. Without advancing any reasons Saxby merely stated this as a fact in his *Birds of Shetland*. Twenty-two pairs noted as especially savage, pressing home their attacks to strike, were, with one exception, among the earliest laying birds on the grounds and therefore probably among the older birds. While the average laying date of these pairs was nine days in advance of the norm, they were, however, less successful as breeding birds, rearing only 0·87 fledgelings per pair compared to the average of 0·98 per pair. Twenty-seven per cent of them were pale-plumaged birds compared with twenty per cent of all breeding birds.

Day by day the number of pairs mobbing increased and by the middle of May there were some twenty-five doing so with varying degrees of severity, and pair 19, who had then been sitting for a fortnight, would put up a most impressive show. Taking full advantage of a strong north-easter the two of them hurtled down the steep of the Head at tremendous speed, one after another again and again, to brake hard with banking wings and a shrill scream of air when full upon me and zoom up sideways an inch or two from my head. By the end of the month, at the peak of ovulation, mobbing was so general and regular that I no longer recorded it unless of particular significance or severity. As soon as a number of pairs began mobbing there was a distinct stepping up of territorial tension. There was fighting when third birds alighted on mounds occupied by pairs, and there was more aerial chasing and buffeting of territorial intruders than previously.

We have seen that there were two aids to indexing the current breeding history of each pair of bonxies—their possession of a territorial mound and their habit of attacking intruders approaching their mound. Given time and patience these were adequate aids to locating every egg laid. That I did not find every egg on the day it was laid was solely due to lack of time, for it was not always possible to locate the eggs by observing at what point the pair mobbed most fiercely. A few pairs did not mob at all. Others might mob me until I was near the nest and then stop mobbing: in contrast to those pairs of which one bird would attack first, but the other not until I was close to the nest. Other pairs nesting in small scattered colonies or on the outskirts of large colonies might select nesting sites forty or fifty yards from their mounds. In this respect the overall average distance of nest from mound was seventeen yards: but two pairs with no proper 'made' mound nested actually on the place where they were accustomed to stand.

Others, again, first mobbed me when they were in possession only of empty hollows—deep rounds of grasses in wet clumps of *sphagnum* moss so many feet or yards from their mound. Some pairs made three or four such hollows, none of which might be the ultimate receptacle of their eggs. This making of trial hollows was all a part of the heightened threshold of the reproductive urge—for here is one bonxie with hackles raised running at another, which has alighted on the heather after a

There was much white speckling on the heads of some Bonxies

A Bonxie exhibiting emotion

considerable fly round, barging against it in an amorous manner
and then waddling round it with head pointed to the ground:
whereupon the newly arrived one walks away and settles down
to 'round a nest'. The amorous bird then squats beside its fellow,
evincing interest in this rounding operation; but the impulse
soon passes and the two sit side by side quiescent. Similarly, on
the male of another pair alighting, the female solicits him with
the usual outstretched head: whereupon the male raises his wings,
with two or three little jumps, and finally jumps on to her back
and balances thereon, with wings waving, for two or three
minutes, during which the mating is consummated on several
occasions. Fifteen minutes later the female again pokes round
and round the male, but nothing comes of this invitation and the
pair begin to round a nest, up-ended bill to bill, the male imitat-
ing the more vigorous and assiduous rounding of its mate; but
after twenty minutes of this mutually interesting work both take
up position on separate mounds thirty yards apart. From time
to time, however, the female is seized with the urge to rise and
peck about, and after five minutes she takes a short flight and
alights on a mound forty yards from the male and 'rounds'
again. The next day she laid her first egg.

Thus it was that, inexperienced in these matters, I did not find
the eggs of the earliest pair until May 11th, though they had
been laid on or about April 30th. In this instance, however, I was
abnormally misled by this pair's habit, already described, of
mobbing me from the steep of the Head as much as one hundred
and fifty yards from their territorial mound. Despite their mobbing and the existence of mounds the bonxies' eggs were by no
means easy to locate, and only one clutch did I find by chance
without deliberate search. Searching in widening circles round
the mound was often not sufficient, and I might have to retreat
to a distance and lie down. It was in this way that I discovered
pair 19's eggs, after they had attacked me savagely from the
Head, returning again and again to their anxious watch on the
siding. By this date they were the savagest pair on the island and
near their standing-place on the Head was the fresh carcase of a
herring-gull, battered and bloody about the head and opened at
the belly. After I had lain quiet for a quarter of an hour the

ruddy-plumaged female made two or three brief alightings at a place only a few yards from my retreat, and I then discovered that this was their true mound, one hundred and fifty yards from the false mound they had foxed me into pegging out on the steep of the Head above! A few feet from it a hardly perceptible hollow, with a quantity of bent strewn around it, contained one golden-brown egg and one stone-brown egg. When the female flew down to the nest on my departure her mate began to tear at the gull's carcase. (Eggs were laid at 48-hour intervals and the majority incubated from the first laying, though in one or two instances eggs were found cool or cold on the third day.)

On the same day I watched a pale-plumaged pair flying round and round, mobbing me only mildly, waiting to alight on their mound. For half an hour the pair flighted and alighted, flighted and alighted, before I discovered that they had a nest with two olive-brown eggs eight yards from the mound. Again, there was much bent and *sphagnum* moss lying around, for within a few days of the beginning of incubation an untidy litter of grass and moss was commonly scratched out round the nest, which was usually situated on damp ground or on patches of *sphagna* in the heather. Normally heather and short sward were avoided, but one pair nesting on a little flat far down the grassy siding above the Cradle Holm, and two hundred and twenty yards from their nearest neighbour, had a substantial nest of dead grasses; another pair nesting on short sward had a neat round plate of bent and heather for a nest; while a pair nearby had laid their eggs in a small trench in the peat. Some nests were sheltered on two or three sides by little hillocks of heather, moss, or bent: just as those few pairs nesting on flats on the steep of the Head constructed large nests of bents in the great clumps of green *juncus*.

It was a characteristic of the bonxie that while it was so confident that it would almost allow one to touch it on its mound, it was exceedingly reluctant to return to its nest while an intruder was obvious in the vicinity, and not once during the season did I flush a bonxie off its eggs. As soon as an intruder appeared every sitting bonxie would leave its eggs and take up position on its mound, until the intruder had passed on or had lain quiet for a while. Thus, on my approaching one pair, whose two yellow-brown eggs, stained with black and brown blotches at their fat ends, had been laid a week previously, the female, distinguished by a patch of white behind the eye, rises from her nest to attack me and is joined by her mate. I retreat twenty yards from the nest and lie down, whereupon the female alights one minute later, but takes off again and the pair display on the wing twice, before the female alights once more and settles on her eggs immediately (rising again to mob me when I depart), while the male alights on one of his two mounds and eyes me watchfully. Similarly, another pair mob me hard on the morning their first egg is laid. On my retreating, the male alights, struts about and barges his mate who, for her part, solicits him, bowed forward low and pointing her bill against him. Reassured by his alighting, she finally settles down on her nest, twenty yards from the mound, after the lapse of a quarter of an hour. A third pair mob me hard when I approach their mound—they had first mobbed me gently two days earlier—whereupon I retreat and lie down. Five minutes later the female *walks* up twenty yards from the heather and settles down thirteen yards from the mound. She has one warm maroon egg. This habit of walking on to the nest normally distinguished the female from the male. No matter how far away she might alight from her nest she would waddle or run to her eggs after her initial alighting, though this might be as much as fifty yards from the nest: whereas the male flew from point to point until close beside the nest.

Not until two hours after this does the male, the darker of this pair, desert his mate and is absent for half an hour. On his return he alights by the peg on his mound and *gyangs*: but the female takes no notice of him. Again, four afternoons later, this male flies up from his resting place off the mound and gently prods up his mate from her eggs with his bill, but she opens hers aggressively at him, and after a little jump and wing-raise he stands off from her and finally settles down again a couple of yards away. Other males, however, are more successful in their attempts to incubate, and I catch a glimpse of another pair changing-over a couple of hundred yards away, one bird taking a hop or two forward off the nest and leaving for sea immediately. At the same time a neighbouring pair are stimulated to rise from their nest and mob me by a similar action on the part of another bird, which had just returned from sea after an hour's absence from his territory. They alight very shortly, however, arching wings and *gyang*ing together. Eight minutes later the female is back on her two eggs again, of which the first—an unusual grey-green in colour—had been laid six days earlier. Though the breeze is chilly the sun is hot and she yawns and pants and very soon her mate relieves her on the nest, without protest on her part. After being relieved, however, she stands preening on her mound only four yards from the nest for twenty-five minutes, before she too goes away west to sea, soaring to a great height Bard-wards, and I follow her with the binoculars for several minutes, until I lose sight of her at a point that cannot be very far from the Sand Vatn.

III

THE GATHERING HILL

The general stepping up of the emotional threshold late in May coincided with a completely new aspect of life in a bonxie colony. Before I first came into Noss my interest had been aroused by the description given me of their social display on one of the eminences at the south end of the Maiden's Paps. H. N. Southern and L. S. V. Venables had suggested that the purpose served by this social gathering was that of stimulating pair formation and the consummation of the mating. (The *Field*, 11th July 1936.) Against this view had to be set the facts that the gathering had been reported by James Jamieson as early as 1923, when only fourteen pairs of bonxies were nesting on the island; and that the following year, when fifteen pairs nested, a flock of no fewer than thirty gathered together for some three weeks in July. By 1928, when about thirty pairs were nesting, the gathering still numbered thirty.

There was no doubt as to the actual location of such a gathering hill: for, just as in the case of the small territorial mounds dotted about the island, so the whole flat top of one of the Paps had been trampled bare of heather and bent, leaving a sparse growth of grass and sorrel that hardly covered the peat. So, confident of the locality, I built myself a breastwork of turves in the first days of my coming, from behind which I might observe at my leisure this interesting *lek*. But day after day passed and no bonxies gathered on this eminence or anywhere else on the island at any hour of the twenty-four. To be strictly accurate there was one place where a number were accustomed to gather and where up to a score might be seen at any time of the day— and also the night at high summer. This gathering place was the Loch of Pundsgeo: for though an occasional bonxie would bathe briefly in one of the little rainwater pools that pitted a great part of the island and particularly the Setter Hill flat, their main resort for this purpose was this tiny lochan, which was also visited occasionally by such small game as rock pipits, skylarks, wheatears and, infrequently, a pair of hoodies, while an inquisitive fulmar would plane round it from time to time. But it was predominantly a bonxie reserve and only once did I ever see an arctic skua bathe there. Here the bonxies would bathe and sit about on the sandy sward at the edge, preening, sleeping and occasionally scrapping. Invariably drinking on first alighting, they would then bathe for five or ten minutes at a time, cleaning their bills under water in a curious way with scratching claws.

As the weeks passed and there was still no sign of any gathering of the clan I was much puzzled and chagrined, and it was evident that such a gathering could not bear any relation either to pair-formation or to mating, so far as the majority of pairs were concerned, for most were already in pairs, some already had eggs, and many consummations of mating had already taken place on territorial mounds. Two alternatives remained: either that the gathering when it ultimately materialized would consist of the off-duty mates of sitting birds or that it would comprise non-breeding birds.

More than five weeks had passed since the return of the first bonxie to Noss, when, on making my way up the moor on the very cold afternoon of May 14th, I observed with some surprise that a number of bonxies were sitting together, not on the traditional gathering eminence, but on one of the middle eminences of the Paps, where there was only a little trodden ground and much untrodden heather. On approaching them two hours later I found upwards of twenty gathered on the heathery slope of the hill: twenty being the maximum at any one time, for birds were continually arriving and departing. Despite the foul weather they sat for the most part on the windward slope, facing into the north-easterly squalls of sleet. Some territorial significance seemed to be attached to individual sitting-places, for every now and again a sitting bird would float upwards a foot or two, poised on the gale with hanging legs, and make as if to drop on to the next bird, when the latter would either float up likewise and make way for the other to alight or, standing up, rear its head with menacing open bill. Some pecking and exchange of blows might then follow. One bird deliberately tried to pick a fight with a number of other birds, bumping into them in that chest-stuck-out way that the male of a territoried pair sometimes employed when soliciting its mate for coition, and pecking at them with reared head until it was ultimately put in its place by one of those it had attacked. For the rest, there was the familiar wing and voice display by one or two sitting birds whenever a newcomer alighted among them—they tended to sit very close together despite this intermittent undercurrent of aggressiveness among them—while the jumping or floating upwards, as if to alight on a neighbour's back, was of frequent occurrence; but by 4.15 p.m. I had still seen no sign of any set social display, nor indeed was I expecting one, in the light of their behaviour during the preceding weeks. What I did see, however, was that several of the birds were very palely plumaged and exceptionally hoary about the head and mane. At this juncture therefore it seemed possible that the gathering might be instituted by those older (and probably hoarier plumaged) mates of sitting birds, now that incubation was getting under way: but against this possibility had to be set the undoubted fact that it was extremely rare to find a pair with eggs and not find both birds present in their territory.

The gathering was still in being at 7.5 p.m., its score or so of members still sitting in a clump facing the wind—and the next morning too, despite a north-easterly gale and almost continuous and very heavy squalls of rain. On the 16th, when the gale had abated to a strong breeze, great numbers of bonxies were on the grounds between 11 a.m. and 2 p.m. and a clump of birds were to be seen sitting quietly together on the gathering hill, dispersing from time to time, only to be reconstituted almost immediately. Thereafter the gathering was in perpetual being.

It was at this time that I concluded the initial pegging out of occupied mounds, attaining a maximum of 170, a figure that approximated more closely than one might have expected to the 160 pairs I had estimated that there might be before I began putting out pegs. But within a few days of the establishment of the gathering hill, I noticed that some of the mounds I had pegged were no longer occupied. At first I attributed this to the fact that some pairs occupied more than one mound and that on different days I might have pegged two or three mounds used by the same pair; but by the end of the month, when as many as thirty-five birds were to be seen at one time on the gathering hill, I was finding that there were fewer bonxies on the breeding grounds than previously. No doubt this falling off in numbers could be attributed partly to the fact that ninety per cent of the pairs were now sitting on eggs and were thus less conspicuous; but it could not wholly account for the fact that I had ultimately to pull up fifty-seven of my pegs, and it was not insignificant that this latter figure approximated to that of the fifty-plus bonxies which might be seen on the gathering hill at one time when it reached its maximum strength early in June.

Let us consider these facts in relation to procedure on the gathering hill. Day after day a glance at the Maiden's Paps, which could be seen from almost every quarter of the island, revealed a number of bonxies, usually about thirty, sitting quietly together, always facing the wind on whatever might be the windy slope that particular day—sitting quietly in fair weather or foul, fog or shine, except for an occasional bird standing up to arch its wings on the arrival of a newcomer, or for the customary intermittent strutting around with reared head, and for the little scraps and aggressive runs or flights at one another and at those members occupying choice sitting places. Sit quietly as they might, there was always in being that excited undercurrent of latent aggressiveness of one bird for every other. This, considering that the bonxie's normal role on the breeding grounds was to stake out possession of a private mound, was very natural. Intermittently the assembly would break up, as all its members rose and floated away, at some disturbance. Mounting and circling, soaring like buzzards for many minutes over the Paps, they might rise to a height of a thousand feet perhaps: gradually drifting away to sea, but never alighting on any territorial mound within my field of vision; nor was any newcomer ever observed to have left a mound to join those birds on the gathering hill. All through the light nights the latter was occupied:

yet never throughout the day did I find more than one or perhaps two incubating pairs, and often none, that had not both birds present at the territorial mound or in the vicinity of the nest. After prolonged observation one noticed that many of the *habitués* of the hill sat in pairs and that there was sexual excitement, with a pair walking around, heads reared, bill to bill. On one occasion a male attempted a mating, with the familiar little jumps with uplifted wings around the female, endeavouring to get behind her: but the latter refused him and there was general excitement and some fighting among those present—of whom sixty or seventy per cent were always white-streaked and tawny birds with a generally ragged appearance, while even the darker birds showed some degree of white. Indeed the exceptionally pale plumage of the majority of the gathering was its most striking feature.

As, from the laying of the first egg until the fledging of the young, one or other parent (and most commonly both) was in continuous attendance either at the nest or on the mound, it was evident that those brief and infrequent intervals during which only one of the parents was present in the nesting territory allowed barely sufficient time for the absent bird to procure food or to bathe in the lochan. Therefore, those birds that sat for long periods on the gathering hill could not be members of breeding pairs. We have seen, moreover, that no bonxie was ever observed either to come into the gathering hill from a breeding territory or to return to one. On the other hand there had been an apparent surplus of occupied mounds before the gathering was established, and there was a noticeable sitting in pairs on the gathering hill by many of its *habitués*. Taking into account the predominance of pale white-marked birds among them, and presuming such a plumage to denote longevity, I concluded that the gathering was composed, predominantly at any rate, of aged individuals and possibly pairs which, after returning initially to traditional mounds, had either failed to pair up or were psychologically or physiologically incapable of proceeding further with the reproductive cycle. Certainly the gathering held no pairing or mating significance for the majority of breeding pairs. That, however, potentially fertile birds might exist among its members was suggested by the fact that after the peak of the laying season had passed eggs were laid by three pairs—on May 30th, June 11th and June 20th respectively—on the edge or actually within that ground occupied by the gathering; while eggs were also laid by two further pairs on June 6th and June 21st within 110 yards of this area. Three of these pairs laid single eggs and all seven were abnormally coloured, belonging to the pale type with little or no dark blotchings,[1] while three were abnormally long. Four of the pairs never mobbed me—none, of course, had 'made' mounds—and three of the nests were only 15, 21 and 32 yards apart, constituting the densest breeding group of any. One of the three fashioned an unusual nest of heather and reindeer-moss on the bare and trampled ground. A photographer put up a hide on the gathering hill on June 22nd and two days later I found that this pair's eggs had been sucked by a bonxie, their shells being intact but pierced with the beak-holes that were characteristic of eiders' eggs sucked by bonxies. Neither parent was present, and this was my only experience of both parents deserting the nest immediately after the loss or addling of eggs—an abnormality accounted for no doubt by the presence of the idlers in the adjacent gathering. Three of the remaining four pairs, however, successfully reared young.

For two months there was no change in procedure on the gathering hill. Incidental to this is the note that in the second week of June a solitary bonxie began mobbing me from the Hill of Papilgeo. This was the only one that ever came inside the hill-dyke, except those that prowled about looking for placenta during the lambing month of May. After mobbing me a number of times in the morning, it made straight away to the moor: but it was again on Papilgeo when I came down in the afternoon. Thereafter its presence on the hill was sporadic, but it was still flying out to meet me, though without mobbing, as late as July 11th.

About the middle of July the numbers on the gathering hill began to decrease, and on the morning and afternoon of the 24th there was a departure from normal procedure when the alternatively fifteen or twenty-five bonxies present were in a

[1] See Section VII.

state of unprecedented restlessness, deserting the hill from time to time to sit on breeding pair 80's unusually large mound on the moor two hundred yards below. I presumed this restlessness, which coincided with the fledging of the first batch of young bonxies, to be the prelude to the permanent breaking up of the gathering preparatory to departure from the island. This state of restlessness continued for the next four days and when disturbed the members of the gathering would drift away to settle on any mound on the moor below. The big one, however, remained the favourite alternative, and at a given time some might be seen sitting on the gathering hill and others on this mound. When on the morning of August 4th there were only six birds present at the gathering hill I concluded that the majority had indeed left the island. What then was my confusion when twelve hours later I found no fewer than fifty sitting on the hill, a number considerably greater than any recorded for five or six weeks past! Thereafter thirty or thirty-five sat quietly on the hill, hardly noticeable—for they no longer settled on other mounds—until August 17th, after which day the gathering was deserted permanently. As the first bonxies normally began to appear in non-breeding waters in Shetland in the latter half of July, I concluded that the unprecedented restlessness among the members of the gathering at this time did indeed signify its break-up, and that the sudden influx in August was composed of birds from the twenty-nine pairs that ultimately lost eggs or young, for it was in the last days of July that one or two breeding pairs abandoned their territories.

IV

YOUNG BONXIES

It was 4.15 p.m. on May 27th and dense sea-fog swathed Noss Head, where a raven was croaking. So thick was the mist that I found it almost impossible to locate the pegged mounds of those bonxies on the Setter flat I knew so well, and I was weary after spending the previous night out at the gannetry. Suddenly, when I was groping round in the mist uncertain of my precise whereabouts, my old familiar, the male of pair 19, swooped down on me and I found myself close beside its nest, the bleached bedding of which was now well littered around. From the nest I heard cheeping and there, just free of its dark golden-brown shell, though the smaller end was still linked to its neck, was a wet dark-purplish nestling. (Two hours earlier I had found my first arctic skua's egg.) The nestling, which struggled vainly to rise to its feet, was surprisingly bonxie-like and, though only a central slit of its eye was open, its black beak, with diamond-shaped egg-tooth, was well developed. The other egg was still intact, though the embryo cheeped from within.

From the very first hour of fracturing the shell, observable from thirty-six to eighty-five hours before it hatched, the embryo might be heard cheeping. After working for from nineteen to seventy-three hours it would succeed in forcing up a few pyramidal flakes of shell: but once a sizable hole had been made in both envelope and shell further progress was slow and the chick might rest for the next five hours. Finally the shell collapsed and the chick emerged after an incubation period of from twenty-eight to thirty-two days, though as much as twenty-six hours might elapse between the collapse of the shell and the emergence of the chick.[1] The majority apparently hatched dur-

[1] Full data on period of incubation, etc., will be found in Appendices.

ing the night or in the early morning, but ten were known to hatch between 8.45 a.m. and 2.45 p.m.

Though the male of this first pair to hatch out young mobbed me very severely on this occasion, his mate only *keked* around, standing sentinel on her mound after my departure, while he displayed the customary wariness in returning to the nest. Three-quarters of an hour later, when the nestling's eyes were fully open, revealing a dark-brown iride with a dark-blue pupil, the parents changed over on egg and nestling.

At six hours the chick is half-dry and at ten hours, when it is still not quite dry, it *peeps* immediately it sights me and threatens me with its beak, with an angry little *kek-kek-kek*, half tottering as it rears up, one pale-blue foot out of the nest. A partially eaten whiting, nine inches long, lies near the nest. At twelve hours it is sleeping on the rim of its nest and *kek-kek-keks* on my waking it: but it is an effort to hold up its head at this tender age for any length of time, the head falls forward and it sleeps with its beak buried in the ground. By this time it has dried off into a beautiful fine-haired fawn down, darker on the head. Other nestlings, however, took up to twenty-two hours to dry off.

At 1 p.m. on the second day, when the top half of the shell was still in the nest and both parents mobbed me very severely, the nestling was three or four feet out of the nest. It snapped at me and screamed when handled, reiterating a swift *gyer, gyer,* its menacing open beak revealing a pale mauvish-pink interior. A piltock's backbone lay near the nest, while another one-day-old chick had a twelve-inch herring near it. On my retreating, the male settled on the egg, but not on the chick (which I had replaced in the nest), for the latter left the nest immediately its parent returned.

The remaining egg had still no more than a chip of shell off its top end, but twenty-four hours later this egg had also hatched, and the chick was a little way out of the nest, which still contained one eggshell, with the female brooding it. (The normal hatching interval was forty-eight hours, twenty-four hours in some cases and seventy-two hours in a few.) This chick was much darker than its bigger fellow, a dusky fawn, darker on the head, paler on the belly, with pale greyish-blue legs. Unlike those of the arctic skua, however, bonxie nestlings were remarkably uniform in colouring—though one pair hatched two velvety mole-brown chicks from dark golden-brown eggs, another pair a blackish-fawn chick from an olive-brown egg, and a third a sooty-fawn one from a dark-brown egg.

On my moving away the nestling followed me, with a 'teezing' cry. Two other chicks, less than thirty-six hours old, belonging, like this one of pair 19, to pairs with plenty of territorial space, also followed me, with a diminutive triple *kek*, apparently for the purpose of settling against my boot. The elder chick, however, continued to crouch quietly when I squatted beside it. When I sat beside the other the male parent struck me lightly on the head. On my departure this chick followed its parent around, but the latter led it to the nest before brooding it.

On the fourth afternoon, when both parents were mobbing me severely, the younger chick was nine yards from the nest and the elder was not to be found; and on the fifth afternoon, with the parents still savage, both were nine yards out, apart as always, sheltering from the rain against tussocks of grass. Another pair of the same age in a large territory were already two or three score yards apart. In one place, a few feet from pair 19's mound, were six partially or fully cleaned piltock backbones and a rabbit's leg-bone, while another five-day chick had a half-eaten herring on its mound. In other territories were the skins of young rabbits, and a pair of old birds on the wing might sometimes be seen chasing a young rabbit down the hillside.

At 6.45 p.m. one of pair 19 fed one of its chicks by disgorging on to the ground. Its mate eventually joined it and both assisted in finishing up the mess, before going off for a drink at a nearby pool, while the unfed chick wandered around at a little distance. In the far background two other parents were each feeding one chick, four and five days old respectively; and half an hour later another parent left its nest, where it was brooding a day-old chick, to feed or to assist in feeding its other three-day-old chick —for I missed seeing whether its mate, now standing apart a little, provided the disgorge, as no doubt it did. The young were fed at any odd hour of the day.

On the sixth day, when only one parent of pair 19 was present at 11 a.m., one nestling was seventeen yards from the nest and the other scuttling away from its vicinity. After they had been put together and photographed first one and then the other shortly scuttled off a few yards and settled down on a clump of *sphagnum* in the shelter of a tuft of bent, panting with the heat of the sun: for even when a cold breeze was blowing the chicks evinced distress at the sun's rays, and on those infrequent comparatively hot summer days, with only a light breeze, many chicks were to be seen sitting in pools of water or on clumps of wet *sphagnum*.

After the third day two chicks of a clutch were never to be found together either in the nest or out of it, and it was unusual to find even one chick in the nest; and once they had passed the tenth or fifteenth day many wandered far from nest and mound, so that it was not only difficult to find them, but still more difficult to assign each chick to its proper nest. Hence the paramount necessity of ringing the chick as early as possible after the eighth day, when the precocious development of the 'ankle' made it possible to ring perfectly without 'overlapping' the band.

On the seventh afternoon, when the elder chick was twelve yards out and nipped my fingers hard, both parents were very savage, striking my spaniel's back with swinging smacks and knocking off my beret, which no wind could displace, when I bent down to examine the chick. For that matter, as soon as the embryo began to cheep within the egg the adults' mobbing reached its peak of intensity, and I noticed that near the mound of one pair which had a chick working away at a punctured shell, there was the carcase of a kittiwake eaten except for wings and legs; while in other territories were the beaked skull of a puffin and a dead snipe.

The elder chick was now very much bigger than its fellow, which scuttled off into the heather immediately I placed the two together: but development varied from pair to pair, and some elder chicks were only slightly bigger and more active than younger twins, despite their one or two-day advantage.

By the eighth day, when both parents mobbed me very severely, striking me hard several times on the back of the head, the younger chick, now a foxy-brown in colour, was sixteen yards out: but the elder was not to be found.

The next day the latter was again missing, while the younger was crouching in a drain thirty yards from the nest. For a quarter of an hour I lay fifty yards away from this chick. Though both parents mobbed me very severely, the male hitting me repeatedly and most unpleasantly, they were as usual very wary where the chick was concerned, and not until I had retreated another fifty yards and lain down again in partial concealment behind a hillock for many minutes, did first one and then the other parent brood the chick for brief periods.

To judge by the number of fishbones it was still being fed on the mound, but a parent of a neighbouring pair dropped a herring from a height near its seven-day-old chick, probably disgorging from anger or nervous reaction at the unusual presence, in addition to my accustomed self, of my wife and son and the two dogs, all moving around looking for chicks.

At the end of the first week of June there were gales and heavy rains, and some well-known nestlings disappeared. One clutch of embryos lay dead in their shells with bills broken through: though one parent still sat on them and both parents mobbed hard. Another dead chick, about five days old, appeared to have been pecked over the eye. This chick belong to a pair in a congested area on the extreme south edge of the Setter flat, where four pairs nested in a circle whose diameter was only forty-eight yards. Here also was a dead eider duck. Rather than dead you would have deemed her crouching to escape notice, for she sat with her head bowed forward on a little bank. But her beak and the back of her head were bloody, and as I stood looking down at her I could enact the little tragedy—the poor duck trying to run back to her nest, tripping up in the long grass and on the uneven ground from time to time, and those mad devils of bonxies, now at the height of their territorial savagery, continually striking her on the head, until weakened and bemused she was ultimately unable to rise again from her last rest, and just sat there and died.

But on a calm sultry afternoon all would be quiet on the bonxie grounds, except for the songs of larks. Now and again

The initial attack was normally head-on

Curiously Buzzard-like when banking

An incubating Bonxie would sit panting

an adult bonxie would drink from a little dub, before taking wing and sailing out over the Rumble Wick cliffs or down over the Maiden's Paps to the Voe of the Mels. Yet, as we have seen before, it was the rarest thing to find a mound that had not both birds of the pair in attendance. No doubt the sight of a score or two of their fellows on the wing above their particular breeding colony would bring back those bonxies not too far distant. Even at 2.30 a.m., when flights of as many as fifteen bonxies at a time might be seen leisurely circling and planing out to sea, I would find myself still being mobbed by *pairs* of birds, notably those with young, and I could never definitely determine any mound that had not its pair present. On those occasions when the mass of the adults had been disturbed, and were on the wing over one of the colonies, the bigger chicks might be seen scuttling for cover, their pale-fawn down rendering them most conspicuous against the green hillside. When the majority of the adults had settled again the chicks would emerge from their places of concealment, perhaps to feed on slugs and other small game.

In the third week of June there was a second period of heavy rains and there were further casualties among those chicks in process of hatching: one pair, not fully uncurled from the embryo position, dying in a pool of water. After heavy rain had set in shortly before 11 a.m. on the 18th I noticed, an hour later, that the majority of the chicks were very wet and had not been brooded, despite the weather conditions, and I found only one pair of one-day-old and three-day-old chicks dry in their nest. Another pair about ten days old were crouching in hollows filled with water, and black slugs were in the nests and under some of the chicks. But when, after nearly three days' continuous rain, I was fearful that I should find heavy mortality among hatching chicks, I was intensely relieved to find only three dead, and on this occasion not a single wet chick was to be found, even the biggest being dry.

Throughout this period the adults were most savage and of forty pairs visited on the 19th ten were exceptionally severe. One pair, which had smacked me continuously since their chicks first hatched, were so determined and incessant in their striking that

I found it beyond human endurance to examine their nine- and ten-day-old chicks for more than a few minutes at a time; while another bird, with a two- or three-day-old chick and a second clambering out of the nest only half dry with a piece of shell adhering to its neck, struck me on the brow with both its feet; and a third with eggs struck me severely above the right eye.

When first I went upon the bonxie grounds I had been inclined to scoff at Laurence's tales of strangers to the hill beating a hasty retreat from the mobbing bonxies. I did so no longer.

Among those chicks that disappeared during the first spell of bad weather were those of pair 19, and the mobbing of this pair immediately became much less severe, though they continued to frequent their famous stand on the Head and to swoop down on me mildly until June 15th, and did not finally abandon their territory until more than two months after the loss of their young.

V

YOUNG BONXIES ON THE WING

Continuing the day to day history of a young bonxie I found that by the thirteenth day the chick's down was a much paler fawn than previously and was being shed on the scapulars, where blue quills were appearing, while its legs were now a very pale and patchy blue. Differences in development were noted among chicks of the same age, a single chick being heavier than one of a pair, though not so forward perhaps in the development of its quills.

At this age a chick belonging to a pair with a big territory might have wandered as much as eighty or ninety yards from its parents' mound, though others in small territories might be only five or six yards from their nests. One three-weeks-old chick, well down on the moor below the Maiden's Paps, wandered no less than two hundred yards over No-bonxie land, with its parents circling over it. When their chicks wandered to these distances the parents would mob the more fiercely as the intruder approached their mound and *not* the chick, and it was at this stage that I found an adult arctic skua lying dead near the mound of one of the fiercest pairs of bonxies with a sixteen-day-old chick.

Between the fifteenth and eighteenth day black feathers began to sprout from the blue and white quills of the chick's wings and scapulars, and it had lost much of its down, except on the head and rump. Very quiet were these dark-eyed big chicks, doing no more than peck sharply at me a few times with their powerful beaks when I handled them as they squatted head up against tufts of grass, in watery hollows, even in deep pools of water, or sheltered in little peat-recesses a score of yards apart and forty yards out of their nests. It was exceptional for one to struggle when I handled it, though occasionally one would vomit up an indigested fish.

After the lapse of three weeks tail-quills were prominent, the legs and enormous feet were now greyish-black, and the scapular-feathers formed two large black patches on either side of a ridge of fawn down. And now, for the first time since the initial thirty-six hours after hatching some pairs, though not all, were at last associating together, and a pair of these monster nestlings might be found sitting side by side with their heads stuck, ostrich-like, into a peat-bank, only nine yards distant perhaps from another pair of monsters. And there they just sat, rising occasionally to preen and take up new positions a yard apart. One pair, however, of which the elder was very much more advanced than the younger, remained 150 yards apart until they fledged.

At a month old, when both parents would still be striking me, the chick's scapulars and also its secondaries were almost completely feathered, its primaries were an inch and a half long, and it had lost most of its down except on head and belly. The bite of its great bill was strong enough to draw blood from my fingers and the interior of the bill had changed in colour to ivory-blue and mauve.

A week later it had assumed almost full fledging plumage, with only a few wisps of down remaining on its head, though birds of the same age varied considerably in the amount of down they retained, and some twins had reversed their age status, the younger being more advanced than the elder. On the belly all were sheathed in a smooth pale copper-brown mail. On mantle and wing the majority were a dark-brown, lightly or heavily linked with copper or chestnut, and in some individuals this coppering on the back and shoulders was so heavy as to obscure the brown; while one or two wore light-yellow manes of down and had yellow throats, which gave them a very curious appearance. Ten or eleven, however, out of the 114 ultimately fledging, bore no copper links on their upper parts, which were instead an almost uniform drab-black.

When thirty-six days old the far-wandering chick on the lower moor returned to its nest-territory and I found it sitting in a drain only twenty-five yards from its parents' mound. With only a few wisps of down still adhering to its head, it seemed per-

Pair 80's nest and three eggs

Bonxies disturbed at the Gathering Hill

Nestling Bonxies—Posed: the two chicks of a brood were never to be found together thirty-six hours after hatching

fectly plumaged for flight, and it gave me great pleasure to sit beside this splendid young bonxie, whose fortunes I had followed since the day, more than two months before this, the egg had been laid. It crouched quietly by me, observing me with its fine clear eye, still dark-brown of iris and dark-blue of pupil, while its parents mobbed me, one occasionally brushing my head with its feet. But when I threw it up into the air it made no effort to fly. Two other thirty-two- and thirty-four-day-old young ones were floating a yard apart against the bank of a large pool, and the younger, after allowing me to handle it, swam quickly across to the other side of the pool. When the elder of these two ultimately fledged, the younger still swam round and round the pool, not now allowing me to catch it.[1] Two days later it, too, rose on to the wing at the second attempt, after first swimming across the pool. Of another pair, forty and forty-two days old, one sat on a little grassy island in a pool, while the other swam alongside. Others, again, crouched in the long swampy grass.

Another six-weeks-old chick in a beautifully smooth black plumage, faintly scalloped with a copper lacquer, with a few wisps of down on its throat, also seemed ready to fly. (Despite its sooty plumage one of its parents was an exceptionally pale-yellow-streaked tawny bird and the other a pale-streaked dark-capped bird.) When I had handled and released it, however, it just ran away, with shoulders humped and head bowed forward like a pheasant. At this age those young ones inhabiting big territories would run a great distance, and there were casualties among them: for I found one forty-day-old chick dead in a deep drain and another, much battered about the head, lay dead in another pair's territory.

The days passed, and still these enormous, perfectly plumaged young ones did not get on the wing but sat sluggishly in their hollows. The forty-sixth day dawned and, when I was walking up the moor from the hill-dyke at 10.25 a.m. on July 15th, I perceived that at long last the wanderer was flapping laboriously round on a light easterly breeze, accompanied by its parents.

[1] In all the studies in this book I use the term *fledge* to denote the act of first taking flight, not of assuming flight-plumage.

When mobbed by the adults of other pairs, which its parents drove off, it uttered a squeaky form of the female's screech, before making a clumsy alighting after a short flight. Though on the ground it had seemed as big as the latter, it was much inferior in size when in the air, though its wings were long in comparison with its bulk. The whitish markings on their undersides were almost as conspicuous as those on the adult's—though those on the upper sides were only thinly perceptible at the end of the ninth week.

Five days later this fledgeling, still the only one on the wing, would get up off the ground when I was as much as a hundred yards distant. One or other of its parents were now spending longer periods away from their territory and on July 18th, when both it and the other sooty young bird were sitting in holes, only one parent was in attendance on each for the first time on record. At 10 a.m. on July 20th the latter, now also in its forty-sixth day, was sitting with its head sloping up against the wall of a drain, characteristically. After I had examined its plumage, smoothing its head and back with my hand, and admiring the smooth perfection of the pale copper mail on its underparts, it ran off and, when I approached it again, laboured off into flight as if the most natural thing in the world, though this was almost certainly its first flight. It remained on the wing quite easily for a couple of minutes, mobbed by other pairs of adults, before alighting clumsily.

A week later there were fifteen young ones on the wing, for the average fledging period proved to be forty-six days, though some fledged in forty-two days and one, slow to develop, did not get on the wing until the fifty-sixth day. Some were able to take off into immediate flight: others could only just lift themselves clear of the ground and would scuttle along it in between flights. One such forty-six-day-old scuttler disgorged a partially digested twelve-inch fish on my approaching. Another, just able to fly, was mobbed by the gulls nesting on the seaward edge of the North Croo. You could see the parents dropping lightly on to the backs of those fledgelings that were strong on the wing, shepherding them back to their territories and forcing them down to the ground; and a pair in the small colony above the

Setter *crö* evinced much anxiety when their fledgeling flew sea-wards. Some fledgelings on the moor might settle temporarily among the *habitués* of the gathering hill on the big mound already mentioned or on the hill itself. As soon as they fledged they adopted for the first time a standing posture: whereas pre-viously they had, without exception, invariably sat or crouched; but in contrast to the adults, which stood four-square with head and neck at right angles to the horizontal axis of the body, the fledgelings stood with humped shoulders, and were thus distinct from the adults at any distance.

In the last days of July it became very quiet on the bonxie grounds. But on a sunny breezy morning in the first week of August, when there were sixty-four young bonxies fledged and the eldest, now three weeks fledged, was playing on the wing with one parent, there sounded from all quarters a squeaky rippling hunger-cry—a cry heard only from those that had fledged. Though occasionally the cry might be uttered by one on the wing it came predominantly from those standing in ones and twos on their mounds, with or without parents: for now, for the first time, some fledgelings between fifty and seventy days old were being temporarily deserted by both parents. Hence this new cry from those deserted, this three- to seven-note reedy rippling, which bore a faint likeness to the skirling of a curlew or, more faithfully perhaps, the softer skirling of the whimbrel. Temporary desertion, however, did not imply that the adults had ceased feeding their young, for here at 10.15 a.m. is a parent disgorging to both 'her' fifty-two- and fifty-four-day-old fledgelings together, after which she takes the customary drink at a dub and washes her beak. Subsequently, she is approached by another pair's fifty-four-day fledgeling, which is waving its spread wings, bowing its head, and 'rippling': whereupon she makes a little flight away from it. Such dancing was to be ob-served up to the sixty-first day—that is for about a fortnight after fledging.

By the second week of August the majority of the fledgelings were to be seen alone most of the day and as many as eleven might be lined-up on and off a single mound—though here and there one might still be seen with two parents in attendance. The latter continued to mob me, though without striking, until their fledgelings were seventy days old. Only for an hour or so after sunrise, however, was there aerial chasing and mobbing by the adults in any way comparable to that of earlier days.

Between three and four weeks after fledging some young ones and their parents disappeared from their territories, and by the end of the third week of August about one-third of young and old had left the island. Yet, with one exception, none of the fledgelings had ever been seen to leave the approximate vicinity of their territories, other than to circle around on the wing or alight temporarily on another mound or gathering place a few hundred yards distant. Only once was a fledgeling seen to venture out over Rumble Wick, though the old birds were continually there, making abortive attacks on the gannets.

Though the last remaining fledgelings were still dancing and hunger-crying up to the middle of September and one adult, which had lost its young, was still mobbing me in its territory at that date, the bonxies had at last surrendered their six-month dominance of the island's hinterland, and the few adults present during the day tended to gather in such unwonted places as the North Croo, though an occasional pair might still float over the breeding grounds with the whistling *keeyuk*. The sheep, which all through the spring and summer had grazed by day mainly on the Head, the green holms and those coastal sidings where no bonxies nested, now ventured over the moors again at all hours; families of hoodies were raucous over the gathering hill; and round the carcase of a rabbit on the Maiden's Paps might be seen together a swaabie, an immature herring-gull, a pair of hoodies, and two bonxies. Only two young bonxies remained on the Paps, where the sixty-six-day fledgeling of one pair kept company with the forty-day-old chick of another pair.

It was on September 15th that I was on the bonxie grounds for the last time, between the hours of 10.15 a.m. and 1.30 p.m. There were now only about a score of adults and young remaining on the island: but the strong west wind kept them at a great height when they rose at my approach, and I could not identify all of them. With one sixteen-day exception, however, all the young had been fledged for three weeks or more: so we may assume that the last of them would have left Noss before the end of the month.[1] Accompanying them presumably would be the faithful parents of a crippled fledgeling, finally deserting it at the age of 115 days, having watched over it and fed it for more than six weeks beyond the normal span. As far back as August 7th their then sixty-one-day-old fledgeling had broken its right wing. For a week or two after this both parents had mobbed me very fiercely, and it was perhaps significant that the only dead adult bonxie ever found on Noss was one freshly dead at this time in this pair's territory. Big though the adult bonxie always appeared, I had not realized how big it was and how massive its head, until actually handling this dead one.

Though both parents were still feeding the fledgeling a month later they stooped only rarely at me and visited it only briefly, though frequently. By this time, being ninety-two days old, the latter was assuming its first winter plumage. The marked uniformity of the fledgeling dress had given way to a rich mottled chestnut, darkening to brown on the crown of the head, at the shoulders of the wings and on the primaries. On September 15th one parent was still present with the cripple and stooped at my dog—as did both parents of the youngest sixty-five-day-old fledgeling on the Maiden's Paps; but thereafter, we can only conjecture as to its fate, and as to the fate also of more than one hundred other fledgelings I had ringed and which would probably not return to Noss until their third or fourth year.

POSTSCRIPT

In the New Year of 1947 I received news that one of my fledgelings had alighted exhausted on a French fishing-smack off Nieuport, West Flanders, on January 6th. The skipper unfortunately took it home with him and it died the next day, seven months after it had hatched from the second egg laid by one of those pairs with a look-out on the Maiden's Paps and a territory in the corrie above.

---

[1] Two young ones were still on the Island on 18th October, 1947.

VI

KILLERS AND PIRATES

Thus far we have observed the bonxies on their breeding grounds, but what of their *extra*-territorial activities? We have seen that from the first day of their return to Noss they did not restrict these activities to the island and its adjacent waters, but passed to and fro across the Sound, going over to bathe in the big lochs of the Sand Vatn and also of Grimsetter, veering to and fro over Bressay and the waters of the Harbour. We have seen that their passing out of Noss was a cause of concern, not only to gannets and gulls, but to such diverse species as oyster-catchers and eiders, rockdoves, hooded crows and starlings, though no bonxie was ever seen to display any evil intent to-wards any of the three latter species. Nevertheless the cause of alarm was present.

As early as April 7th, the second day of their return to Noss, I had seen a bonxie mobbing an immature swaabie over the White Hill of Bressay, though on this occasion it had appeared more a matter of one inter-mobbing with the other than definite piracy on the part of the bonxie; but it was not until my first day in Noss that I observed the latter in the act of obtaining food. If I ever gave the matter any previous thought I suppose that before I visited Shetland I conceived the bonxie as obtaining its food mainly from piracy on the gannets, especially on an island such as Noss, where a large colony of gannets was established on the very edge of the bonxie grounds. It was therefore with some surprise that lying on the cliffs above Rumble Wick that first morning, with an occasional pair of bonxies or a solitary one flapping to and fro along the wall of cliff, I saw first one and then six of them disembowelling a kittiwake on the sea at the base of the cliffs. Two would sometimes tear at the carcase to-gether, but for the most part there was continuous fighting among the six and two or three at a time would rear up in the water and strike with their talons, hammering savagely at one another with their beaks and threshing with their wings. Throughout the proceedings a pair of swaabies swam around the carcase, without, however, ever venturing to touch it, and they eventually retreated when assaulted by one of the bonxies: whereupon, to my still greater surprise, a fulmar swam into the *mêlée* and pecked up the tit-bits floating off the carcase.

Four days after this I noticed that the bonxies were already flapping purposively to and fro the cliffs at 5 a.m.; and at 7.15 p.m. on the 28th three were again tearing at a kittiwake's carcase. When they finally drew off, satisfied, I was surprised, once more, to see a fulmar swim up and rip at the carcase, while a swaabie swam around impotently; and what was more surprising, on another bonxie approaching, the fulmar shot at it with wings busked (its feeding posture) and actually drove the bonxie away. While I was rubbing my eyes, in my ignorance, at this astounding act, the fulmar returned to tear at the carcase with, if you please, two bonxies and two swaabies, besides other fulmars, swimming around, awaiting his lordship's pleasure. The inoffensive fulmar, the Lord of the Seas! This was indeed an unexpected facet of the fulmar's biology, and cast a new light for me on its status as possibly the most numerous of all sea-fowl. As further evidence of its mastery this particular fulmar subsequently again chased a bonxie away from the carcase, and then two bonxies together, and then another, and then a swaabie. Finally, having finished feeding, it busked its closed wings and twice drove off a bonxie: but in this instance the latter retained final possession of the carcase, the fulmar no doubt being full-fed.

Two afternoons later I learnt more of the bonxie's methods. Every now and again, as was their way, colonies of kittiwakes would suddenly 'shoal' out and down from, and return to, the cliffs. On one such 'shoaling' I perceived that one of the bonxies continually prowling along the cliffs was dropping on top of a kittiwake and forcing it down to the water, where it began to peck it about the eyes and possibly drown it deliberately. On being joined by another, no doubt its mate, the two began ripping up the still living victim, tearing at its neck, with the customary pair of swaabies swimming around. White feathers began to float away on the water and a red dye spread outwards. On an empty stomach I felt rather sick at this butchery, before being astounded to see a fulmar swim up and chase *both* bonxies away from the carcase! While ripping vigorously at the carcase the fulmar was disturbed by one of the swaabies which, however, was chased off by a bonxie. The fulmar then chased away the latter but, having fed well, finally lost possession to the two swaabies.

Similarly, at 8 a.m. the next morning a fulmar was tearing at the carcase of what appeared to be a guillemot, with the usual bonxie and swaabie awaiting its pleasure. Subsequently fulmar and swaabie fed together, with the bonxie still waiting-on. Other bonxies flew to and fro close along the cliffs, but no kittiwakes shoaled off at their passing, and it seemed that the bonxies made only chance kills during their sporadic and spontaneous shoalings. On the other hand a bonxie flapping close past the cliffs two afternoons later, twice brought off clouds of kittiwakes, but made no attempt to strike; and similar phenomena were observed the next evening.

For two weeks, then, I had watched the bonxies at their killings, but not once had one even so much as stooped at a gannet: their sole source of food had been kittiwakes—though sole source was not quite correct, for on the morning of May 3rd a bonxie had harried a swaabie over Gungstie, causing it to release some object, the bonxie going down after it; and the next day another, harrying a herring-gull over the Sound, finally dropped on to it to the ground, knocking some feathers out of its back, when the gull surrendered a six-inch, silver-bellied piltock, which the bonxie gulped, after standing with it in its beak for a minute or so; while, on another pair harrying a herring-gull into disgorging a fish, a swaabie and a hoodie were first at the place of its fall and the bonxies could do no better than alight together on the brae and arch their wings in protest: before taking off to harry another gull unsuccessfully.

By this date the earliest bonxies were beginning to incubate and henceforward their presence at the cliffs was not so con-

A fifteen-day-old Bonxie

Five weeks old

Bonxie mobbing: note the dropped feet

stant; nor were they to be observed at all frequently with carcases of kittiwakes, for shortly before the middle of May the
latter began nest-building, and a ceaseless procession of them
shuttled to and fro the cliffs and the muddy dubs down by the
hill-dyke, passing either over the bonxie grounds, where they
were permitted safe passage, or coast-wise, hugging every indentation of the geos. During a period of bad weather prior to the
eighteenth, indeed, there were no entries of any killings in my
notebook, but that evening numbers of bonxies were working
the cliffs and waters of Rumble Wick in familiar manner, and
one, in company with a swaabie, was tearing at a guillemot's
carcase.

Up to the end of May I had still not witnessed any act of
piracy on the continual stream of gannets alighting on the cliffs,
with the sole exception of one bonxie stooping briefly at a gannet on the 22nd—the day that my first gannet nestling hatched.
A couple of weeks later, however, on the afternoon of June 3rd,
when two pairs of bonxies also had nestlings, I at last saw one
harry three or four gannets in succession, tweaking the tail of
one of them; but it sheered off very quickly from each victim,
evidently not obtaining the proper response from a gannet
carrying undigested fish. Subsequently I just missed seeing
another bonxie forcing a gannet to disgorge, but did see it
dropping down to the water after the fish which, however, two
swaabies gobbled up before the bonxie could get to the spot.

It seemed clear, then, that the bonxies did not begin to seek
food from the gannets until the latter had nestlings: but what was
the nature of the stimulus that initiated piracy at this juncture,
and why should gannets be carrying undigested fish to the gannetry at a time when their young were, in fact being fed on regurgitated and digested fish and not on disgorged whole fish?

After this initial day of piracy, however, there were no further
instances, nor any killings of kittiwakes, which were now incubating; and though there were always bonxies circling over
the Wick and flapping along the cliffs, bringing off clouds of up
to two hundred puffins at a time, I witnessed no attacks on them.
The presumption was that the bonxies, most of whom now had
nestlings to feed, were obtaining their main source of food at the

Atlantic fishing grounds of all these sea-birds. On the other hand, so short were the absences of one or other of a pair of bonxies from the nest, it did not seem possible that they could reach out to any great distance from Noss.

By the fourth week in June pairs, trios, and solitary bonxies were to be seen circling and planing over the Wick and working the cliffs at all hours of the day from as early as 2.25 a.m., yet an hour might pass and I would not see even one bonxie stooping at a gannet. Not until the evening of June 24th did I see one make four abortive stoops at gannets. At 3.15 p.m. the next afternoon there was a similar incident. For once it was fine, with only a light westerly breeze, and at 3.58 p.m. there was a second abortive attempt, and a third at 4.15 p.m., when a swaabie surprisingly seized the harrying bonxie by the tail. Five minutes later a bonxie, hotly pursued by a swaabie, forced a gannet to disgorge and may have retrieved the falling fish, though I did not actually observe this. The attack did not appear to be pressed home, the bonxie flying beside and beneath the gannet. At 4.22 p.m. there was a fifth (abortive) chase, and eight minutes later a sixth bonxie dropped on to a gannet's tail, with what result was not seen. There followed three more apparently abortive chases, the ninth a very long one. Thus in seventy-five minutes only one, possibly, of nine bonxies had been successful in its piratical attempts, and my impression was that these activities over the Wick could hardly be considered primarily food-productive, for all but a few pairs of bonxies now had nestlings, some three or four weeks old, which would demand a great deal of food.

Again, during an hour's observation on the late afternoon of July 1st, when for the first time for many weeks two bonxies were tearing at a carcase—probably a guillemot's—there were three instances of piracy. One was abortive; a second was a very long chase, for the most part on an even keel, and so long that when the gannet ultimately alighted on the water and submerged, the bonxie had passed out of my field of vision; in the third instance the bonxie apparently recovered the fish and swallowed it before the attendant swaabie could filch it.

The next morning a bonxie was waltzing round the cliffs, as they continued to do all and every day. Nine times did this bird make tentative slanting stoops at those gannets continually circling off the cliffs or coming into the Wick. Twice it struck a gannet on the back with its feet, at which the latter looked up inquiringly but took no stronger evasive action than to descend a few feet. Once it upset a gannet's balance by tweaking its tail: but though following this bird for a considerable distance ultimately broke off the chase. Its piracy appeared to be a matter solely of trial and error or success, the bonxie having no definite knowledge of which gannets were carrying whole fish: while those gannets with empty crops displayed no active fear of their persecutors.

Towards the end of the second week in July the first young guillemots began to leave the cliffs for the sea, and at midday on July 12th six bonxies were significantly sitting on the reef at the base of the Noup, below the great townships of guillemots, of whose young ones they would take toll during their nightly fledging. Though present at the Wick for two hours I only noticed one bonxie stooping to retrieve a fish in mid-air disgorged by a gannet, and part of the fish falling to the water was taken by the inevitable pair of swaabies.

At the end of July another cycle was reached when the young kittiwakes fledged and the bonxies were once again to be seen ripping up carcases on the water—this time of young not adult kittiwakes—as late as 8.15 p.m. Nor were the fledgeling kittiwakes their only victims at this season, for on the evening of the 31st one was killing a fledgeling herring-gull on the sea off Pundsgeo, though repeatedly struck, or near-struck, by the latter's parents. When the gull was dead the bonxie's mate then joined it in ripping off the feathers. A hundred yards away another bonxie was killing a second fledgeling gull, pecking at and then standing on its head to drown it, while balancing with raised wings. Once again, its mate waited until the gull was dead, while fulmars and tysties swam around curiously. Other bonxies were successfully harrying adult swaabies over the Bressay croftings and there was much harrying of gannets and also of lesser black-backed gulls over the Harbour.

In August fledgeling kittiwakes were the bonxies' staple food supply off Noss—though it must be remembered that the latter's

young were fed almost entirely on fish—and the waters of the
Wick were strewn with their corpses. As early as 3 a.m. the
bonxies would be at their butchery, with fledgeling swaabies as
jackals. Yet I never actually saw a young kittiwake knocked
down and on the only occasion on which I saw a bonxie stoop
at one, it avoided the stoop with a quick roll. Though the bonxies were continually over the Wick their harrying of gannets
continued to be as sporadic and mainly unsuccessful as hereto-
fore, and in one instance a gannet without a fish lunged up at its
attacker with its beak.

Towards the end of August nearly all the fledgeling and adult
kittiwakes had left the Noss cliffs, and yet another food-cycle
was reached when, shortly before noon on August 26th, as
many as six bonxies at a time were continually working, though
without result, a spiral of some 150 gannets milling over the
Wick. One even pulled a feather out of a gannet's tail but, not
provoking a favourable response, sheered off immediately. And
then I was a witness for the first time of that incident of which
I had heard so much and which had so often been recorded off
Hermaness, when a bonxie suddenly and most unexpectedly
seized a gannet by its wing. The latter crashed—though under
full control—and shot almost flatly into and just under the surface of the sea, disgorging on emerging. Its fish, however, was
captured by two other bonxies, alighting simultaneously with
a swaabie, and the pirate itself made no attempt to drop down
and retrieve the fish from the water.

Shortly afterwards another bonxie seized a gannet by the tip
of its wing. Though this victim was not knocked off its balance,
it nevertheless disgorged, and its assailant, passing immediately
below it, neatly caught the fish before it had fallen more than a
few feet. This incident was followed by yet another seizure of
a wing-tip and disgorge, when however the fish fell to the water
and was retrieved by another bonxie, two others also alighting.

It was ironical that I had had to wait five months to see this
famous manœuvre. But what was the actual position? Nearly
all the gulls, kittiwakes and auks had now left Noss. Apart from
the occasional adult gull or fledgeling only the gannet remained
as a potential food source. On September 1st a bonxie was

attempting to kill a fledgeling herring-gull on the Hill of Papilgeo, returning twice to knock the screaming juvenile on its back, but finally sheering off, distracted by two hundred milling gulls and the mobbing parent. Though large numbers of both young and old bonxies had also left the island, those that were still on the breeding grounds had big young to feed and were hungry, pressing home their attacks to the full. As gulls and kittiwakes also nested in large numbers at Hermaness, it was difficult to understand why the piracy on gannets should be intense there and not at Noss, though had I myself found time to visit this other gannetry the reason might have been apparent by comparison with conditions on Noss. However that might be, August 26th remained the one and only occasion on which I observed this wing-seizing manœuvre. The probability is that most observations at Hermaness have also been made in August when, as on Noss, the gannet is the only remaining food source. In September I observed a new technique when a bonxie, swimming with raised wings behind a gannet on Bressay Sound, constantly forced the latter down, whenever it attempted to rise from the water, itself rising from time to time to hover above it. In the end, however, the gannet was allowed to fly off. And on my last visit to Rumble Wick in the middle of the month there was the more familiar spectacle of four bonxies, one possibly a fledgeling, tearing at the carcase of a young gull, with the usual fulmar swimming nearby; and very shortly the latter flew at them with busked wings and tail spread and raised, chasing all four from the carcase! The Lord of the Seas!

VII

SOME STATISTICAL ASPECTS

We have seen that in the ultimate event there were not 170 but 113 breeding pairs of bonxies, plus a minimum of fifty non-breeding birds and possibly one or two pairs which lost their eggs before I began pegging the territorial mounds and did not lay again. Thus, the complete colony on Noss numbered not far short of, or possibly as many as, 300 individuals, and their breeding colonies were contained in about 300 acres of moor and hill. Where no colony was distant from another by more than 200 yards, and where each colony had its outlying solitary pairs and half-way links with other colonies, no one could be said to be truly self-contained: but there were eleven distinct groupings, with Colony I on the Setter Hill flat further subdivided into four sub-colonies distant as much as 100 yards from each other.

The average laying date in two colonies and one sub-colony showed a marked variation from the overall norm, which was May 18th to 22nd.[1] The average date for the seven pairs in Colony V on the gathering hill, for instance, was June 4th, none laying before May 20th; the antecedents of this colony have already been discussed. The average date of eight pairs in Colony II was May 27th. Lying above the Setter crö, this was the most isolated colony on the island, its nearest neighbours being 150 yards distant in Colonies III and IX. The presence of made mounds indicated, however, that if small, the colony was yet an old-established one, though not of course as old as Colony I, wherein the bonxies had originally established themselves on the island.

The third late-laying group was Sub-colony Ic (May 28th), a colony of half a dozen pairs, some with made mounds, on the southern edge of the main colony not very far in from

[1] Full data for each colony will be found in the appendices.

the Rumble Wick dyke. In spite of this late-laying group, the thirty-six pairs comprising the whole of Colony I were, as we should expect of a large and long-established colony, able to maintain the early overall average of May 17th, five pairs laying before the end of the first week of May and only four pairs as late as June.

No correlation between density of nesting colonies and early or late laying could be consistently established, though the eight colonies with mounds most closely spaced averaged May 18th and the seven with those most widely spaced May 24th.

The 113 pairs laid 219–223 eggs in the period April 30th to June 29th, comprising ninety-nine clutches of two eggs (two double clutches), four clutches of one or two eggs, ten clutches of one egg, one clutch of three eggs and one clutch of four eggs. In the case of a species laying a normal clutch of only two eggs, no very great differences in the colony average of eggs per pair could be expected. It may be put on record, however, that the lowest average clutch per pair of 1·7 eggs was found in four colonies in the later-laying group; and that the only colonies to exceed an average of two eggs per pair (with the aid of double-clutches and abnormal-sized clutches) with 2·3 eggs per pair, were three colonies in the earlier-laying group.

Of 206 eggs colour-recorded 70 per cent were brown (mainly golden-brown) or olive, or a combination of these colours, darkly blotched to a greater or lesser degree with brown or black; 25 per cent had a stone or cream ground, tinted in some cases with brown or olive, and only palely blotched or not at all; and the remainder were pale grey, green or stone. Of clutches of similarly coloured eggs, varying however in intensity of colouring, 90 per cent belonged to the first category and 10 per cent to the second; and there were some significant colour-groupings. Nine each of Colony II's fourteen eggs and Colony V's twelve eggs, for example, had a ground-colour of stone or cream, while of the fourteen pairs that did not lay until June eleven laid eggs of these pale types.

Significant facts were also recorded of the ten pairs known to lay only one egg. Eight were laid after the average date. Seven were laid by birds in small colonies, three belonged to outliers, and two were laid by pairs on the gathering hill. Two were abnormally shaped (only 6 per cent of all eggs laid were abnormally long, round or small) and seven were of the pale type.

Of the two pairs laying abnormally large clutches, pair 80 was the most northerly in Colony III. When I found the nest on May 20th, forty-four yards from that very big mound frequented by the non-breeding bonxies late in the season, the three eggs were already being incubated. One egg was stone-coloured, one pale-olive, and one olive-brown, and there was no reason to doubt that they were all laid by one bird. Immediate neighbours laid golden-brown x golden-brown and golden-olive x stone eggs.

On the 25th two eggs of this clutch were cold and one cool, but thirty days later the eggs were still being incubated and both birds were still mobbing me. On the thirty-eighth day, however, one egg had disappeared and another was outside the nest.

The pair with four eggs, number 135, belonged to Colony Id on the south-west edge of the flat immediately above the Cradle Holm. This was the most remarkable sub-colony on the island with, as we have seen, four nests in a circle whose diameter was forty-eight yards, with two more pairs forty yards and fifty-six yards respectively outside the circle, while the average distance between their mounds was only thirty-two yards and between their nests twenty-seven yards. When I found pair 135's nest on May 29th it already contained its full clutch of four eggs, of which two were olive and two a rich chocolate-golden-brown cicatrized with minute excrescences. The colours of the other three clutches within the circle were olive-green x olive-green, olive x golden-brown, and olive-yellow x stone-brown. So unlike were 135's two sets of eggs that there could be little doubt in this case that they had been laid by two different females, though in view of the special territorial technique of the bonxie it was difficult to imagine how this could have come about; and though I watched this nest for forty-five minutes on this occasion (and often subsequently) it was evident that after laying her eggs one of the females took no further share in their incubation. The present female was a very dark-crowned bird and the only one I observed as being bigger than its mate, which was also noteworthy as being an exceptionally pale, almost white-headed bird. A further abnormality was that this was the only female which returned to its nest in short flights, contrary to the usual practice of females of walking to the nest. In the light of these unusual features I at first presumed the latter to be the male bird, though the white-headed bird was in that case strangely uninterested in the eggs; but as on subsequent occasions it was always the dark-headed bird that displayed much anxiety to return to the eggs when I had disturbed the pair, I was forced to credit this bird as being the female. As in the case of pair 80, this pair's abnormal clutch also failed to hatch and on June 27th one egg of each set had disappeared. The dark-headed bird was, however, still incubating one stinking egg on July 2nd.

In all, fourteen clutches of eggs proved infertile or were chilled by the heavy rains and flooding in the middle of June, when six pairs had their eggs lying in pools of water or actually submerged. Lifting the sodden grass or moss on which they lay, I rearranged them on drier nests at the side of their flooded hollows: but by the next day all the eggs had been moved back into their pools of water again, and five clutches out of the six failed to hatch, while the chicks of the sixth disappeared on the third day after hatching. The fourteen failures were spread evenly over the different colonies and showed no colour significance.

In addition two pairs of eggs disappeared, though in view of the fact that a bonxie's eggs were never voluntarily deserted for a second from the time that the first egg was laid, and that there were no predatory mammals on Noss, it was difficult to understand what agency could be responsible for their loss. One clutch disappeared without trace, and of the other only a few fragments of shell remained. It is possible that one pair's eggs were taken by the adjacent arctic skuas during a *mêlée*, though normally both skuas and bonxies sucked eggs in the nest and did not remove them. Both pairs laid again in the same nests on the sixth day after losing their eggs. Pair 76's second clutch were the same colour as those of its first. Pair 95, however, after laying stone-brown x golden-brown in the first clutch, followed this with pale-stone x olive-black. Pair 76 successfully fledged two chicks and pair 95 one chick.

A third pair, 125, one of the fourteen infertile pairs abovementioned, sat on a clutch of abnormally shaped, very rounded olive x golden-brown eggs from May 16th to June 18th, by which date they were addled. Nearly six weeks later, on July 26th, I found a single stone-brown egg in this nest, which disappeared nine days later. It seemed hardly possible that this could have been laid by the same pair. Normally, after incubating and mobbing for 40 to 49 days, when the eggs would be soft and cracked, and possibly minus a quarter of their shells, those pairs with addled eggs gave up the struggle. One of those pairs, indeed, whose eggs were lying in water, abandoned incubation on the twenty-seventh day.

Some unsuccessful pairs continued to mob me for a few days after their eggs had finally disappeared: but those pairs, such as 95, that lost their eggs shortly after laying did not mob me until a new clutch was laid, flying around me quietly, uttering the monosyllabic *kek*, or sitting peacefully on their mounds.

A rather similar case to that of pair 125 was that of pair 23, whose chicks were both dead in their shells with bills through holes on the thirty-fourth day, June 7th. On June 27th and 29th two more eggs were laid in this nest, but these were subsequently smashed and sucked by bonxies three weeks later.

One hundred and fifty-five eggs hatched in the period May 28th to July 15th. The variations in numbers hatching from colony to colony were striking, but showed no correlation with either date of laying, size of territory, or number of pairs per colony. The three lowest hatching percentages, however, were those from colonies that had the highest clutch figure, while one colony of only four pairs hatched 100 per cent of their eggs.

One hundred and fourteen nestlings fledged in the period July 13th to August 30th. One hundred and twelve of these I ringed, plus eight that died before fledging. There was thus a 30 per cent loss in eggs and a 26 per cent loss in chicks. There were some interesting developments during the pre-fledging stage. Four colonies fledged all their nestlings and a fifth lost only 7 per cent of theirs. On the other hand one colony lost

44 per cent of theirs, another 37 per cent, and seven others from 20 per cent to 30 per cent.

At least three young ones died after fledging: so that the 113 pairs reared slightly less than one young one per pair—a satisfactory ratio, taking into consideration the fact that the bonxie was probably a long-lived bird (attaining to an age of twenty-four years in captivity), even if a proportion of the aged birds were unable to reproduce, as events on the gathering hill suggested.

Part III

A STUDY OF A BREEDING COLONY OF ARCTIC SKUAS

(Stercorarius parasiticus)

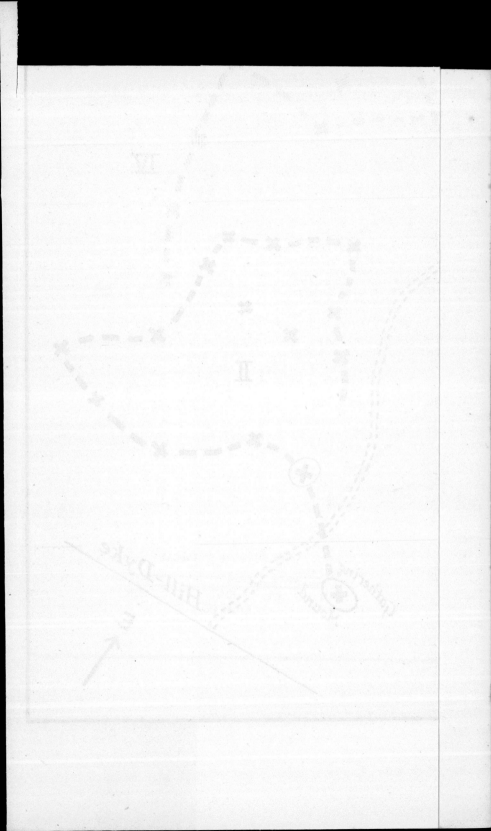

I

THEIR HOMING

It was on the afternoon of April 28th, when I was watching bonxies bathing in the Lochan of Pundsgeo, that a strange cry rang out over the Head, like, and yet not like, the yodel of a herring-gull. Twice more I heard it, but still could not trace its origin. And then two couples of big dark birds, their lines as sharp-cut as those of terns, came swooping and falling headlong over the lower part of the Head. Again the cry rang out, resembling now the jubilant *wick-gewr*, *wick-gewr* of a kittiwake, and the first homing arctic skuas, harried by and harrying the already resident bonxies, dived down to the little Corrie of Pundsgeo. In comparison with the gigantic bonxies they appeared fine petrel-like birds with exceedingly long wings.

This was almost certainly the initial return to their breeding grounds of any of the Noss Skuas—as I shall refer to them hereafter—from wintering in the South Atlantic. One couple, pair 1, took up their position on a hillock forty-five yards south of a small peat-stack in the middle of the corrie and couched down in the hot afternoon sun. They were a little shy in their new environment and when I rose from the slope of the hill seventy yards distant, to improve my observation point in relation to the angle of the sun, one of the pair made a little flight from the hillock. On my lying down again, however, at a distance of fifty yards, it relaxed and drank from a drain, before settling twenty yards from its companion. This restless bird was handsomely plumaged a uniform sooty-brown except for a just-perceptible darkening on the crown of its head. Its mate was a rather paler shade of brown and, with the sun shining full upon it, there was the suggestion of a cream pigment underlying the brown. Especially was this so on the nape and the sides of the neck, in contrast to the dark-brown cap.

The third bird, 2, of the four—another uniformly dusky one —settled on a prominent grassy mound fifty yards north of the peat-stack. On the ridges on either side of the corrie, and from 150 to 200 yards from the peat-stack, were six pairs of bonxies, and there were other pairs on the Maiden's Paps to the south. Only northwards were there no bonxies. That way the corrie shelved down to the steel-blue sea with, in the far background, the long low brown ranges of Mainland curving round to the high island of Whalsay and the long chain of the Out Skerries, which terminated in the tall white light-stack on Bound Skerry.

For a long while nothing exciting happened, and there was no sign of the fourth bird. Rabbits ran around the stack and a wheatear sang from its dome; the jingling bells of piping oystercatchers sounded intermittently from the green holm of Pundsgeo; the crying of kittiwakes passing endlessly up-coast never died for a second. And then, after an hour's interval, number 2 was joined by a beautiful bird with a white nape and belly. A pale greyish-brown band, barely meeting across its breast, alone marred the white expanse of its underparts. This bird was more active than the other three, which had just sat quietly, and pecked about its mossy mound. None of the four, however, displayed any apparent interest in the occasional bonxie passing over the corrie, though those bonxies on the knolls overlooking it acknowledged such passers-by with the customary arching of wings.

After an hour and a half and just as I was about to approach the four more closely, for cloud was veiling the sun and rain threatened, the dusky bird of pair 1 rose and stretched its wings, spread them to preen—revealing a faint white lattice effect on the primaries—and then took off and flapped steadily east out to sea, leaving its mate still sitting on their mound. Its departure evoked a single *ayer-yah* from pair 2, though they remained sitting. This was the cry so much resembling that of the kittiwake and also recalled the kaaloo's 'bagpipes'.

A quarter of an hour later the other three also took wing. Almost immediately, however, three flighted into the corrie again, with soft *pewk*ing calls, and the two dusky individuals pitched down on the heather a score of yards apart, the white bird going out again at once.

After a ten-minute interval 2 moved up on to its mound and 1 to a spot near its original alighting place—for there was no obvious mound in this bird's territory. But on its brown mate coming in five minutes later, it at once took flight: whereupon the brown bird joined 2 on its mound! Almost immediately five more (four dark and one white) circled over the corrie with soft *pewk-pewk* calls and that ringing *ayer-yah, ayer-yah*. The two on the ground appeared to ignore them, though one of them was the dark bird 1. The latter came down to circle close around my head, as dusky as a swift or a stormy petrel, and alighted in its territory: whereupon the dark bird 2 took wing in its turn.

The latter alighted again a quarter of an hour later, when seven skuas were wafting and swooping around the corrie and then chasing out to sea—whence five returned still in pursuit of one another, and two white and two dark birds settled amicably on pair 2's mound and one dark bird near pair 1's mound. Then they were up once more, with wild *ayer-yah, ayer-yah, ayer-yah*: to settle yet again, this time with the two white birds on pair 2's mound and three dark ones near pair 1's mound. Ten minutes later one of the three dark birds rose and alighted *between* the two white ones, without any offence being taken. But in another five minutes the most of them were on the wing again, and the two white birds chased each other with characteristic upward zoom, before making off to sea with other partners, leaving behind the dusky bird 1 and its brown mate. The former was restless, for it first moved across to pair 2's untenanted mound and then, when I flushed it, rose and settled by its mate again.

At this juncture I left, after two and a half hours' watching, but returned again an hour later at 6.15 p.m., when a group of four dark birds were standing *ayer-yah*ing, with some arching of wings. Two made off at my coming, leaving pair 1 *in situ*. Subsequently, after first walking and then flying a little way from its mound, the brown bird flew back to its mate. The latter —the female, as events showed—greeted him with a high-pitched *pewk*, throwing up her bill nearly vertically; and he, bowing his head and turning up wide-open bill sideways, with wings loosened at the shoulders and tail spiked up, uttered a violent cry and nuzzled into her: whereupon she too bowed her head to him. This ceremony was enacted more quickly than I can recount and immediately afterwards they took a fly round, alighted separately and walked far apart, apparently feeding. At 6.45 p.m., when I left for the cliffs, another bird passed over the corrie and both pair 1 departed seaward, leaving the dark bird of pair 2 sitting alone on its mound.

In all, about a dozen skuas had visited the island on this initial day of homing. Of the dozen only three pairs had taken up what would presumably be territorial mounds—a third pair of dusky birds being present in the evening on the grassy siding above the Cradle Holm, where they were harrying members of the small colony of lesser black-backed gulls, which were then beginning to take up territories there. Pair 1 had demonstrated that they were a mated pair. Pair 2 showed every appearance of being such. No ill-will, however, was shown towards other skuas visiting their mounds. Little groups of birds, indeed, took pleasure in each other's company and in pursuit on the wing.

On the 29th there was neither sight nor sound of any skuas about the island from 6.35 a.m. until 2.20 p.m., when two pairs appeared over the Pundsgeo corrie, but made off again immediately; and I saw no more of them up to 5 p.m., when I left.

At 6 p.m. the next evening, however, both pairs 1 and 2 were sitting on their mounds and another pair, 3, had taken up their position fifty yards west of the peat-stack. Of this pair one was dusky and the other a rather darker brown than the male of pair 1, the brown shading into pale grey on neck and throat. Very shortly four more came playing over the corrie with their customary cries. Very dark and sharp were their silhouettes against the heavy grey sky on this evening of light rain. At their noisy coming the male of pair 1 stood up and answered them with the customary *ayer-yah*. But after this brief surge of feeling both pairs 1 and 2 walked quietly about their territories, occasionally chasing insects with little runs and leaps, as a wagtail might do. Then pair 2 took a little fly round and, on alighting again, the white male circled round its mate with spiny tail elevated. On a third bird joining them, however, the three stood together with heads thrown back and *ayer-yah*ed, their wide-open bills revealing a pinkish-white interior.

Meanwhile three others were stooping at a bonxie on the North Croo, beyond the ridge on the north side of the corrie (though none had paid any heed to my dogs), and I heard a new cry; a musical *yeh-yeh-wow*, and remembered Selous: 'Oh, that cry, that wild, wild cry, that music of the winds, the clouds, the drifting rain and mist—like them, free as them, voicing their freedom, making their spirit articulate! . . . Let it live for ever in the memory of him who has sat on the great Ness-side, on the dividing-line of sea and sky, and heard it pealing so clearly, so cheerily, so gladly wild, so wildly, madly glad. So let it come to him again in his own soul's music, scudding with the clouds, driving with the driving mists, ringing out like *the wild bells to the cold sky*. And never let that sky be blue that it sings to, unless in pale, moist patches, drowning amidst water clouds; and never let there be a sun, to be called one, but only a glint and a gleaming, a storming of stormy light, a wet beam flung on a rain-cloud. Child of the mists, of the grey-eyed and desolate northland, what hast thou to do with the robes of the vine and the olive?'

Pairs 1 and 2 were still present at 6.40 p.m. and it was possible that they, and perhaps other pairs, passed the night in their territories, for I heard their cries at 4 a.m. the next morning, and a quarter of an hour later found both in the corrie, besides other pairs on the North Croo, and as many as seven together would come crying over the corrie, continually going to and fro the sea.

By the afternoon of May 3rd, when both pairs 1 and 2 had third dusky birds with them on their mounds, the skuas were returning in numbers to their breeding grounds, at least sixteen being present. When I went out of Noss in the evening a dark pair rose from Ullins Water, that little lochan beside the road in the dip between the Ander and the Ward. To this freshwater lochan the skuas had been accustomed to repair from Noss, for the purpose of bathing, from time out of memory. And the next evening, when there may have been a score of pairs in Noss, a pair of white birds were bathing there, dipping and rearing heads and breasts, with frequent *pewks*, and lying on their sides, white bellies turned up. On subsequent days as many as eight might be seen bathing at one time and pairs would be going out of Noss, Ullins-ward, as late as 9.30 p.m.

At the end of a week's residence on the island there was a raising of the threshold of territorial awareness among the skuas. On the male of pair 1 joining pair 2 in their territory, but off their mound, on the evening of May 5th, for instance, and all three pointing their beaks to heaven with the wonted joyful *ayer-yah*, its mate immediately mobbed the white male of pair 2, which retreated therewith to its mound. (As it happened these were the only pairs present on the island at this hour.) Again, when a brown bird alighted midway between the mounds of these two pairs the next morning it was harried by one bird from each pair: while a dusky stranger subsequently alighting beside pair 2 was driven away solely by the two throwing up their heads and *ayer-yah*ing. But for the most part pairs 1, 2 and 3 were quiet, sitting or standing about in pairs or solitary, rising from time to time to fly round after others of their fellows. When, however, a bonxie crossed the corrie pair 1 broke into a chorus of *yeh-yeh-wows*—the cry associated with the aggressive impulse—and rising for a short flight, alighted on another of their several mounds; while on two pairs suddenly leaving the corrie the cry of the peregrine was heard immediately after their departure.

These three pairs, together with that pair above the Cradle Holm and a white couple in the south-west corner of the moor at the head of the Voe of the Mels,[1] were still the only pairs to be seen regularly at their territories—though some nights at any rate they passed out at sea, for there were no skuas on the island between 9.30 p.m. and 12.15 a.m. on the 10th. Though all were in possession of regular territories, so far as area was concerned, none except pair 2 used the same mound at every alighting, but stood indiscriminately on any slight eminence within the territorial area: the reason being that pair 2's territory alone included a salient hillock, a well-developed mound trodden flat into grass and moss and comparable to those of the heavier bonxies.

By the 10th, however, two more pairs, 18 (both brown) and 39 (dusky and brown), had taken up territories at the extreme

[1] A pair of white birds have occupied this territory for at least twelve years.

south and north ends of the corrie; and morning and evening now there was wonderfully swift aerial chasing by twos and threes over their territories, with lightning-sharp turns, stoops, and sixty-foot vertical climbs, to the ringing *ayer-yah, ayer-yah*: but at midday hardly a pair or even a solitary bird was to be found on the island.

Ten days later another pair, 4, had taken up their position west of pair 3. Of this pair one was dusky and the other brown with paler underparts and a distinctly yellowish neck-ring much lighter in colour than the necks of those brown birds already noted. In addition a seventh pair, 5, had established themselves 100 yards north-east of the peat-stack. One of these was a white bird—probably that second white bird present on April 28th—and the other, like 4, a yellow-necked bird. This new white bird and pair 1 inter-mobbed over the corrie at breakneck speed with rush and 'scrap' of wings, to the accompaniment of that incessant tern-like *pewk* and sometimes the ringing *ayer-yah*. Even when the pair alighted on their mound the white bird continued to mob them, forcing them to bow their heads—at which indignity the two, standing side by side, lifted their heads, with the customary protest—and it also mobbed all other birds present in the corrie, while its mate stood on the peat-stack. After all had settled down once more on their mounds, but were as yet a little uneasy at my newly arrived presence, I could hear a quieter form of the aggressive *yeh-yeh-wow*. But tension was unprecedentedly high among all the skuas present, the entrance into the corrie of any newcomer being the signal for a general aerial inter-harrying. The cause of this raising of the emotional threshold became apparent when at 12.40 p.m. the male of pair 4 after *yup-yup-yup*ing, while his mate pointed her bill to the ground, jumped on and off her back three times and finally mated with her, at which she turned her head up to him, screeching. A number of other pairs were also to be observed mating in various parts of the island on this twenty-third day of residence, including those solitary pairs which, nesting among gulls or bonxies hundreds of yards from the nearest neighbours of their own species, lacked any social stimulus.

At this stage one or other member of those pairs that had taken up territories were probably present in these at all hours of the twenty-four; but except for an occasional song from a lark it was quiet in the corrie at 8 p.m. on the calm evening of May 23rd, with the sun still well up a little west of north after a perfect summer day—though banks of fog and cloud resting on the Ward were a reminder of a chill easterly air. Shortly after my arrival, however, I became aware that the paler bird of brown pair 18 was uttering a strange mewing cry, as if in pain, while bowed forward almost vertically. Evidently the urge to round a nest was upon her, and after a little of this anticking the male made his way to her, and I heard a thin whistling note, resembling the tystie's penny-piping. This apparently excited the male of pair 1 in the adjacent territory, for he flew up and mobbed the couple persistently, and for several minutes the peace was broken by persistent *ayer-yah*ing and *pewk*ing, as the three mobbed and flighted round and round. Ten minutes earlier this disturber of the peace himself had mated five times, to all appearances at the female's invitation, as she bowed forward a little, pecking at the ground; while, on the male of pair 3 running to his mate, the two got together excitedly, head to head, and the latter bowing forward and turning up her bill to him, solicited him to feed her. This he did, disgorging some morsel on to the ground, which she picked up. Having swallowed it she pivoted around on her breast before him with spread tail elevated. Then, after a fly round, she solicited him again, and he disgorged a second time in a different place. (Courtship feeding continued as late as the ninth day after eggs had been laid and it was also observed in a non-breeding pair.) All the pairs in the corrie—at least nine being present—displayed every intention of staying in for the night, as they sat on their mounds or walked and ran around chasing insects; and they were still present at 10.30 p.m., when the Maiden's Paps were swathed in mist.

By May 25th I had twenty-five territorial mounds pegged and numbered, and there were between thirty and thirty-five pairs of skuas present on the island. Their mounds were very much more difficult to site than those of most of the bonxies, on account of the already noted absence of salient hillocks and their habit of pitching down anywhere in a territory, and also because of their shyer nature, which led to their taking flight and indulging in aerial pursuit at the least disturbance—though once I had settled down near a territory or colony they would perform their antics without concern at a distance of no more than thirty-five yards.

During the last week of May two non-breeding pairs, 7 and 28 (the first pair brown and white and the second both brown), had established themselves in the corrie east and west of the peat-stack, and on June 17th another brown and white non-breeding pair, 29, took up position in the extreme north of the corrie well down towards the sea. There were thus now ten pairs of skuas in the corrie, their territories covering an area of about seven acres, with maximum axes of 255 yards x 240 yards: while the average distance between the mounds of the breeding pairs was seventy-five yards, with a range of from forty yards to one hundred and ten yards.

Finally, by the end of June, when the last of the non-breeding pairs had taken up territories on the island, the skuas' total strength was thirty-seven and a half pairs, of which thirty-one were breeding pairs, and six and a half non-breeding—the half pair being a solitary bird which, after associating with an isolated pair west of the Setter *crö* on June 24th, subsequently occupied a territory east of the *crö* for a few days, but failed to acquire a mate.

The thirty-seven and a half pairs had distributed themselves in two main colonies—one in the Corrie of Pundsgeo, the other on the moor south and east of the hill-dyke. There was an extension from the latter colony on to the North Croo, and there were isolated single pairs at Setter, on the moor immediately below the Maiden's Paps, on the sidings above the Feadda Ness and the Cradle Holm, and at the east corner of Rumble Wick. There were fifteen pairs in the second main colony, that on the moor, two of them non-breeding. This colony covered an area of about sixteen acres with maximum axes of 380 yards x 330 yards: the average distance between the mounds of breeding pairs being sixty-eight yards, with a range of from thirty to one hundred yards. Thus each pair occupied rather more than one acre, compared with the seven-tenths of an acre to each pair in the Pundsgeo colony. Excluding isolated pairs the total area within the skuas' sphere of influence amounted to about 100 acres though, as we have seen, the bonxies had driven wedges into the west moor—North Croo colony and extension and also between the Croo and the Pundsgeo corrie.

A Dusky Arctic Skua

A Brown (intermediate) Arctic Skua

An Arctic Skua nestling

II

YOUNG SKUAS

On the afternoon of May 27th the scene in the Corrie of Pundsgeo was one of great animation, with any number from one to ten skuas in the air at a time harrying the west-bound stream of kittiwakes, which were passing down to the Voe of the Mels in quest of building material. As many as eight skuas might be harrying a single kittiwake, striking at it with their feet, as it twisted and turned with agonized *zoo-oo-oo*. The mobbing of bonxies was also persistent, and there was a continual chorus of *ayer-yah* and a circling and rushing at breakneck speed of these giant swifts low over the corrie. Yet hitherto they had ignored the constant passage of kittiwakes over their territories. What was the cause of this unprecedented excitement at the end of their first month of residence?

I had not been five minutes in the corrie before I perceived that the dusky female of pair 2 was behaving in a strange manner, 'sitting back' on her tail and thrashing partially spread wings unstably, to the accompaniment of an abnormal wheezing cry. Presuming this curious behaviour to indicate that she had eggs I walked towards her mound to find them, but could not. A quarter of an hour later, when I was still searching for her nest, she displayed again. The spreading of the primaries, drooping to the ground on either side of her, revealed the two long white quill-stripes which, in flight, formed a thin white margin to the front edge of the wing. Though, by her displaying again, I supposed myself to be close to the nest its whereabouts still eluded me, and it was not until a third attempt ten minutes later that I found one warm egg on a little round of dead bents in the thick herbage nineteen yards from her mound. The round of bents was just laid flat on the ground and no attempt had been made to hollow out the ground, as the bonxie

149

normally did. The egg—very small in comparison with the latter's—was a dark olive-brown heavily mottled with brown and dark-brown blotches.

The next morning she had laid a second similarly marked egg. She was still the only Pundsgeo bird with an egg, though the male of a pair on the west moor had mobbed one of my dogs— the first to do so—while his mate displayed in the curious manner already described, but I was unable to find their nest. Though the Pundsgeo corrie pairs were quiet on this morning of thick mist there was great activity on the moor, with those bonxies on the southern edge of the skua colony mobbing me and the skuas harrying them, playing with them as they pleased, with their marvellously swift flight, and striking them with their feet with tremendous and audible force, without the bonxies re-taliating.

On the evening of the 30th, I observed that the male of pair 1 was waving spread wings to the accompaniment of a chittering *ik-ik-ik*: but he did not return to a nest the while I leant up against the peat-stack; so, eventually I circled his pegged mound in widening rounds and found one pale-olive egg lying on a few wisps of bent ten yards off the mound. And though neither of pair 18 in the adjacent territory displayed, I very quickly located a single olive egg belonging to them on a little mat of dead bents thirteen yards from their mound. As I hurried Gungstie-wards, after nine hours on the hill, two screaming pairs on the moor were falling about with waving wings, and I happened by chance on two dull-olive eggs belonging to one of them lying on the bare sward of a little ridge eleven yards from their mound —twenty-five yards off the mound being the maximum dis-tance from it that any pair laid their eggs. It was evidently high time that I was ascertaining the precise stage reached by all the pairs, and, after intensive search the next day, I located a further six clutches, including a pale olive-green egg, with a blurred brown zone, belonging to pair 3; but details of these and subse-quent stages of the reproductive cycle, and also of the varied patterns of display and mobbing, will require separate chapters, while full data is given in the appendices.

I was surprised to find that pairs 1 and 18 still had only one cold egg apiece on the morning of June 1st and both females were absent. Pairs 2 and 3, however, had laid theirs on consecutive days and pair 39 on the first and third days. Though pair 3's eggs were cool the female displayed, running crouched along the ground, with an incessant *jig-jig-jig*. In the afternoon both pair 1 were present and their egg was warm, though neither displayed. I found ultimately that the second egg might be laid on the second, third, or fourth day: though only pairs 1 and 18 allowed the maximum interval of seventy-two hours to elapse between the laying of their two eggs. The male skuas were more often out at sea than present in their territories, but they did a certain amount of incubating: the change-over on the nest being conducted without ceremony.

A fortnight elapsed. Then on June 17 I found that one of pair 2's eggs was just perceptibly fractured, and the next day the fracture though still slight, extended half the way round the top of the egg. Two days after this there was a small hole in the shell and a cheeping chick was working away within. Though both parents were present they neither displayed nor mobbed me, but stood quietly on their mound. Five hours later the diameter of the hole had increased from half to three-quarters of an inch and the egg had turned over, with the hole to the ground.

On the morning of the 21st, about ninety hours after the first fracturing and on the twenty-sixth day of incubation, the chick had hatched, and on the bents, just free of its shell, its purplish hair barely covering its raw-pink skin, was the nestling. Its fellow was working at a half-inch hole in the other egg. Again, both parents were present and the female displayed slightly, but I was not subjected to any mobbing until I had examined the nestling and had retreated forty yards, when the white male attacked me once.

The next afternoon the other chick had also hatched on the twenty-sixth day, less than forty hours after the first fracture, and had nearly dried off into a velvety blackish-brown down of a peculiarly silky mole-like texture. (The period from hatching to drying-off in the one instance recorded precisely proved to be thirteen hours.) Its irides, like those of the bonxie nestlings, were brown with dark-blue pupils; its gape was pale-pink; its legs and feet palest pinkish-blue, the latter being semi-transparent. By this time its fellow nestling was two feet out of the nest, and both parents were again present, the female displaying only slightly, as on the previous occasion.

By the 24th, when both nestlings were seven yards out of the nest, no marked increase or disparity in their size was noticeable: whereas the three-day-old nestling of another pair was very much bigger than its imperfectly dry fellow. The latter pecked repeatedly at the elder and gripped it by the bill when I placed the two together in the nest: just as all these skua nestlings, in contrast to those of the bonxies, pecked at my fingers, while one almost ready to fly would first peck at my fingers and then, with characteristic confusion, at its own carpal joints. This morning pair 1's first nestling (also hatched on the twenty-sixth day, twenty-five to twenty-six days being the normal incubation period) had already moved towards the edge of its nest, though only three parts dried, and the female mobbed me, as she had been doing since June 8th. Twenty-four hours later this nestling was under a bank four yards out of the nest: but the second chick did not hatch until the 27th—an interval complementary to the seventy-two hours that had elapsed between the laying of the two eggs.

As soon as a skua nestling gained sufficient strength its main objective was to get out of the nest and away from its fellow, and thirty-six hours after the first had hatched the two nestlings were never to be found together in the nest. On the 26th, indeed, I rescued one pair's three-day-old nestling from a burrow halfway down the far side of a drain two feet wide, while the female mobbed me.

By July 1st pair 2's younger nestling, now ten days old, was twenty-seven yards away from the nest and its elder fellow was not to be found. The sooty female sat unconcerned on her mound, while I hunted around, for when their young hatched some of the adults became much more confident, allowing me to approach to within eight yards of them without betraying uneasiness. The female of pair 1, however, and both pair 5, whose young one had hatched on the 23rd, continued to mob me directly I approached their territories. Once the nestlings reached the age of ten days I had the greatest difficulty in finding them in their lairs in the long grass, and to keep track of them it was essential that they should be ringed as soon as possible after the ninth day, by which age the 'ankle' was of a size to retain the ring without its overlapping. Moreover 80 per cent of the casualties among young occurred in this first ten days after hatching. Such evidence as there was suggested that this mortality—30 per cent of the total hatch—was caused mainly by the adult skuas themselves attacking those nestlings of neighbouring pairs wandering into their territories which, as we have seen, were very crowded in the two main colonies. On July 4th, for instance, the older of pair 39's nestlings—a six-day-old chick—had wandered into pair 2's territory and lay dead by the latter's mound, seventy-five yards from its own nest; and previous to this on June 29th, when neither of another pair of adults on the west moor were present in their territory, I found that their elder nine-day nestling had been killed by pecks on the side of the head, though this territory was far removed from those of any bonxies—which in any case were never permitted to alight in the skuas' territories. Where, however, the latter were adjacent to those of the bonxies, then there was a tendency for the parents to attract the young outwards from the bonxie territories. It was possible that both nestlings of one pair on the North Croo were killed by a bonxie whose big nestling had strayed near their territory: while those of another pair on the Croo may have succumbed to a lesser black-backed gull which also had chicks there. On the other hand a third pair, whose isolated territory was adjacent to that earlier mentioned savage bonxie, reared both their young successfully.

It has been noted that both parents of one pair were absent from their territory when their elder chick was nine days old. In marked contrast to the behaviour of the bonxies the majority of the skuas began to desert their young temporarily about the tenth day, one pair indeed deserting theirs for a short interval as early as the fourth day. There were, however, exceptions to this practice, for the females of pairs 1 and 2 were never observed by me to leave their territories during the hours of daylight, though their mates put in only intermittent and brief appearances.

On the evening of July 8th I watched the female of pair 2 feed her two young, about forty yards apart, disgorging on to the ground to them, while the male sat on his mound. She then went out to sea and did not return for the next hour. On her departure the two young ones started walking about, taking no notice, however, of the white male sitting on the mound in full view of them. Though they were 150 yards distant from me I could see the rings on their legs flashing in the evening sun. After ten minutes' exercise both went into cover, though the elder made a brief appearance a quarter of an hour later. On my return nearly two hours after this, the female was back again.

Three evenings later the male of pair 3 arrived from sea and, alighting on his mound, circled with little paces about his mate in courting posture with head stretched out low to the ground. Both then flew off a little way to (as I supposed) drink from a drain, and on their return a young one approached them: whereupon both flew to it and the male, with that same courting posture, brought up a thin silver fish which the young one took from his bill, dropped, picked up from the ground, and swallowed. The female took an active interest in the proceedings, during which they were persistently mobbed by adjacent pair 4. The latter, having lost their first clutch of olive eggs, were now completing the incubation of a second clutch—olive in colour like the first but of a rather duller pigment with heavy brown blotching—in a new 'nest' twenty-five yards from their first one. On the 15th this pair triumphantly hatched one velvety blackish-brown chick, but on August 7th Laurence Sutherland found the latter dead near pair 1's mound.

III

FLEDGELINGS AND PIRATES

On the fine calm night of July 15th I was making my way along the sea edge of the North Croo, bound for the guillemots' cliffs, when I was astonished to see a young skua on the wing in slow flapping flight. With golden-chestnut head, mane and breast gleaming in the evening sun it was a breath-takingly beautiful bird in its first flight plumage, which bore not the slightest resemblance to any of the adult phases and for which none of the pre-fledging plumages had prepared me. This unseasonable fledgeling belonged to a pair of whose territory I had been aware since the earliest days, but whose eggs—they being one of the non-displaying pairs—I had never had time to find on the Croo's shorn plantain-pasture devoid of landmark, though these must have been laid more than a week earlier than any in the Pundsgeo colony. Mobbed by other pairs of adults on the Croo, at which the one parent present stooped, the fledgeling threw-up a fish in mid-air, the disgorge being caught by one of its assailants, and alighted clumsily. Two days later it was quite strong on the wing. On this day, July 17th, the island was entombed in its thickest sea-fog and there was a great chorus of *eyer-yah*ing in the Pundsgeo corrie in the afternoon, with that swift chase of urgent wings I recalled from other foggy days in a time that now seemed aeons gone.

By the 20th, pair 2's younger chick also seemed all set for its first flight. In contrast to the golden fledgeling this was a dark-brown bird with copper-coloured underparts and ivory-blue legs paling off into an ivory-white patch at the base of the black webbed feet. But it was the next afternoon, on the thirtieth day after hatching, that it first rose on the wing as I approached its territory and, after a seventy-five-yard flight across the corrie, tumbled on to its head on alighting. It still, however, preferred walking to flight and on my retreating walked around for long distances. Forty minutes later both young ones of this pair were walking about on pair 39's ridge attended by the female, while the male sat on his mound, tern-like, stern and spiky tail projecting in a long upward slant. On this rare summer day, with wisps of fog-cloud clinging to the Noup, I could make out the bright rings on the chick's legs at a distance of 250 yards and the elder chick shone a glossy black, much blacker than its sooty parent. After drinking twice ten minutes later the male went out to sea—returning after forty minutes—and when I subsequently approached the elder chick it, too, took wing (on the thirty-first day) with less effort than the younger, and also made a seventy-five-yard flight with a good alighting, followed by a two-minute flight round the corrie, terminating in a partial tumble.

On the moor a uniformly dark-brown fledgeling was sitting *upright* beside its crouching and still unfledged younger fellow, a black bird with a tawny mane and throat and copper underparts. As soon as the young skua got on the wing, but not before —and the average fledging period was twenty-nine to thirty days, with extremes of twenty-seven and thirty-three days—it assumed this upright posture when sitting, in contrast to the crouching posture to which it adhered consistently throughout the pre-fledging stage, even when fully feathered. Similarly, it was only during the last week before fledging that pairs of young were to be found sitting together.

By the 25th both pair 2's fledgelings were strong on the wing on the fifth day after fledging, even twisting and turning a little in flight, and when the male parent took wing from his mound the elder fledgeling flew after him and solicited food from him with the same antic as the courting adult; but I could not see whether it was fed or not though, as the parent subsequently drank, it probably was. On the male returning to his mound the fledgeling harried its fellow, swooping up vertically and hovering above it like an adult, striking it with its feet. After this exhibition it again solicited its parent; whereupon the latter flew away to sea and the fledgeling took its place on the mound. The male returned after an absence of twenty minutes and this time

The round of bents was just laid flat on the ground

Posed! Two nestlings of a brood were never to be found together
thirty-six hours after hatching

A beautiful bird with a white nape and breast

As dusky as a Swift

disgorged a fat silver sand-eel to the fledgeling, which it picked up and swallowed, after which its parent flew down to a drain for the customary drink.

The next morning both fledgelings were sitting on the mound with the female, who however went out to sea a quarter of an hour later. For the first time for many weeks the female of pair 1 was also absent—though she returned very shortly after my arrival—and parents of other fledgelings came and went at frequent intervals. Now that the latter were between four and five weeks old the parents raised no objection on finding fledgelings of other pairs associating with their own young in their territories and even sitting on their mounds. On the other hand two casualties occurred during this earliest stage of the fledging, pair 5's single fledgeling and pair 1's younger one disappearing. The chances were that they had been killed by those bonxies with territories on the east ridge, up on to which it was their custom to fly from time to time; for I had previously noticed one of the North Croo fledgelings, just on the wing, being mobbed by both bonxies and lesser black-backed gulls, and on alighting close beside me it disgorged two fish, one of which it swallowed again. Another fledgeling had a feather knocked out of it by the swinging feet of a bonxie. When, however, the latter fledgeling had been on the wing for fifteen days it itself mobbed an adult of its own kind, while another ten-day fledgeling mobbed a bonxie in company with its parent, and a second fledgeling of the same age was sufficiently confident to mob an adult lesser black-back and ten days later to mob a young bonxie.

There were days in the first week of August when all was quiet in the Corrie of Pundsgeo morning and evening. Few adults were present and they did not mob me. There were none of the recent aerial pursuits and the cries now came from the fledgelings, which at the age of five or six weeks occasionally *ayer-yah*ed squeakily or *yeh-wow*ed thinly. But the cry most frequently heard and directly associated with the long absences of both parents was a new cry on the island—an incessant hunger-cry, an unforgettable plaintive mewing *wiv-wiv-wiv-wiv-wow*, which proceeded from those groups of four or five fledgelings gathered together for company on one pair's mound, or moving from mound to mound without interference from the few adults present. This new cry had been anticipated by a single nestling which, on the fourth day after hatching, had uttered a reedy little rippling note, additional to the normal squeak.

Their parents were, however, still feeding the fledgelings and at 5 p.m. on August 7th, when for the first time both pair 1 were absent, the male of pair 2 fed both his young.

Where did the skuas obtain their food supplies? Until the third week in June when, it will be recalled, the earliest nestlings were just hatching, Noss provided no answer to this question. Occasionally one would glide leisurely out over Rumble Wick and on June 3rd one harried a herring-gull over the Sound. But that was all. It seemed that they must obtain their food at the source—that is, at the fishing grounds of the gulls and kittiwakes off the west coast of Shetland: for the latter were not yet returning to Noss with food for young. (G. T. Kay and L. S. V. Venables have, however, drawn my attention to the fact that much harrying of kittiwakes and also terns takes place in the sea area a couple of miles or so north of Noss, and the former has observed that only homeward-bound kittiwakes are harried and that the latter tend to fly at a greater height than those outward-bound from Noss.)

By the third week in June, however, both skuas and bonxies were to be seen circling and planing over Rumble Wick at all hours of the day: yet it was not until the afternoon of the 21st that between 12.45 p.m. and 2 p.m. I for the first time saw guillemots twice chased by skuas and once forced down on to the waters of the Wick. This was also the first day that I was able to make out a guillemot carrying fish and the first day that I saw puffins bringing up transparent grey fry to their nesting burries. Strange that the pirate and his victims should all hatch out their young at the same date!

Four afternoons later at 3.15 p.m. a skua, darting into the cliffs from several hundred yards out in the Wick, forced down a guillemot with a clearly perceived fish but made no attempt to descend to the latter on its submerging. Five minutes later a second guillemot was forced down in a nose-dive, with what result I could not see. The speed of these pursuits was terrific, complicated to follow, and often ultimately lost below the over-hang of the cliffs. Moreover the field of activity was too vast to be covered by binoculars. One had first to spot a likely looking skua with the naked eye and then put up the binoculars at the appropriate moment. Even so, these sharp-cut dark skuas were exceedingly difficult to keep in view against the steel-blue and grey sea. At 3.24 p.m. there was another apparently unsuc-cessful force-down of a guillemot and half an hour later yet another after a chase right into the cliffs, followed by two more.

On the afternoon of July 1st there were more of these appar-ently abortive chases, the victim twice escaping by diving, after being chased along the surface of the water by, in one instance, two skuas. Never once, however, was a skua seen to stoop and retrieve a fish either in mid-air or from the water, though in one instance a gannet made one of those beautiful flat dives into the glass-green waters of the Wick and retrieved a fish dropped by a guillemot forced down by a pirate. One could only presume that piracy at the deep-sea fishing grounds was very much more productive than off Noss. Were it not so, it was difficult to understand how the adult skua or bonxie could secure enough food for itself, let alone for its young. Two evenings later, for instance, a skua chased a tern (also fishing for young) over the Nesti Voe without result, another harried a lesser black-backed gull unsuccessfully, and though I witnessed many chases of guille-mots (and of a puffin on the 6th) all were abortive or the result obscured by the cliffs; and on the 12th I distinctly saw a guille-mot, forced down to the water, retain its fish. Pursuits of guille-mots continued until July 31st, when there were very few of them still on the wing in Rumble Wick, and there was one pur-suit of a fledgeling kittiwake over the Nesti Voe; but not once throughout the season did I observe a skua actually rob success-fully any species of bird except fledgelings of its own kind!

Throughout the second week in August, in contrast to the first week, large numbers of adults were present and noisy on the breeding grounds at all hours of the day, and as early as 3.25 a.m. on the 8th there was a general chorus of *ayeh-yah*, *ayeh-yah* over the moor from birds gliding with decurved wings, like joy-flighting redshanks, or standing with heads thrown back.

Once again I heard that high rush of wings and saw those incredibly swift stoops and anglings of pairs chasing in rhythmic flight. With a sudden renewal of territorial emotion the female of pair 1 stooped at me, brushing my hair with her feet. At sunrise, nearly two hours later, there were more aerial pursuits and mobbing of bonxies than there had been for some weeks. Ten minutes after sunrise the first fledgeling was fed, after dancing for a short space before its parent and waving extended wings, hollowed so that the closed primary tips touched the ground. This dancing was identical with the feigning display of the incubating or brooding adults and also with the hunger dance of the young bonxie.

What was the significance of this sudden raising of the emotional threshold? On August 11th I noticed that the Cradle Holm fledgeling, now eight weeks old, was missing, and though large numbers of adults were again present next day more fledgelings were absent, while those present were sitting about anywhere and were continually on the move from one territory to another. That earliest missing fledgeling was present again on the 13th but, even as I drew near, it left its one parent on the ground and, taking wing, flew out over Rumble Wick. Ignoring two adults returning Noss-wards from sea it glided a great way out over the Wick, before making a brief stoop at a kittiwake, after which I lost sight of it. On the same day another fledgeling, ten days younger, circled widely out over the Voe of the Mels from its territory outside the hill-dyke and stooped at a young herring-gull, while one of the Pundsgeo fledgelings chased a rock-pipit down into a geo. Complementary to these excursions was the fact that the hunger-cry was now only occasionally heard, and when pair 3's two fledgelings, neither of them quite eight weeks old, danced frenziedly with waving wings before one parent, the latter moved away from them and ultimately flew out to sea. It was evident, then, that between the seventh and eighth weeks the parents stopped bringing food to the young and the latter began hawking their own food, foraging ever farther afield. With only their own food to seek the adults were thus able to spend much of their time on the breeding grounds.

On the morning of August 17th I noticed that the numbers of

Cataleptic!

The peculiar 'injury-feigning' of an Arctic Skua

Arctic Skua mobbing: note the feet swinging down

both adults and young were fewer than for the past nine days, and that evening there were no fledgelings on the North Croo. The next day a fledgeling accompanied by one parent was bathing at Ullins Water, and by the 21st all the adults and young on the North Croo and most of those on the moor had left the island for good, when eight and nine weeks old and from three and a half to five weeks after fledging. On the 22nd fledgeling 18, now eight weeks old, was still uttering its hunger-cry to its parent flying above it, but by the end of the month all the Pundsgeo colony had left the corrie, parents and young leaving together. The only fledgelings then remaining on the island were two on the west moor. These two, both singles, had not hatched until July 5th and 6th; but they, too, left on September 5th or 6th. Thereafter no skuas were seen on Noss, though it will be remembered that the previous autumn two were present as late as September 10th.

Of the seven non-breeding pairs, one pair and also the unmated bird occupied their territories for a few days only after their initial return in June, but the remaining five pairs were more or less regular attendants at their territories from late May or June until the middle of August, at which date those breeding pairs that had previously lost eggs or young began to disappear. In the middle of July up to seven of these non-breeding or unsuccessful breeding birds might be seen in a little group on or near a non-breeding pair's mound far down in the north corner of the west moor. They did not, however, do anything exciting and this was the only form of sociality recalling the big gathering of non-breeding bonxies.

In addition to these non-breeding residents the island was visited by one or two immature-plumaged birds, and on the evening of June 23rd one such bird was attempting to associate with various of the breeding birds—I noted it with five different pairs in the space of two hours. This was a white-phase bird with a pure white nape, but with greyish-white bars and mottling on its belly and the undersides of its wings, and with dark bars across the white patch on the upper part of its tail, of which the central streamers were as yet only half as long as those of the adult birds. On the 28th this bird was present all day, teaming

up first with one pair and then with another: sometimes tolerated, sometimes driven off. But after this I saw no more immature until August 4th, when two white-phase birds—one of
which stayed until the 10th—were associating with the Pundsgeo
colony.

IV

ATTACK IN DEFENCE, ALSO CATALEPSY

The peculiar antics of a skua, either male or female, when its eggs or young were approached by a human being—but so far as my observation went, no other animal—depended, I found, upon the precise mental and emotional reactions of a particular individual to such a situation. The skua's 'injury-feigning' display very obviously had no conscious luring-away purpose and showed every evidence of being induced by shock to the nervous system, which in the more extreme cases resulted in a temporary and partial paralysis resembling that induced in the rabbit by the hunting stoat. Such display was naturally never indulged in by any of the non-breeding birds, even though some of them occupied territories from May until August: for no bird displayed until the day it laid its first egg. Display might continue, however, for seven days after the loss of a clutch, and in the case of one pair there was both display and mobbing until the seventeenth day after the loss of a clutch. Possibly this indicated a second laying, though no eggs were found and no young reared.

Fifteen pairs—except where otherwise indicated the term *pair* in this chapter signifies one or other of two birds of a pair—displayed on the day the first egg was laid and a further five pairs at some stage during incubation. Five others, however, did not display until their chicks hatched and one not until its chick was fledged—when it would do so at a distance of 100 yards from me. This pair continued to display extravagantly for a fortnight after the young one was on the wing, and display might continue as late as the twenty-first day after fledging. Three pairs did not display at any time, though they mobbed me when their chicks hatched, and it was not without significance that these were the three pairs whose eggs I was never able to find. One pair was never observed either to display or mob.

No factor, except the psychological, would seem to account for the many exceptions to the rule. And just as there was this variation in displaying and not displaying from one pair to another, so there was variation in the degree and frequency of display. Pair 2, for instance, which was one of the pairs I watched most often, displayed only three times, to my knowledge, throughout the season—on the day the first egg was laid; on the day the first egg was fractured (about ninety hours before the chick hatched); and on the day the first egg hatched, when one of the pair, the male, mobbed me on the only occasion throughout the season. Note this coincidence of the raising of the emotional threshold with definite biological stages in the reproductive cycle.

Another pair displayed only once, on the seventh day after its young one had fledged, when it alighted on the Voe of the Mels and displayed on the water! Another, 39, displayed only once or twice, after its chicks hatched, *teez*ing and dancing up and down with flapping wings only fifteen yards from me when I ringed its twelve-day-old chick. This pair also mobbed me once only throughout the season, though persistently mobbing other adults from their territorial ridge when the latter attempted to drink from a pool on the ridge. Finally, one pair displayed once only, on the day their single egg was fractured—though the shell was not punctured until seven days after this and the chick did not hatch until the eighth day!

In contrast pair 5, both male and female, displayed intensively and also mobbed me severely throughout the season, while two other pairs, though displaying extravagantly throughout, never once mobbed me. As a general rule it could be taken that when a skua displayed it had eggs and when it mobbed it had young. Fourteen pairs, however, never mobbed me: among the seventeen pairs that did there was the same variation in severity and intensity from one pair to another as there was in display. Seven pairs mobbed me during incubation—two as early as the third day—though the majority of these did not begin to do so until the eleventh day, which was the first day I was struck on the head. One pair mobbed me once only, the day their egg was fractured (seventy-two hours before the chick was hatched); two

pairs not until a day or two before their young fledged; and
seven pairs from the first day after their chicks hatched. The
majority mobbed me on some occasions, but not others: but
there were certain pairs, among them 1, 5 and 3, which were in-
veterate mobbers right through the season, once they had begun,
and they were also liable to display violently. Pair 3 was striking me from the thirteenth day of incubation but, generally
speaking, mobbing was most intense during the first ten days
after the chicks hatched, and tended to decrease in severity once
the young were on the wing—though 1, as we have seen,
stooped mildly at me on the thirteenth day of fledging. The
latter, the most severe mobber of them all, did not actually
strike me until the day her first chick hatched, though she had
been mobbing me since the fifth day of incubation. Note again,
as in the case of display, the coincidence of initial mobbing with
the initial days of fracturing, puncturing, hatching, and fledging.

Again, the psychological factor seemed to be the only one
accounting for all the variations in the frequency of mobbing
and its degree of severity: though it was probable that in the
crowded territories of Pundsgeo corrie the exceptional fierceness
of pairs 5, 3 and 1 may have subdued the remaining pairs. When
mobbing me or other pairs of skuas the three fierce pairs would
range over the territories of their fellows, dominating the situation—though this did not prohibit pair 18 from being very
severe on that pair of bonxies a hundred yards south of them—
while an isolated pair would mob me more than fifty yards distant from their mound. Similarly, one bird of a pair—invariably,
I think, the female—was much more severe in its mobbing than
its mate. The male of pair 1, indeed, may never have mobbed
me throughout the season; and while both birds of a pair would
display, the female was again—invariably I think—the most persistent and extravagant in her antics: as one would expect.

In addition to the variations in the frequency and intensity of
both display and mobbing there were also variations in the pattern of both. As we have noted, the first bird I saw display, the
female of pair 2, leant backwards in a broken-bodied manner
on its tail, threshing spread wings on the heather, to the accompaniment of a *teez*ing cry. The female of pair 1 substituted the

more normal *ik-ik-ik* or *jig-jig-jig* for this wheezing note. Pair 3 shuffled along the ground with wings drooping from the shoulders—all these on the day the first egg was laid.

On the second day 3 *jig-jig*ed incessantly, running crouched along the ground; while the female of another pair staggered about with waving wings fully extended and primaries curving to the ground, twenty-five yards from her mound, and her mate tore at the heather with his beak. He did this again on the day the first egg was fractured, while on the day the first chick hatched the female danced up and down in an extravagant manner.

On the third day of the incubation period the female of pair 5 hopped about, cheeping, with expanded wings and also mobbed me; and by the ninth day she was mobbing me severely, with a sudden, almost perpendicular stoop and a swish of dropping feet, attacking me from the front as much as from back or side.

On the fourth day the female of one pair *yeh-wow*ed, while waving wings only slightly; and both birds of another pair waved wings and fell about (but did nothing the next day); while the female of a third pair uttered a hissing scream (palest of mauve gapes well-extended) when I touched her eggs, and fell about extravagantly within fifteen yards of me, wings rocking to one side or the other. Eight days later she showed every sign of being cataleptic, as she rocked about, leaning sideways on stiff unflexed legs, allowing herself to be blown about by the wind, hissing and screaming the while.

It was on the fourth day, too, that one of a pair on the North Croo waved only slightly extended wings, but mobbed me, with legs hanging perpendicularly—very delicately in comparison with the mobbing bonxie. Nine days later, after both had displayed together with waving wings and a peculiar twisting of spread tails from side to side, the female mobbed me the most severely of any at that time. With legs hanging perpendicularly (which one did not observe in the bonxie) and striking at me with her feet, to the accompaniment of an incessant *pewk, pewk*, she missed my head by a hair's breadth again and again. On my retreating the pair proceeded to peck holes in a pair of oystercatchers' eggs.

On this day pair 3 also struck me for the first time on the back and sides of the head. The next day both the North Croo pair again displayed and mobbed me very severely, hitting me on the back of the head, *yeh-yeh-wow*ing continuously. But on the fifteenth day, when only the male was present, the latter did not mob me, attacking instead two ewes and lambs when they were close to the nest and smacking the lambs' rumps with his feet. Dogs, sheep, and bonxies were targets invariably taking precedence of the human. Sheep, however, were not always mobbed, for there were occasions when a pair would ignore sheep only a yard or two away from their eggs.

It was on the fifteenth day that the female of pair 1 mobbed me for the first time with a devastatingly fierce stoop and a near-miss when I ducked my head, and a week later she was striking at me with her feet—the invariable weapon of both skuas and bonxies—with the vicious swish of a whip-lash. Her mobbing was no less severe after the young hatched and on the eighteenth day after hatching she was hitting the stick, which I was now compelled to hold above my head by way of protection, with tremendous force, without apparently causing herself any inconvenience, while the male sat quietly by on their mound. Four days before the young fledged she actually knocked the stick out of my hand with a terrific dunt: but this only quietened her for a few minutes and she was subsequently successful in striking my head despite the waving stick. At this time of the fledging the Corrie of Pundsgeo was a lively spot by day, for in addition to the severe attacks of pairs 5 and 1, the male of pair 3 mobbed me very severely after feeding his young, and I could hear the sound of the blows that one of pair 18 was inflicting on the back of her bonxie neighbour. Yet at 9 p.m. I could walk right across the corrie without a single attempt at mobbing by any of the pairs.

The female of pair 1 was the bird I feared more than any other skua or bonxie on the island. From the time that she first began mobbing me on June 9th she never gave me one day's peace until July 26th when, her young being fledged, she was absent for the first time from her territory; and she continued to mob me sporadically and less violently until August 8th, when her fledgelings had been on the wing for seventeen days. Throughout this period her attacks were continuous so long as I was within fifty yards of her mound. Stooping at me head-on, on my first approaching, she would smack my head in passing, swoop up almost vertically, turn, stoop, and smack me from behind: pass on, swoop up, turn, stoop and smack me head-on; and continue to do so indefinitely, with an occasional side attack thrown in by way of variation. She never drew blood with those small stinging feet of hers, but the cumulative effect of stinging smack after smack on head and ears was intolerable physically, while even more intolerable was the nervous suspense of waiting for the severe blow that would inevitably follow that menacing whip-crack of feet swung down with incredible force—sufficent to lift a beret clean off one's head. To spend more than a minute or two in search for her crouching young was a torment.

V

SOME STATISTICAL ASPECTS

I separated the seventy-five resident skuas into four colour-phases—the uniform sooty-brown phase; the brown phase with distinct dark cap and paler cheeks; the brown phase with yellow neck-ring; and the parti-white phase displaying every degree of motley, from four individuals with dazzlingly white underparts and slight shading only at the sides of the throat, through those with a light or heavy, greyish or mole-brown band across the white breast, to two individuals with white napes only and intensely shaded greyish bellies: all, however, bearing a broad or narrow white band at the base of the bill. (The second and third phases are sometimes known as the Intermediate phase.) I could, of course, following Selous, have subdivided these four phases into innumerable categories, but such splitting was valueless from the practical point of view, for no two skuas were precisely identical in colour or pattern and the individual itself altered colour from minute to minute according to light variations.

Actually, there was an even gradation of colouring from the uniform dusky phase to the yellow-necked phase, and intensive field-work was necessary before some individuals could be definitely allotted to any particular phase. Ultimately I separated a fifth phase, recognizable in the field, of uniform brown, paler than the dusky type, but with crown and neck-ring much less salient than in the two other brown phases; but for the short-term field worker the only practical working distinctions are between dark phase and white phase.

Of the seventy-five individuals twenty-three (31 per cent) belonged to the parti-coloured white phase. In 1934 L. S. V. Venables had estimated 17 per cent of the hundred skuas then on Noss to belong to this phase. With these percentages we may compare those of 31 per cent for three colonies on Yell and 23 per cent for two colonies on Fetlar counted by G. K. Yeates in 1946.

Eleven of the twenty-three white Noss birds were located in the west moor colony—no fewer than seven being distributed among eight pairs in a sub-colony with a nesting area of only three acres —and represented 61 per cent of the eighteen individuals in this colony. A further five were located on the North Croos extension, forming 38 per cent of that colony: whereas there were only four, two of them non-breeding, in the Pundsgeo colony, forming 20 per cent of that colony. No fewer than fourteen out of the twenty-three were paired together, and six of these seven pairs were located in the Moor-Croo area: the seventh being the non-breeding Rumble Wick pair. (The percentage of white x white pairs was 19 per cent, compared with Yeates's figures of 12 per cent on Yell, and 6 per cent on Fetlar; of dark x dark pairs 57 per cent—53 per cent Yell, 55 per cent Fetlar; and of dark x white pairs 24 per cent—35 per cent Yell, 39 per cent Fetlar.)

The implications of this concentration of one colour-phase do not require stressing and they were confirmed by the grouping of the other phases. Excluding eight yellow-necked birds, there were forty-four brown or dusky individuals. 73 per cent of these were paired together, and 70 per cent of the Pundsgeo colony were of this phase. The seventeen individuals of the uniform dusky phase (and also the eight yellow-necks) were all breeding birds, but 26 per cent of both brown and white phases (and also 28 per cent of white x white pairs) were non-breeding.

Fifty-seven to sixty-one eggs were laid in the period May 20th to June 11th, comprising twenty-five clutches of two eggs (one pair, 4, losing its first clutch and laying a second between June 10th and 19th), three clutches of one egg, and four clutches of either one or two. The concentration of pairs in colonies might be said to stimulate egg-production, for of eight isolated pairs only 62 per cent laid eggs compared with 87 per cent of those in colonies; but against these figures must be set those of the densest breeding colony, I, in which only 70 per cent of the pairs laid eggs.

Of fifty-two eggs found, thirty-four (65 per cent) were

coloured pale olive (twenty-two), olive or drab-olive. The remainder were various shades of brown, yellow and green. Of the three single-egg clutches found, one was pale olive, a second pale stone-green, and a third olive-yellow: the second being addled and the third lost. Of ten eggs laid by white x white pairs 40 per cent were of the less normal colour category, and of nineteen laid by pairs including one or more white birds 47 per cent belonged to this category: against 38 per cent of twenty-nine eggs laid by brown x brown pairs. Whereas 42 per cent of the dominant colour category hatched, only 31 per cent of the minor category hatched.

Forty-six to forty-eight eggs were hatched (76–83 per cent of those laid) in the period June 15th to July 6th. White x white pairs hatched 77–83 per cent of theirs: pairs with one or more white birds 65–68 per cent: dark pairs 70–75 per cent. If close colony-nesting did not necessarily stimulate egg-production it had, on the other hand, a marked protective value. Whereas 96 per cent of those breeding pairs nesting in colonies succeeded in hatching their eggs, only 40 per cent of the isolated pairs were successful. No psychological factors were involved: losses in eggs being almost certainly directly due to the activities of gulls and bonxies adjacent to, or actually surrounding, these isolated pairs.

Of forty-one nestlings found—twenty-eight of which I ringed —thirty-two varied only slightly in the colour of their down (when they had dried off) from dusky-brown, through sooty-grey, to sooty. Seven others were a dark mole-brown, and these were the progeny of three white pairs, one white x brown pair, one brown pair, and two yellow-neck x brown pairs. The remaining two were a distinctive pale tawny-brown and belonged to a white pair and a sooty x yellow-neck pair. The predominance of white pairs among the parents of this paler-downed minority, and the inclusion of only one sooty parent, was too marked to be discounted. It was further confirmed by the fact that white pairs produced only three dark nestlings out of eight, and that of fourteen nestlings produced by parents including one white bird only four were sooty: whereas out of twenty nestlings belonging to dark pairs no fewer than seventeen were sooty.

The majority of the nestlings had large or small, white or fawn belly-patches and tips to their wing-arms. In 75 per cent of those nestlings belonging to dark pairs, however, this pale belly-patch was absent or hardly perceptible; and while some nestlings of white pairs or white x dark pairs might have fawn instead of white belly-patches, there was naturally a tendency to presume that those nestlings with prominent white bellies and wing-arm tips might develop into white-bellied fledgelings and thence into white-phased adults. This, however, did not prove to be the case and it was not possible to forecast the fledging plumage of any nestling, despite the predominance of the pale-downed type hatched by white parents.

By the tenth day after hatching, tortoiseshell-coloured feathers were beginning to unfold from the chick's scapular-quills, and from the secondaries on the seventeenth day. By the twenty-first day primary feathers were well developed in some birds and most of the down had been lost, though the bird was not yet quite fully feathered. A week after fledging the white wing-edge was showing on the primaries and, two weeks after, the central tail-feathers had become prominent points.

There were three distinct phases of fledging plumage and several sub-phases:

1. Uniform black (twelve) with,
   (a) drab bellies and whitish undersides to wings (nine);
   (b) copper belly (two);
   (c) cream nape and white belly (one).

2. Dark brown (ten) with,
   (a) all-over rufous feather-tips (two);
   (b) copper head and light fawn belly (six);
   (c) greyish-white belly (two).

3. Light brown (six) with,
   (a) copper or tawny head and belly.

Eight of the twelve black fledgelings originated from sooty or sooty x brown pairs: the four exceptions being two that belonged to sooty x white pairs, one with a white belly belonging to a yellow-neck x white pair, and one with a cream nape and white belly belonging to a white pair. All twelve originated from dark nestlings. Of the six light brown with copper or tawny heads and manes each had one or more white parents, with the exception of one with two yellow-necked parents.

It will be seen from the above that four dark nestlings ultimately developed into fledgelings with mottled white underparts (first obvious on the twenty-first day), though two more —both with white parents—which were white on the belly in the fourth week ultimately turned fawn on the belly. Two of the four white fledgelings had white parents, a third had white x yellow-neck parents, and the fourth sooty parents. Presuming that these four would mature as white-phase adults—one was almost certainly killed before leaving the island—they represented 14 per cent of all young fledged. It will be noted that the three white pairs of adults bringing off young reared two white and two light-brown fledgelings, and that five white x dark pairs reared four light-brown fledgelings, one white fledgeling, and two black ones.

Of the forty-five to forty-eight nestlings twenty-nine fledged and twenty-four to twenty-eight ultimately got away from the island; or about eight juveniles to every ten pairs. With regard to this proportion of young reared we may note that the potential life-span of a skua is probably considerable, an unusually small dark-phase female returning to the same territory beside a croft on Foula for thirty-one consecutive years. She was, incidentally, sufficiently confident to accept food, mainly oatmeal, from the hand, having been tamed as a nestling. In 1941 she broke a wing and was not seen thereafter. On Hermaness another tame bird, a male, returned to the vicinity of the watcher's hut for about thirty-two years, bringing a number of different mates— certainly more than three—to his particular nesting spot. He mated successfully for about thirty-one years, but was unsuccessful in the thirty-second year, when his previous year's mate paired up with another bird.

No one colour phase proved more markedly successful in the reproductive cycle than any other, dark x dark pairs rearing 0·9 fledgelings per pair, dark x white 1·0 per pair, and white x white 0·8 per pair. On the other hand those breeding pairs nesting in

colonies enjoyed a certain advantage over widely scattered and
isolated pairs. The seven pairs in Pundsgeo Corrie took away
1·0 fledgelings per pair and the thirteen pairs on the west moor
0·8–1·1 per pair: whereas the six pairs on the North Croo
averaged 0·7 per pair and five isolated pairs 0·4 per pair.

Part IV

A STUDY OF A BREEDING COLONY OF GANNETS

(*Sula bassana*)

The Noup
The Gannetry is contained within the whitened area

The Control Gannetry

Reading from right to left (in left corner) are pairs I, II and III. This photograph was taken in 1947 when all three pairs had much more substantial nests than in 1946. Pair VI occupied the white-stained

I

LIFE IN A GANNETRY

From that grassy promontory at the south corner of Rumble Wick I could look down and directly across at some hundreds of gannets nesting on the back wall of cliff, from a score or two of feet above the waters of the Wick to within a few feet of the cliff-top, which at this point reached a height of 350 feet. The nearest half-dozen pairs were on a level with my eye, only thirty feet distant, and nested nearest to the cliff-top of any gannets on the island. In the dead ground below the overhang of my observation post were more gannets, but all those nesting on the back wall could be observed from the O.P. except for a few pairs in dead ground in the upper portions of a central recess of flattened 'stalls', which shelved back and upwards, tier on tier, into the cliff.

Along the upper limits of the gannetry, where there were no gannets' nests, occasional fulmars occupied niches under slabs of rock and vomited over any gannets alighting nearby, causing them to depart again immediately; while, thinly interspersed among the even rows and tiers of gannets and squeezed into the cells with which the weathered sandstone was honeycombed in places, were a few kittiwakes. Here and there a small township of guillemots huddled up on a platform in an angle of the cliffs. Others were packed tightly, a dozen together, among the gannets, where the latter were nesting less evenly, and there were even solitary pairs shrinking up against the cliff-wall between the nest-drums of two pairs of gannets. Their humming *oo-oo* was an amusing and familiar accompaniment to every untoward movement on my part or the rustling in the breeze of the leaves of my big notebook. What sharp eyes they had, bowing their heads in mutual unease at my appearance no matter how far their township from the cliff-top.

M

Photographs illustrated how great had been the reduction in the numbers of guillemots in this gannetry in the past fifteen years or so, complementary to the increase in gannets—not that there had ever been any active persecution on the part of the latter. Those remaining little groups of guillemots huddled up within beak-range of sitting gannets, but the latter did no more than nip a restless guillemot very gently with their bills, infrequently; nor did the threat of that potentially dangerous beak deter these diminutive neighbours from fighting incessantly, driving one another hard up against the gannets' nest-drums, nor from mating beneath a gannet's very beak. In the hurly-burly of one gannet being turned off a ledge by another an adjacent pair of guillemots, which had just mated, would be shocked into such characteristic mental confusion that they would fight severely, before realizing their error. Did a gannet, which had not yet laid, leave her nest temporarily the chances were that one of the neighbouring guillemots would take possession of it immediately, beating a hasty retreat on the owner's return.

No, the infiltration of the gannets had been peaceful, but none the less inexorable, mainly because of their size, the bulky nature of their nests, and the relatively small space of a foot or so between the nest-drums—a space, covered by the lunge of one sitting gannet at another, in which a pair of guillemots might stand or even walk quietly about, but in which a resident group was not tolerated.

Each pair of gannets, then, was in possession of a nest-drum, or merely a territory on the bare rock, a foot or so from its neighbours on either side and above and below, except at the outer limits of the gannetry and in those places where a sheer slab of cliff contained perhaps only one small shelf or honeycomb cell with room for only a single pair of these huge 'boobies'.

These beautiful 'boobies', sitting each in its place with black primaries crossed, tern-like, over snowy mantles, were now at the end of April at various stages of the breeding cycle. Some two-thirds of them had big nest-drums raised on previous years' foundations, which were so concreted to the rock and whitened with the excrement of both gannets and guillemots that it was impossible to distinguish where rock ended and nest began. On top of the drum perhaps might be an impressive round pile of dead grasses, nine inches deep, with fresh green grass surmounting the whole structure. But, generally speaking, surprisingly little new material appeared to have been added to the permanent structure of these big ancestral drums.

Other pairs had no drums and only rudimentary nests, their occupants sitting rather on raised lumps of less-weathered sandstone than on nest-stuff comprising a wisp of dead grass or a white feather or two—which some swimming birds were retrieving at the base of the cliffs, shooting through the water after them, with wings loosened a little at the shoulders and primaries crossed over their tails. Nevertheless, material was continually being brought up to both rudimentary and drum-nests, the newer parts of which had every appearance of being fashioned of wet hay—as indeed they were, for much of the material was dead grass, which the gannets plucked from high up on the green West Noup, more especially during the hours before and after noon. At this source as many as fifteen or twenty gannets at a time were to be seen tugging hard at bunches of grass or plantain, paddling about on unsteady feet and balancing with the aid of their tails pressed down against their precarious perch on the sheer face of the siding, while another score circled off-cliff preparatory to alighting.

Besides gathering material from the sidings and from the reefs and waters of the Wick the gannets flew many miles to the shores of Mainland in search of tangle; and when one was sailing well out to sea off Bressay they might be seen coming up in ones and twos with huge beakfuls of bladder-weed from farther north than the binoculars could pick them up.

Another source of supply was contained in the gannetry itself, where a regular feature of nest-building was the filching of material from other gannets' nests—not those, of course, of incubating birds, which never left their eggs unattended for a second day or night, but from those of pairs which had not yet laid and which were in perpetual process of building and losing nests. It was clear that those old-established pairs with ancestral nest-drums, or at least the foundations of drums, must hold a considerable breeding advantage over younger pairs. On their initial return to the gannetry—and no doubt more often than not to the same nest-drum—late in January or early in February they would have substantial nests on which to sit, and would tend to sit more assiduously than younger birds, so that it would matter little whether fresh material was accumulated on the top of the old drums or not: whereas it seemed to some extent a matter of chance whether pairs returning to, or prospecting, bare ledge-sites ultimately succeeded in retaining a sufficiently big proportion of the material they collected, or filched from other vestigial nests, to form a nest; and what actually happened was that these later-laying birds did not accumulate any permanent nest-structure until such time as they laid their eggs and sat perpetually—at which juncture the material continually brought up by their mates became a permanent addition to the nest, being no longer subject to the incessant depredations of other building gannets. It might be true to say that no pair of gannets ever succeeded in building a nest until after incubation began.

The difficulties with which these later-laying pairs had to contend in their endeavours to establish any sort of permanent nest-foundation were exemplified by those pairs on that top-ledge immediately opposite my O.P. This ledge was probably first colonized between 1935 and 1938, a photograph taken in the latter year showing one pair on the ledge. Now, on April 25th, there were four pairs. Pair 1 at its north end, with an egg on a nest composed entirely of white feathers was, however, the only pair with a permanent nest, though not an ancestral drum; and my attention was drawn to another gannet filching an enormous beakful of nest-stuff, including feathers, from an unoccupied vestigial nest, 5, farther along the ledge. With this it flew out into the Wick, returned to the robbed nest again, flew out again, and finally returned to another unoccupied vestigial nest immediately adjacent to pair 1's and some thirty feet from the robbed nest. Here it deposited its beakful of stuff and sat on it. Subsequently this bird, 2—which occupied the site photographed in 1938— filched more beakfuls from pair 3's unoccupied nest, adjacent to

it on the south side: but, on itself going off later, its own nest
was robbed by a bird from another part of the gannetry—and
so it went on.

By the 27th, for instance, pair 2 had acquired some green
thrift, three white feathers and a stick of dead thistle. Almost
immediately after my arrival in the morning, however, neighbour 3 filched the attractive thrift and flew off with it: but in the
evening 2 was again robbing 3's nest. A morning or two later,
however, the male of pair 2 made no attempt to prevent 3, which
had just arrived with nesting material, from taking in addition
an enormous beakful from *his* nest. On the contrary he flew off!
Whereupon 3, having filched a second beakful, also flew off!
(In those places where I refer specifically to male or female it
must be understood that they are identified by the act of mating
or by some physical peculiarity.)

As in the case of many other species I had studied it was
apparent that the fashioning of a nest was to a greater or lesser
degree fortuitous, and a gannet alighting without nesting-stuff
at an unconstructed nest would seize up a beakful of stuff lying
nearby on the ledge, as if to consummate a forgotten, but now
remembered, mission: just as 6, a pale-headed bird, alighting
empty-billed at its solitary niche above and north of pair 1,
characteristically, at the moment of alighting, seized in one
motion with the braking of its feet on the ledge a beakful of
stuff from its own nest, which it began to arrange. While, on
one bird of another pair without a nest bringing up a big bunch
of seaweed, neither partner appeared to know what to do with
it, and it was ultimately purloined by a bird sitting on a nest
below. In another instance one male bird alighting with a small
billful of stuff deposited it on an empty place on a ledge, not
without difficulty in ridding its beak of it, then picked up a
fragment and hopping along the ledge to a bird with almost no
nest, deposited it there and subsequently mated with her.

There was much mandibulating by sitting birds of the nesting
material brought up by their mates and, when 2 was standing
fiddling with some stuff it had filched from pair 3's nest, both of
pair 1 were encouraged to begin fiddling with their nest, the
pale-headed male twisting his head affectionately over his mate's

head in order to do so. Then the two played lovingly with a beakful of green stuff, before the female took it ultimately from her mate's upstretched beak and the two together bowed down with it to the nest, where the female arranged it delicately. A bird sitting on a big drum-nest would continually fiddle with little bits of disturbed nest-stuff, and mandibulate them precisely inwards to the egg with a curiously delicate vibratory movement of the just-parted tips of its beak—that grey-blue, black-lined dagger-bill which, when distended in a yawn, revealed a black interior; and when pair 4, a late-laying pair on the north side of the gannetry, ultimately settled down to incubation, the sitting bird was continually digging into the rampart of its new nest of seaweed and then raising its head and shaking its bill.

The bringing up of nesting material and its idle mandibulating by the incubating bird were not only almost the sole direct acts of nest-building, but also provided the major stimulus maintaining that tempo of high activity and vocal expression which, while crescending and diminishing in intensity, never wholly slackened for more than a few seconds at a time during the hours of daylight. In April most of the gannets would still be sleeping at 5 a.m., with few coming up to the ledges, and there would be little noise in the gannetry. Not for another half-hour is the first nest-stuff brought up, and it is an hour before the first mating takes place.

By 4.30 p.m. there are signs that another busy day is drawing to a close, and the last bird has plucked its billful of grasses from the sidings of the West Noup. An hour and a half later, when 90 per cent of those present on the nesting ledges are single birds, several are beginning to sleep and only their orange crowns and napes can be seen above beaks buried in scapulars. At 6-15 p.m., however, some are still bringing up seaweed from more distant sources, and when I leave the gannetry three-quarters of an hour later, with the sun pretty low in the west, the tempo of activity and vocal refrain has not materially decreased.

The effect of stepping back a yard or two from the cliff-edge dyke is startling. Instantaneously and incredibly all visual, aural and olfactory evidence that tens of thousands of sea-birds are nesting immediately below me is gone. The effect of the sudden quietude is similar, in its sudden contrast of extremes, to that of closing behind one the doors of the Parrot House in the Zoological Gardens. All that remains of the tumult is the cawing of fulmars high up on the West Noup; and as I go down the boggy hill into the westering sunlight, through that other-world of skua-held hinterland, I hear all around, instead, the *kyee-ek* of protesting bonxies and the 'creaking' of snipe twisting up at my feet.

On returning at 9.45 p.m., however, the gannetry is almost completely quiet, with half its inmates sleeping with heads buried so deeply in parted wings that their foreheads are hidden, and only five birds are on the wing in the Wick at one time. An hour later all are on the cliffs and most are sleeping, though from time to time a sitting bird gets up, with a quiet *urrah*, to flap its wings and wag its tail, or to arrange its egg. An occasional outburst comes from guillemots and kittiwakes, a fulmar caws, and an oystercatcher pipes from the siding above the Cradle Holm.

At 11 p.m. on a May night, when the wind is blowing distinctly warm off the sea, it is still light enough to pick out the white heads of kittiwakes sixty yards away with the naked eye and the white bellies of the more distant guillemots with the binoculars. Herring-gulls and an occasional dusky bonxie are the last birds on the wing before 11 p.m., though half an hour later occasional kittiwakes are still circling out from the lower parts of the cliffs and their *kit-kit* is to be heard frequently, penetrating the sullen roar and surge of the cold relentless sea. Then for a while—a long while it seems, though it lasts only from 11.30 p.m. to 12.45 a.m.—the lonely night knows only the wretched being huddled for warmth in the lee of the cliff-dyke and the winking beams of distant lighthouses. The night grows neither appreciably darker nor lighter, and none of the sleeping sea-fowl show any reaction to my torch's beam playing upon them. At 12.45 a.m., however, a faint red glow is perceptible east of the Noup, and I hear the crying of unseen herring-gulls and swaabies over the Wick. Ten minutes later larks begin to twitter over the bonxie grounds and the Head. By 1.15 a.m. it is distinctly lighter, for I can make out the faint grey outline of the southern hills of Mainland, but the gannets are still sleeping and the gannetry is

dead-silent. At 1.30 a.m. the first fulmars and kittiwakes are on
the wing, and a quarter of an hour later, when I can see to write
my notes without the aid of a torch, the gannets waken at last,
after more than two hours' total inactivity, and the first one leaves
the cliffs, and a second two minutes later. By 1.50 a.m. most are
stirring on the ledges, and at 2 a.m. there is a brief display of
affection between a pair without a nest (and a mating twenty
minutes later), for some non-breeding birds also spend the night
in the gannetry. At 2.10 a.m. roosting birds are leaving the cliffs
at regular intervals and twenty-six leave my gannetry between
1.45 a.m. and 2.30 a.m.: but it is not until the latter hour that
the first alighting bird arrives. By this time I can bear the cold
of the stiff on-cliff dawn wind no longer and, rising with difficulty
from my four-hour couch on the bare rock, I am forced to leave
the gannetry when the tempo of activity is still low.

As early as 2.10 a.m., however, a gannet standing alone on its
nest-drum, or one of a pair, might be seen to display with those
antics that were of minutely occurrence throughout the hours of
daylight. After first wagging its head the displaying bird then
bowed forward, turning its head sideways in the same motion
to, or under, one or other of its wings. These were either 'hung'
open, cormorant-wise, with primaries closed, or loosened at the
shoulders and depressed—so loosely perhaps as to rest on the
ledge—with the black primaries crossed, like open scissors, over
the upper part of the tail, whose spine-like point was spiked
upwards. Thereupon, as likely as not, an adjacent pair would
briefly enact the same ceremony. The head-wagging antic, which
was often coupled with the pretence of picking up nest-stuff,
was continually indulged in: just as the head-bowing-to-wing
antic might also be coupled with the pretence or actual picking up of stuff, and also with the waving of it—no matter
whether it was a ceremony between a pair of birds or the antic
of a solitary bird. One might be seen bowing its head incessantly,
first under its left wing, tilting up its tail with every bow, and
then under its right wing. And just as the bowing of one bird
or pair would stimulate an immediate neighbour to bow, so six
solitary birds sitting on a row of nests would have spasms, either
together or one after another, of bowing under primary-crossed

wings. Nor was the antic confined to nesting birds, for a solitary gannet alighting on a ledge devoid of nests would stand on its edge, wings fully open—though not of course stretched to their full span—tilt its tail up and down and bow forward two or three times.

When a pair wing-bowed together, the ceremony very often culminated in the two stretching up their heads, wagging them, and then fencing bills lovingly. This fencing and clashing of bills might be extremely vigorous—as might the fondling of heads, when one bird crossed its head over the other's neck—and might continue without a break for a minute or more, with constant crescendos in the tempo and violence of the clashing, as one partner stimulated the other should the latter display any slackening of enthusiasm. In between two such bouts of fencing one of the pair might, though infrequently, elevate its bill vertically, with mandibles parted and throat pulsing tremulously, while its blue eyelids were almost closed over the pale grey-blue eye-disks with their tiny black pupils. So, too, infrequently, a solitary incubating bird would indulge in this curious throat-pulsing —the reason for which was obscure, but which was also a peculiarity of the nesting cormorant—without a second's break for several minutes, until perhaps it was interrupted by stuff falling from a nest above. Similarly the head-wagging, and often the twining of heads, might also continue for several minutes without a break and might lead ultimately to a mating or attempted mating, as might also the arrival of one partner with nesting material—the act providing the most frequent stimulus to mating.

The mating was initiated by the male taking a firm beak-hold of his mate's head: an alighting bird, indeed, normally gripped its mate by the nape. (Note the salient ochre colouring of a gannet's head.) It might even fly direct to its mate's head, gripping it before its own feet were on the ledge, or alight with one foot on its mate's back. Either method might lead to the mating or to that extremely vigorous and prolonged clashing of bills and fondling of heads. Thus, when the male of pair 2 came up to alight he did so with such a direct lunge at and grip of his mate's head that he appeared to be, rather, a rightful owner returning to find his nest being robbed than a fond husband. Nevertheless he subsequently mated with her, flew off, returned with the same vicious lunge, and trod her for the second time in ten minutes. Having failed on another occasion, however, to consummate a mating, he became extremely violent in his grip of her head and finally pushed her off the ledge! This contrasted with the behaviour of another newly united pair, who were preening one another's heads and throats with the utmost delicacy, and a third pair, the male of whom was preening the tips of his mate's primaries—at which she gripped his bill in hers more tightly than he altogether enjoyed. One could, indeed, never be quite certain initially whether a bird without a nest gripping another by the head and then standing on its back was about to mate, as one supposed, or in actual fact was only manœuvring to push it off the ledge! If it was with the intention of mating then, having obtained his beak-hold, the male would proceed to paddle about on his mate's back, balancing with waving wings—while she continually shook her head—until such time as he had secured a good grip on the folds of skin he pulled up with his beak; just as the cock fulmar continually rubbed his beak across his mate's brow and beak while treading her, and might begin to do this again after the mating had been consummated, until, pecking her too roughly, she would throw him off.

When the mating had been consummated the male gannet might fly direct from his mate's back to sea—though not, perhaps, without first performing the special antic that usually, but not invariably, preceded a gannet's departure from its nesting ledge—or he might merely step off her back, when a mutual clashing of bills would follow; while the mating of a pair without a nest might be followed by mutual head-wagging and beak-pointing. The departure antic in no way resembled any of those antics already described, and is worth special consideration in as much as the gannet did not normally fly direct from its nesting place like any other sea-bird. No, when the impulse to leave its ledge took it, the gannet seemed to pass into a trance-like state and would begin to paddle about the ledge very slowly, lifting its feet only just clear of the rock and gradually straining up beak, head, and neck vertically, while at the same time slightly busking closed wings, inflating its chest, and elevating its stern or, alternatively, depressing the spiny tail stiffly. Once this unique posture had been assumed the bird might continue to paddle around in an attitude of intense concentration for several seconds and sometimes as long as a full minute, totally oblivious of the surrounding tumult, before approaching the edge of the ledge. At this point it would bow forward, with neck still upstretched and tail tilted, but wings now loosened a little at the shoulders—or, alternatively, with head and tail depressed—and finally launch forth in flight in this looped-up manner, expelling as it did so a sighing *woo-or-er*, not dissimilar from, though louder than, the sighing expiry of a kittiwake when it zoomed down and out from the cliff-face. On a calm sunny morning this departure-note sounded like the last sigh of a departing spirit and reflected the disembodied antic of departure, as with an S-shaped kink in its neck, head still being stretched up vertically, and with spiny tail now depressed, the great white bird floated feebly off into space—a most humorous caricature.

As in the case of so many avian antics this curious departure-antic of the gannet was occasionally, though by no means so frequently as the peculiar antics of other species, provoked by the wrong stimulus. Thus, a gannet wishing to relieve its incubating partner on the nest might begin to assume the departure antic, and one such bird pushed its mate violently aside when the latter was too slow in removing itself from the nest. With similar confusion the mate of one nesting bird performed this antic after shoving a non-nesting bird off its ledge, while another did so before flying to a different ledge on being threatened by the rightful occupant. At 7-15 p.m. on April 27th, the female of pair 2 arrived at the nesting ledge and there was an audible brittle clashing of sabre-bills between the two and a smoothing of one's head down the other's, to the customary vocal accompaniment, which continued without a pause for two minutes and intermittently and less violently subsequently—the female being the more violent of the two—though at this date they had not a scrap of nest-stuff. Half an hour later the male performed the departure antic, but did not leave, clashing bills with his mate instead, and after more strained anticking waved wings twice, but still did not leave. Similarly, on another occasion, after one of this pair had assumed the antic for a full minute its mate nibbled its taut, vertically stretched throat delicately. This led to a mutual and gentle billing and in the end it was the mate that left—returning again in another half-minute. On May 10th both the pair went through the ceremony, but this led, not to their departure, but to one of the two paddling slowly along the ledge and concluding with a gleeful run and hop forward to seize a huge beakful of stuff from pair 3's nest and return with it to its mate! This pirating was repeated and then a minute or two later further anticking did finally lead to this bird's departure, while its mate arranged her latest foundations. Of another pair, which had changed places on their nest, the relieved bird departed with the customary sighing *oo-oo-oo*, but returned in two minutes and mated, proving to be the male—the absence of any nest was no bar to mating—whereupon the female left after thirty seconds, but returned again in another thirty seconds, leaving once more after a similar period.

And throughout these antics of birds continually departing, of others alighting, and yet others displaying, came from the gannetry that incessant vocal refrain, broken only at second-intervals and continually renewed by every new alighting, continually crescending with every wave of bowing and every clashing of bills—that harsh repetitive *gūrrah-gūrrah-gūrrah*, with the accent on the *gurr*, pitched somewhat higher than the similar greeting-cry of a bird coming up to alight, when the *gurrāh* was abbreviated almost to a monosyllable and slowed up, with the accent on the *rah*. Since the cry was emitted through closed bill it was extremely difficult to tie down the refrain to any particular bird amid the general tumult. Nor, as it has been noted, was the refrain limited to those gannets actually *in situ* on the ledges, for one coming in from the Wick to alight, planing up at great speed to the cliff-face and then braking, with tail depressed vertically, would begin *gurrāh*ing when still a hundred yards or so from the cliff-face; and there was a constant chorus from that off-cliff stream of not-immediately alighting gannets, which were in perpetual process of coming up to the cliffs, passing along their front, falling away again, and circling out into the Wick: for the number of alighting birds was only a small percentage of those circling off the cliffs at any one time, and there was a constant falling away from the cliffs of unsuccessful or undecided potential alighters—great white attenuate hawk-moths drooping at head and tail. Despite this constant traffic of birds alighting and departing and others planing along the face of the cliff in a continuous stream, only once did I witness a partial collision.

A non-territoried gannet purposing to alight at some spot in the crowded gannetry, but able to locate only a mere crevice in the face of the cliff, might find itself suspended almost in mid-air, while hanging on to the lower mandible of a bird sitting on a nest at the edge of the ledge above, and scrabbling with its claws for purchase on the cliff-face: for there was much aggressiveness among the occupants of a gannetry, both between neighbouring pairs and against solitary non-territoried birds alighting on unoccupied sites between two nest-drums. The latter were ejected by threatening beak-lunges or pushed off the ledge by the actual pressure of a beak-hold. On the other hand a bird alighting on a ledge containing no nests had no difficulty in forcing off any non-breeding occupants. Incubating birds, however, never left their nests for combat and this was restricted to the savage lunging and actual beak-gripping of one sitting neighbour by its adjacent fellow, whether on the same ledge or on those ledges immediately above and below: while neighbours might tweak the two combatants' tails, which were spread in diamond-shaped fans in their efforts to push the other off its nest. The endurance and sustained powers of pressure of two combatants were hardly credible. For twenty minutes, and longer for all I knew, I on one occasion watched two gannets without nests locked together, beak in beak—those powerful beaks with which the men of St. Kilda were accustomed to peg down the straw thatch covering the oval turf and wood roofs of their houses!—and one, or both, had blood on them. In this homeric contest I saw that the prime object of the beak-hold was for the purpose of exerting pressure to push the rival off the ledge, and it was apparent that tremendous pressure was exerted. Very gradually, but relentlessly, first one combatant and then the other would force back the head of its rival to, one would have thought, breaking-point, or would twist it round over its back—maximum pressure being obtained by pressing half-open or even fully expanded wings and depressed fan-spread tail against the cliff-face. Every now and again one of the two would shake its beak violently in order to obtain a better grip, and this might give its rival the opportunity to exert pressure in its turn and force back the other's head: but never once were the beaks unlocked. With a fresh and bitterly cold up-draft blowing it was too cold for me to await the outcome of this Homeric combat, and I was forced to leave my O.P. after half an hour, when beak was still locked in beak: but it ended some time in the next half-hour. Generally speaking, however, a gannetry was a remarkably peaceful community, and acts of aggression between neighbouring pairs were for the most part limited to occasional menacing beak-lunges, tip meeting tip from outstretched necks at the halfway point between two nest-drums; and this double stretch governed the territorial space between every pair of nest-drums and accounted for those ordered rows so characteristic of a gannetry.

With a strong wind or breeze from south or east causing a stiff draught up the cliffs the circling gannets had the greatest difficulty in alighting, and had to float-drop on to their ledges at right-angles. With the up-draught so strong that I would be thrown off my balance from time to time on the landward side of the cliff-dyke, the gannets would give a marvellous display of aerobatics, and fulmars and herring-gulls performed the most extravagant actions with wings and tails, all soft curves and no rigidity, just above or below the cliff-top: while high overhead, hundreds of feet above the Noup, hovered the falcon peregrine on seemingly motionless wings. On such breezy days there was a continual circling of sea-birds round the Wick and sideways along the cliffs, and an idly-circling whirlpool of sea-fowl off Puffin Holm might contain gannets, bonxies, arctic skuas, kittiwakes, fulmars, herring-gulls and swaabies. In the evening great numbers of gannets, fulmars and kittiwakes would soar over the Wick at scores or hundreds of feet, and pairs of bonxies would wheel, like buzzards, in overlapping circles out to sea. Such aeronautics were not to be confused with the milling out of a cloud of inquisitive gannets on those infrequent occasions when a yacht sailed into Rumble Wick or a tramp-steamer or shark-boat chugged close past the Noup, and 500 gannets would circle off the cliff and fall like plummets in the boat's wake; while on a calmer day after a gale the sea would be dotted with solitary swimming gannets almost as far as the eye could reach.

II

NINE WEEKS A'GROWING

By the end of the third week in April two-thirds of the pairs in my gannetry had eggs and the majority, though not all, of those pairs with drum-nests appeared to have laid: some eggs being stained brown by a few days' incubation; but I could only make out two drumless nests with eggs, of which one was that nest composed entirely of white feathers belonging to pair 1. There was much billing of the egg inwards by those incubating to their black feet, with their curious pale-green veins, set far back on the bird. I observed that one webbed foot was not placed on top of the other over the egg when incubating, as traditionally stated, but after first placing one foot along one side of the ridiculously small egg, the other foot was then placed along the other side, overlapping its fellow; and this operation might take quite a while before the bird finally sank down on its feet. From time to time one would rise to flap its wings and then re-arrange its egg.

Incubating birds sat for long periods without being relieved by their mates, a bird here and there becoming heavily stained with green excrement voided by those sitting above. The operation of relief was seldom seen except in the early morning, and the alighting rate was at its maximum in the three hours after sunrise. On being relieved the sitting bird might fly directly out to sea or might delay its departure for anything up to three minutes, clashing bills or fondling heads with its mate; and this would be followed by the appropriate antic preceding departure, after which it might circle off the cliffs for the few minutes that it could be distinguished among the throng of its fellows.

As no birds with big drum-nests ever left their eggs unattended none of the latter were ever lost and the percentage of infertile eggs was apparently extremely small: but losses occurred among

192

Pairs I, II, III and V—reading from top right to bottom left (1947)

A characteristic pair of Gannets

pairs with new drumless nests. All these rudimentary nests were situated on the outside ledges of the gannetry. On April 22nd, for example, pair 1's nest of feathers was the only nest on this ledge, which contained no foundations from previous years. We may surmise with some confidence that these outer ledges in a gannetry were occupied, predominantly at any rate, by the younger adults. Certainly the female of pair 1 behaved like one unused to incubating. She never performed any of the various ceremonies and antics of display and courtship perpetually indulged in by the vast majority of the members of the gannetry, whether solitary or in pairs—though her abnormality might be attributed to the absence of stimulating neighbours above and for some distance below her, to the irregular attendance of the three other pairs without nests on her ledge, and to the long absences of her mate, a very pale-headed bird, who was not seen at the nest until April 27th and was only observed on five occasions thereafter throughout the season. His absence was naturally most felt in the early morning, the most popular hour for relief, and at this hour she would leave her egg unattended and make fifteen-minute flights round the Wick—which no other gannet ever did—returning, with a pathetically brief *urrah* and no display antic, to stand over her egg, without covering it with her feet, for long periods. Though bitterly disappointed I was not, therefore, surprised to find on the 28th, when the male alone was present, that this pair had lost their egg, filched no doubt by a gull during one of the sitting bird's intermittent absences.

Pair 2 were bringing up nesting material on April 25th (and no doubt previously) and began and lost many nests between that date and May 13th, finally laying an egg sometime between the 25th and 29th on a wretched jumble of feathers, dead stalks of angelica and other flotsam. The egg was already stained on the 30th and the next day I noticed the pair changing over.

Pair 3 had a rudimentary nest on April 25th and probably laid on May 11th. As, however, the male visited the nest very infrequently—May 23rd being the only occasion on which I noted both birds present—and the female sat very tightly, I did not actually see their egg until June 1st, by which date they had acquired quite a big nest.

The fourth 'pair' of birds on this ledge, pair 5, were first noted on May 23rd. By June 7th their permanent nest comprised one feather and on June 24th one bird was still sitting and sleeping on the bare rock! 'They' laid no egg, and this was possibly an un-mated bird, for I never saw two birds at the 'nest'.

Finally, the pale-headed partner of pair 6 first occupied its solitary niche above pair 1 on May 6th and by the 10th she had a fair-sized new nest of dead grasses and greenstuff. All this day and for at least five days subsequently she never budged an inch or raised herself from her nest during long periods of observa-tion, sitting in an attitude abnormal for an incubating gannet with fully erect head. I presumed that she laid during this period of intensive sitting, but I was never able to catch a glimpse of her egg. Then on the 19th my observations at the gannetry suf-fered a second mortifying setback, when two companions stood too far out on my O.P. Their sudden appearance proved too much for the nerves of this peculiar bird and she flew off her egg. Immediately, a herring-gull (whose kind I had hardly noticed about this end of the Wick previously) appeared from nowhere, seized the egg, and flew off with it almost before I had realized that the felonious act was being perpetrated. Thus, I had lost my two closest observation nests with eggs. The pale-headed bird—a mate was only once observed, on the 7th—continued to visit the nest until the 23rd, but was not seen thereafter.[1]

Meanwhile, for a week after the loss of their egg pair 1's attendances were very brief and their nest was filched piecemeal. By May 8th, however, they had gathered together quite a good nest again. Attention has already been drawn to the peculiarities identifying this pair, and on the 30th I was astounded to see, on her rising from the throat-pulsing attitude, after I had been watch-ing for an hour, that the female was sitting on a second egg, to-gether with a guillemot's egg which must have rolled into the nest. This second egg must have been laid about the 14th, seven-teen days after the loss of the first, though from that day to this I had never had the slightest suspicion that she was sitting on anything except an empty nest. She continued to incubate the guillemot's egg until some date between June 14th and 19th, and

[1] A photograph taken in June 1947 shows her niche to be unoccupied.

on the 20th the nest was provided with fresh greenstuff for the last time.

Here and there a guillemot might be seen sitting on her egg up against the cliff-wall and within beak range of two sitting gannets. To those already heavy losses among eggs, due to the carelessness and nervousness of sitting birds usual in a guillemot colony, were added those further losses due to alighting gannets, especially non-territoried birds, which knocked sitting guillemots off the cliffs, and to the many eggs that rolled within range of sitting gannets, where the restless endearments of a pair of guillemots were not tolerated for any length of time, though the gannets did not deliberately peck these guillemots' eggs that rolled their way. So long as the guillemot sat quietly all was well, but the excitement aroused by the arrival of its mate was likely to result in the shifting of the egg to a point where the gannet would not tolerate even a quiet guillemot.

As in the case of the two skuas I was working almost in the dark throughout my time on Noss as to the dates I might expect the gannets to lay their eggs and hatch and fledge their young. I was further handicapped in the case of the gannet by the distance from the O.P. of most of the pairs, by the fact that I had arrived too late on the island to observe the laying dates of all but the later-nesting pairs, and by the further fact that long observation was necessary before it was possible to determine precisely what a gannet's nest contained, owing to the extremely tight and prolonged sitting of its occupant. However, as I thought it possible that the earliest pairs might have laid at the end of March, I began to scrutinize the gannetry very closely, early in May, for any evidence of hatching, and it was with some excitement that shortly after the middle of the month I was able to make out that one of the drum-nests, on a broad ledge just above the sea and far down below me, contained a naked and minute greyish-black squab with a grizzled-white head. With eyes still closed it lay spreadeagled helplessly flat on the drum, which still contained the shell. It was, however, the last days of May before chicks were hatching in any numbers; and not until at least a dozen had hatched was there any circumstantial evidence as to their presence. At this juncture, however, the percentage of couples of adults present at nests in the control area at any given time began to rise steeply.

Meanwhile the parents, pair 7, of this first chick, whose egg must have been laid in the first day or two of April, bowed together triumphantly under 'hung' wings, or 'throat-pulsed' in an ecstatic rapture, or clashed bills exuberantly and fondled heads continuously; until the newly arrived parent began to preen the chick, while the much-stained sitting bird performed the departure antic. (By the time it was a couple of weeks old and growing very rapidly into its 'puff' of woolly white down, with black 'lores' and beak, the chick would also 'throat-pulse'.) But the chick was a magnet, and after five minutes of 'anticking' the brooding bird settled down on it again. Though the newly arrived parent had twice opened its bill suggestively, the chick had not solicited food from it, as I had expected it would. A quarter of an hour later the brooding bird got off the chick again, anticked and departed: to return in three-quarters of an hour, when there was more preening of the chick and fondling of heads between the pair; but four minutes later she anticked and left again, returning this time immediately. Once again the chick was not fed. While it *might* be fed by the newly arrived parent, subsequent events showed that the act of feeding was not specially related to the returning of one parent from sea— a routine that aroused no response in the chick—nor with any special hour of the day, feeding taking place as late as 9 p.m. In actual fact it was more often fed—though even so infrequently— at any odd time by the brooding parent.

Feeding took place from the earliest stages and a chick not yet free from the hinder part of its shell, and still wet and black except for its grizzled head, would be fed by its parent regurgitating, at which the chick would peck inside the latter's lower mandible. When older the chick thrust up its head into its parent's gape, commonly five or even six times in the space of a couple of minutes, while the parent swallowed back and regurgitated after every two or three feeds. When the latter drew up its head to swallow or broke off the operation and began bowing, the chick would point up its bill at the other's, to stimulate further feeding. Such importunity, however, was not always effective, for on one fourteen-day-old chick biting its parent's bill the latter ignored it and continued to play with a feather. Occasionally there was a hitch in the procedure. After much importunity, for instance, one chick was fed three times, but then twice failed to put its bill into its parent's gape, though successful at a sixth attempt. Nor was feeding confined to one parent: for nestling 8 was first fed once by its most recently arrived parent and then fed five times by its much-stained brooding parent—a solid white residue remaining on the parent's beak after the feeding. After this the latter subsequently made two further half-hearted and abortive attempts to regurgitate again. Five minutes later, however, it fed the nestling a seventh time, when the other clean-plumaged mate left after an earlier period of 'anticking'.

No regular fishing took place off Noss. After a gale gannets might be seen plunging into the Voe of the Mels for piltocks, or surface fishing for fry off Setter, with much excited croaking, in company perhaps with a school of porpoises and a basking shark; but their main fishing grounds were no doubt among the herrings twenty or thirty miles out to sea. As early as 5.45 a.m. scores were to be seen coming up from the south into Rumble Wick in rhythmic flights, six or nine at a time, before each at its journey's end wheeled off to its own special cliff or continued on round the Noup to the gannetries on the north side. I never saw a gannet cross the island from sea to sea, though one morning I found one standing on the green outside the hill-dyke, unable to get airborne: but it had disappeared by the evening.

By the time the nestlings were a fortnight or so old their parents no longer brooded them and they passed their days in a comatose condition, sleeping with heads stretched full length down the wall of the nest-drum—a characteristic posture—or curled up with head turned round to belly. Seeing a big nestling laid out motionless, or lying curled up on its side, fouled to the very beak with ordure, one's first impression was that it was dead, and I suffered one or two shocks in this way. After long observation, however, with the aid of binoculars, it was apparent that a membrane was nictitating slowly and intermittently three-quarters of the way across the 'dark-blue' eye and up again: but this was the sole evidence that the young one was alive. When one such comatose nestling raised its head, after several minutes' inertia, it was severely pecked on the front part of its head by the adjacent pair of adults: whereupon it cowered its head round for some considerable time, before beginning to preen. Here was a possible cause of mortality among the bigger nestlings, when their bulky size tended to result in their 'overflowing' into a neighbouring pair's beak-territory: though, in actual fact, probably only one big nestling in the control area met its death in this way, when at the age of about forty days, pair 7's chick—the oldest in the gannetry, older by four or five days than any other and by a month than half of its fellows—was lying stretched out in that peculiar comatose way, while its parents bowed to one another. In this instance, however, this did indicate death and ten days later its carcase was almost trodden into the nest-drum, at which one or both parents were still in constant attendance.

By the end of the third week of June, when some sixty-five chicks in white down were obvious in the control area and the eldest surviving were three weeks old, the latter woke up a little, preened themselves, twiddled feathers lying about the nest, or played with their parents' beaks or with nest-stuff with them. Up to this age they had been preened by their parents, sometimes by both at the relieving hour—which was still predominantly in the early morning—and a curious incident occurred when one of two parents 'mandibulated' a grey squab quite severely across the head and neck, possibly to turn it beneath the brooding bird, which stabbed its mate mildly. But still more curious was the fate of a nestling kittiwake sitting on the outer edge of a nest in a row of cells between two layers of gannets: for on its other parent alighting the nestling tumbled off and fell twenty feet, to land beside a sitting gannet. The latter mandibulated rather than pecked this waif, and after a minute or two the nestling crept under the gannet, which had either an egg or a very young squab, and after a few minutes of uneasy pecking beneath her and settling herself, she brooded the strange nestling! The latter, however, was never seen again.

At the end of June, when about one hundred white chicks

could be seen in the control area, the eldest were of a size with their parents and seemed bulkier on account of the great bloom of white down which enveloped them, though black tail-points were now showing. They were spry enough to peer over the edge of the nesting ledge at the sea so far below, ignoring, in their interest, their parents' bowing ceremony. A week later they had learnt to sleep standing on dark-grey feet with heads tucked back into black scapulars. The latter were now becoming prominent and were followed before the end of the sixth week by neat black-and-white wing-secondaries and short black tails. At seven weeks scapulars, wings and tail were almost free of down and the head was beginning to blacken; and it was at this season —towards the middle of July—that after heavy rain a number of well-advanced dark juveniles became prominent in the control area: for heavy rain produced a striking transformation in the gannetry, as did the departure of the ledge-fouling guillemots, which was just beginning. The cliffs, with most of the guano distemper washed off them by the rain, appeared much closer in perspective and therefore higher and of more gigantic proportions, and all *exposed* nests, chicks, and adults were very wet and dirty, the nests appearing once more as drums rather than amorphous hummocks of rock; but whereas those chicks still in full down were so wet and muddy that they were difficult to 'pick up' against the muddy ledges and drums, those that had shed a great part of their down, appearing a mottled grey in dry weather, now stood out very blackly. The former were in a truly dreadful dishevelled state of bedraggled down, which was now scattered all about the ledges. This state, together with their infestation by lice, probably caused them much irritation, and they preened continually, shaking out clouds of down, which settled on the ledges and floated very slowly up to the top of the cliffs like thistledown: for they, and to a much greater degree the older black young, passed minutes together flapping their wings vigorously, clipping a parent on either side round the head, causing them to bow. The black juveniles were now assuming adult manners, and one might be observed with its beak locked savagely in its parent's, while another even stabbed at an adjacent brooding adult, and a third lunged mildly at its parent's head.

They also had a trick of standing with heads elevated perfectly vertical without, however, the customary pulsing of the throat. At eight weeks they were completely black when wet, and when dry and in places sheltered from the voiding of those above, a mottled grey—magnificent birds in a breeding greenshank's plumage of dark or pale grey, speckled or striped with white, smooth diver-like heads hachured in white.

At nine weeks, that is, in the second week of August, when there were some 140 chicks in the control area, the oldest were completely feathered and showed a tendency to wander a foot or two from their nest-drums, disappearing temporarily behind protuberances in the cliffs, reappearing again after an hour or so. This tendency resulted in a further, though small, mortality. One fell on to a ledge below its own and lay on its back all day between two drums, paddling feebly with its feet in the air, and died during the night; a second floated dead at the base of the cliffs; a third, still with down on its head, fell on to the reef at the base of the Noup and survived for two or three days, sleeping for the most part with head tucked back into scapulars, before it disappeared. (Only one dead adult, floating on the waters of the Wick on August 16th, was ever observed off Noss.) At this time, too, one among many hundred parents would fly off its nest-drum and leave an eight- or nine-week young one unattended for a minute or two—the first time the nest-drum had been left unattended for a second by one or other of the parents since the egg had been laid four months earlier!

III

THE YOUNG GO DOWN TO THE SEA

The circumstances attending the departure of the young gannets for sea were somewhat obscure and it was perhaps that event on Noss I was most anxious to watch. It had indeed been witnessed by one or two naturalists, but their accounts were conflicting. According to J. H. Gurney, who contradicted himself more than once in his book, *The Gannet*, the parents stopped feeding the young one after eight and a half weeks, but a further ten days then elapsed before the latter finally launched itself forth on its long unsteady flight down to the sea. E. T. Booth, however, according to his *Rough Notes*, found that his captive gannets fed the young one up to the age of thirteen and a half weeks; while more recently R. M. Lockley had stated in *Letters from Skockholm* that, 'When it is about two months old the adults feed it more and more irregularly and at last abandon it altogether,' and 'We can now visualize the young gannet, deserted by its parents, awaiting at the nest the moment when hunger shall have thinned it down sufficiently for it to be light enough to flap, with wings which have been very much exercised during the last few days, downwards to the sea.'

In respect to this statement, that the parents abandoned the young one, Gurney had been misquoted in the *Handbook* and it was also at odds with my experience the previous September, when I had found thousands of adults on the Noss cliffs outnumbering the young by something like twenty to one. However, as the first young had hatched shortly after the middle of May this year I could, from the above evidence, expect them to begin fledging—that is to say to begin going down to the sea—in either the first or last weeks of August, though it seemed to be generally agreed that it was exceptional for any to fledge before September. Taking no chances, I began to watch out for any parents deserting young as early as the middle of July.

But the days passed and no parents deserted their young. Weeks passed, and still one or both parents were in daily attendance on every young one, and I saw no change in the daily routine. Then, on August 10th, when the oldest were entering upon their twelfth week, I noticed that pair 8's young one had disappeared, seventy-six to seventy-nine days after hatching, though both parents were present and one was sitting on the nest-drum; but though I watched more closely than ever, thenceforward, nothing further materialized until the 14th. At 12.45 p.m. that day a rorqual whale breached at no great distance off Puffin Holm, affording a brief glimpse of white belly, shark-like underjaw, and enormous tail-flukes. Fastening my binoculars on the place where it had sounded again, what was my astonishment to perceive a young gannet on the sea east of the Cradle Holm. Though flapping its wings and threshing them on the water it was unable to lift itself into the air and drifted south-west with the tide. No adults were with it.

A few minutes later I perceived a second fledgeling on the water south of Puffin Holm. Three adults were near it and one 'attacked' it—at which one of the other two drove off the latter, lunging at it with open beak; but then first one and then the other of these two also 'attacked' the fledgeling, persistently flapping forward and alighting on its tail, to peck at its head. They finally abandoned it, however, and flew off, leaving it like the other fledgeling to drift away alone, southwards. Were these its parents? If so, their manners were peculiar, though not dissimilar from those of the alighting adult greeting its mate with a savage grip of her head.

The days passed and I was still unsuccessful in observing any of the fledgelings in the act of leaving their ledges. At 8.40 p.m. on the 16th, for instance, one was on the water on the north side of the Noup; and at 12.15 p.m. on the 17th there was another off Puffin Holm. An hour later a second was close into the Rumble Wick cliffs but, though I presumed that it must have come down quite recently, no adults were with it, as was also the case with the other two. Seven minutes later, however, two adults landed on the water near it, but the fledgeling swam hurriedly away from them, its tail awash. On a third adult also landing, one of the other two threatened it, whereupon both the assaulted bird and the attacker passed into the departure-antic, in so far as they were able to raise their heads from the swimming position, and the aggressor subsequently bowed its head to 'scissored' wings with some difficulty, before all three flew off. At 1.25 p.m., when the morning sun was already off the Rumble Wick cliffs and at the hour of high-water, a third fledgeling swam out from the base of the cliffs; and a quarter of an hour later I perceived a fourth in the north corner of the Wick.

Though a second known young one belonging to pair 9 had also disappeared, about eleven weeks after hatching, and the number of young in the control area had decreased by five or ten, I had not, up to now, been able to observe any signs of one preparing to take this momentous step; and, as I had expected, not one of those on the cliffs had been deserted by its parents, every visible young one, and *also* every drum deserted by a fledgeling, having one or both parents present. On the contrary, the percentage of adult couples present in the control area at any one time had never been previously exceeded and the total number of adults present had only once been exceeded—on July 26th.

At 1.45 p.m., however, I caught a glimpse out of the corner of my eye of a young one flapping vigorously, in characteristic high-standing posture, on a ledge overlooking the sea, and saw it suddenly launch forth and fly steadily and evenly some three hundred yards out into the Wick, gradually descending to make a good alighting on the water. Its departure was too sudden for me to mark the drum from which it originated, but apparently no adults took any notice of its departure and none visited it on the water. Five minutes later I was again taken unawares—it was almost impossible to keep one's eye on every one of some scores of potential fledgelings—when another launched forth from a lower ledge, descending after a flight of only forty yards to a sound, though foaming, alighting. Again I was unable to mark its nest-drum, but no adults accompanied it or subsequently visited it. Thereafter, no more young went down within my field of vision and by 3 p.m. very few were exercising their wings, in contrast to the period 12 noon to 2 p.m., and many were sleeping. The period of tension had passed, and on Laurence Sutherland drawing my attention to the fact that the fledgings had taken place at high-water, this seemed quite a likely hour, though it was difficult to understand the attraction or advantages of such an hour.

The next morning I was at the O.P. by 3.10 a.m. At this hour there was quite a lot of light in the Wick, gathered from the yellowing east, and one or two gannets and also fulmars were on the wing, though there was as yet little noise coming from the gannetry. By 3.30 a.m., however, when it was light enough to write easily, most of the adults and young were waking, though there was little activity among the latter; but five minutes later four or five were flapping hard. At 3.50 a.m., half an hour before sunrise, the gannetry was in full uproar, though only a score of adults were on the wing in the Wick, and I noticed that a black young one and a white-headed one, both without parents, were joined by one and two parents respectively; and then a deplorable scene occurred when an immature-plumaged parent with a little black barring edging its secondaries—the only parent thus plumaged in the control area—attempted to mate with its black young one and, when unsuccessful, characteristically seized it violently by the head and attempted, initially, to push it off the ledge, while the young one resisted, with tail spread and wings loosened at the shoulders, as stubbornly as a female adult would have done in a similar case. After a minute or more the parent's confusion passed and it resumed normal parental behaviour towards its offspring. This, however, was not the first such lapse in the control area. On July 12th a single parent had attempted as late as 9.45 p.m., to mate with a big white chick—one, say, in its third or fourth week; and on the afternoon of July 26th the male of a pair with a white chick had also attempted to mate with it, while the female stood by enacting the departure antic! Matings of breeding pairs had ceased as long ago as the second week in May, though a pair with a large white chick had an abortive mating as late as June 28th, the male striking savagely at the female when she attempted to clash bills after he had got off her back, though they subsequently preened one another. With that exception there had been occasional matings of non-territoried pairs only, up to the end of June, and one thereafter by a pair with a nest-drum, but no chick, on August 17th.

By 4.50 a.m. no young ones had left their ledges, most were quiet, and none were to be seen on the sea. It was clear that the early morning hours were not those stimulating departure. When I returned six hours later, however, two were down on the water—they appeared dark-brownish on a dull day from the cliff-top—and every now and again a pair of adults or a single bird would alight by one of the two and make vicious lunges at its head. At these, it being a calm day, I could hear the fledgeling's guttural, yet falsetto, *crr-eek, crr-eek* (comparable to the adult's *arrg*)—a cry that had been heard in the gannetry only during the past week or so since the fledging had begun.

At 12.20 p.m. a third fledgeling appeared on the water below my gannetry, and ten minutes later a white-headed bird also appeared there—that is one in all probability not more than nine weeks old at the most, though no doubt some young gannets might be slower than others in attaining their fledging plumage, as in the case of the bonxies.

At the end of the first week of fledging there were obvious gaps in the ranks of the young in the control area, some 17 per cent having gone down. There was, however, no decrease in the ranks of the adults, and all those nest-drums from which young had fledged were occupied at all hours of the twenty-four by one or both parents, including both of pair 7, whose young one had now been dead for seven weeks!

At noon on the 21st, when another known young one belonging to pair 8 had left, between twelve and thirteen weeks after hatching, I saw a fledgeling make a flight of some five hundred yards. Again, I missed the instant of its take-off, but no adults accompanied it. No more went down until 12.45 p.m., when a whitish-headed bird appeared on the water; and after that no more within my field of vision up to 3.5 p.m., though for an hour or more one stood looking out to sea intently, incessantly exercising its wings. This was a rather uncommon spectacle, for only those young ones due to fledge within the subsequent twenty-four hours or so *faced* the sea during wing-exercises, the others religiously flapping with backs to the sea. (By 10 a.m. the next morning this bird had disappeared.) Only one other young one displayed any sign of responding to the urge to go down to the sea, straying three feet from its nest-drum, to the complete unconcern of its parents—which commonly paid no heed to their young wandering into the territories of adjacent pairs; but after peering over the edge of the cliff, loosening its wings at the shoulders from time to time suggestively, it ultimately re-turned to its drum after an absence of an hour or so.

Thus far, apart from witnessing intermittent visits by one or more adults to three or four of those fledgelings on the sea, I had obtained no direct evidence as to what part, if any, the parents played at the actual moment of the young one's departure, though it was becoming increasingly probable that these visiting adults were not the fledgelings' parents. At 1 p.m., on the 22nd, however, I noticed a young one standing, with loosened wings, away from its drum and looking out to sea in the customary intent way. That many of a bird's actions belonged to a mechan-istic chain of reflexes and motor responses might be granted, but it was equally evident to the student of animal behaviour under natural conditions that it had its moments of perception. It was difficult to believe that these young gannets were mental vacuums when they stood concentrating for long periods on the world beyond the cliffs. But even as I entered in my note-book the detail that, while this young one was looking out to sea its parent was unconcernedly tossing up nesting material, the former slipped away 200 yards out into the Wick, its parent to all outward appearances completely unaware of its departure and making no pause in its tossing up of nesting-stuff!

At 10 a.m. the next morning there were two fledgelings on the sea and it was evident that the state of the tide had not, after all, anything to do with the hour of departure. There were also two on the sea at 1.5 p.m. on the 25th, and a quarter of an hour later I saw two more go down one after the other. The first made a flight of some 500 yards and the second was still flying strongly, flapping and gliding, about 1,000 yards out from the cliffs, when it was forced down by a bonxie—at which juncture an adult gannet suddenly appeared and landed just behind the fledgeling: whereupon the bonxie sheered off. At 1.27 p.m. I lost another strong flyer in sea-mist beyond the Noup after an unfinished flight on a controlled half-circle. Some of those young ones fledging at this date—when about 30 per cent had gone down—were probably older and stronger on the wing than some of the earlier ones. At 1.40 p.m. a fourth alighted after a flight of only 100 yards and was subsequently 'attacked' by an adult. At 2.5 p.m. a fifth made a flight of some 300 yards; and at 2.13 p.m. a sixth leapt off its drum with half-spread wings, somewhat unsteadily, before gaining its equilibrium with wings fully spread: but by this time the mist was too thick for me to follow its flight to the end. As in the earlier instance, however, its parent continued to fiddle with nest-stuff, without any sign of awareness that its young one—which it had tended unremittingly, first in the egg and then as a nestling, for some eighteen weeks— had, in a second of time, vanished from its ken. There did not seem to be any parallel among sea-fowl to such a phenomenon.[1]

Half an hour later, however, a young one attempting to take flight from one of the ledges in the central recess of my gannetry landed beside a nest-drum nearer to the edge of the cliff. The occupant of the drum and its own young one unexpectedly caressed the newcomer quite gently, the young one persistently 'mandibulating' its fellow's beak and head. On this occasion the newcomer's parent followed it down, threatening the other parent, but pecking its own young one on the head! Very shortly, however, it significantly abandoned the latter and returned to its own drum: while its young one, ignoring its fellow's atten- tions, except for hunching itself as flatly as possible against the rock, proceeded to concentrate intently on the sea below. Similarly, at 2.50 p.m., another young one twice stumbled into an adjacent pair's territory, but twice retreated to its own nest. In this instance its parent ignored its activities throughout, includ- ing its ultimate successful fledging flight.

[1] Since writing the above, I find that Seton Gordon had observed this pheno- menon more than a quarter of a century ago (vide Wanderings of a Naturalist, 1921): but the significance of the record appears to have been overlooked in all subsequent accounts of the Fledging.

By 9.55 a.m. the next morning the first wanderer had disappeared, no doubt taking flight some time after I left the cliff the previous afternoon: for no fledgelings were to be seen on the sea, though one was 'concentrating', and none went down up to 10.25 a.m. An hour and a half later, however, there was one in the Wick and two more off Puffin Holm, and at 12.5 p.m. I saw one make a long flight of 600 to 700 yards, curving southwards out beyond the Holm. At 12.35 p.m., a second actually lifted in the air a little after its take-off from the cliff, a manœuvre causing it to rock dangerously, before it succeeded in straightening out and descending to a good splash-landing some 250 yards off the cliffs.

By September some 60 per cent of the young had gone down, and on the 7th one fledgeling was on the sea at 11.30 a.m., but none went down during the next hour and a half and none were 'concentrating' or exercising their wings facing seawards. At 2 p.m. one made an 800-yard flight southwards, alighting with the usual splash-landing (it being the hour of low-water, with some swell) a few yards from two adults which, however, ignored it. No more went down up to 2.45 p.m., when three were visible on the sea, and though the thirty-two young still unfledged in the control area were livelier than earlier in the morning, there was not a tithe of the wing-exercising there had been in August. It was the rule, rather than the exception, for these remaining young to belong to groups of nests. Ten of the thirty-two, for example, were close together—on or beside their own drums of course—on a broad upper ledge just below pair 1's ledge: while large areas of the control block contained no young at all. Though there was still no decrease in the numbers of adults, the percentage of couples present in the control area at any one time had dropped considerably since the third week in August.

On September 9th one fledgeling was on the sea at 11.10 a.m., but none left the ledges after that up to 2.15 p.m., though several stood looking out to sea or peered over the edge of the cliff, loosening their wings from time to time. One of the latter would probably have gone down, had it not been for the arrival of an adult on a ledge immediately below it. This upset its concentra-

A great bloom of white down

A six-feet wing-span

With a strong wind blowing the Gannets had the greatest difficulty in
alighting on the nesting ledge

tion: whereupon it clambered up to its parents on the drum and began preening. I noted with interest that there was now more building activity among the adults than there had been for some weeks past. At least three pairs were actively constructing nests and a dozen birds at a time were picking up feathers and sea-weed on the water below. Almost certainly one of those bringing up weed to its mate belonged to a pair whose young one had fledged. This 'nest-building' had continued right through the season among all classes of gannets, and even those with black young had been bringing up feathers or clumps of weed or grass, which the latter assisted in spreading about the nest-drum, toying and tugging at it with their parents and passing much of their time in billing the stuff under their breasts in the manner of the sitting adult: just as at an earlier stage, when the chicks were in white down, enormous beakfuls of bladder-campion and other greenstuff were being brought up to the ledges and strewn around, very often over the backs of the young ones.

On September 15th, when there were westerly squalls of rain, a fledgeling was down at 12.15 p.m. quite close under the cliffs. It threshed its wings repeatedly on the water, trying to lift itself into the air, as they all did. Another appeared at the base of the cliffs, where a third was standing asleep on the reef-platform, at 12.40 p.m.: but none went down during this, my last, half-hour at the gannetry. The fledging had now lasted for more than five weeks, more than 80 per cent of the young in the control area had fledged, and only twenty-four individuals (including two still in three-parts white down) remained. Of these, seven were clustered together on that above-mentioned ledge, with two more near-by, and there were other groupings. And still there were no *noticeable* gaps in the ranks of the adults, with the single exception of pair 7, which had also been absent on the 9th, though one had been standing on the nest-drum on the 7th, seventy-three days after the decease of their chick and about six months from the beginning of incubation! One of this pair, however, presumably the male, had been absent since August 17th, as had also one of pair 8. The total number of adults present, however, had never been materially higher and at least one bird was present at all known nests, other than pair 7's.

Pair 1 had successfully hatched their second egg on July 2nd; but thirty-seven days later when this, an under-sized, nestling was only about a quarter the size of its parent, the latter grew restive and left it alone for a quarter of an hour at 5.12 a.m.; and this day was the last on which I observed the male at the nest for more than a month. At 11.45 a.m. on August 14th the female again left the chick for three minutes. Two days later the latter, the smallest in the gannetry, had (not unexpectedly) disappeared when little more than six weeks old. On the 18th the female flew up time and again to her nest-hollow, 'anticking' pathetically, very briefly and, as one would say, dejectedly. By the 22nd the nest had practically disappeared: nevertheless the male was present as late as September 15th.

Pair 2, who had laid their egg between May 25th and 30th, were even less successful, for by July 18th their egg was addled after fifty to fifty-five days' incubation. Both, however, were still 'sitting', mainly standing, on the egg on the 28th, and even changed over on August 7th, the last time the male was noticed. On the 16th the egg was finally smashed after seventy-nine to eighty-one days' incubation, and by the 22nd this nest, too, had almost disappeared. The female, however, was present on September 15th.

Pair 3 were more successful and hatched their chick in the last days of June. By August 21st, when the nestling was between seven and eight weeks old and when I noted the male for the last time, this female was also beginning to desert the chick temporarily: but mother and young one were still present on September 15th, when the latter was not less than eleven weeks old.

Number 5 had never got as far as laying an egg, and on August 5th the only bird ever seen of this 'pair' began to desert the nesting site intermittently, though still present on September 15th.

Pair 4, whose chick had hatched in forty-nine or fifty days, lost the latter when it was about a week old. Both parents were present the next day, but thereafter only one. This bird was deserting the nest temporarily on July 28th but, like the others, was still visiting it on September 15th.

The earliest fledgeling had abandoned its nest-drum on August

10th: but had pair 7's chick lived it would have fledged as early as the last days of July or the first days of August—for the fledging period appeared to be of the order of ten to twelve weeks. My only surviving young one, pair 3's, whose hatching date was known was, as we have seen, still on the ledge, fully feathered, at the age of seventy-eight to eighty-one days: though its parent, being one of those with a rudimentary nest on the uppermost ledge had, abnormally, begun to desert it for intervals of half a minute or a minute at a time (caressing it briefly and lightly on the head on her return) as early as the fifty-third to fifty-sixth day. This unusual behaviour was probably due to the irregular attendances of the male, of whose presence I had no record after August 21st. The young one was one of those slow to develop, retaining some down on its head and much on its thighs as late as the tenth week. Figures for five less accurately recorded fledgings gave an average period of seventy-five to eighty-one days, with possible extremes of sixty-eight to ninety-two days.

Of approximately 116 young that had fledged fourteen had been seen to take off from the cliffs. In no case did the parents accompany them and in three instances, when the fledgeling's nest-drum was also observed, the parent was apparently unaware of, or indifferent to, its offspring's departure. In addition twenty-eight fledgelings had been noted on the waters of the Wick or farther afield—most of which probably came from gannetries outside the control area. Only five were approached by adults when on the water, and these had either treated them in the peculiar manner described or had left them alone. None had been seen to *take off* from the cliffs before 12 noon or after 3.5 p.m., but others had been seen on the sea as early as 10 a.m. and as late as 8.40 p.m. The main departure hours were those between 12 noon and 2.15 p.m., and no associations could be traced between the actual fledging hour and the state of the tide or the weather: but there was a notable raising of the emotional threshold, in the form of wing-exercising and 'concentration', during this period. All on alighting had drifted gradually southwards to sea, though some of those making only short flights probably remained in Wick waters overnight.

Throughout the fledging period none had ever been seen on the wing off Noss—or, for that matter, off Shetland since gannets first began breeding in the islands—after their initial take-off flight. This suggested that an interval elapsed between the initial departure from the nesting ledge and the true fledging—that is, the ability to rise off the sea and fly—and this was in accordance with Gurney's statement that, once down, the young remained 'drifting hither and thither for the space of two or three weeks', without feeding or being fed. Such an estimate was consistent with the interval that elapsed between the earliest departures from Noss in the second week of August and the first appearance of fledgelings on the wing off the coast of Aberdeenshire in the first week of September.

All the evidence went to suggest that those adults visiting fledgelings on the water were not parents, but inquisitive strangers. It would, in any case, be difficult to explain how the parent-birds, of which one or other, or both, of every pair were still present at the abandoned nests at every hour of the twenty-four, could, during their intervals away from the cliffs, locate their young several miles off Noss. I will anticipate the objection that, as it was not possible to ring or mark the gannets on Noss, I had no evidence that it was the original parents or pairs that were still frequenting the abandoned nests after the fledging of their young, by pointing out that, as I was actually counting more *occupied* nests in September, *when* 80 *per cent of the young had left,* than at any previous time, it would be necessary to replace the parents of these 80 per cent by non-breeding birds —if it be held that the latter are the new occupants of abandoned nests.

I was not able to ascertain how long one of a pair of gannets was accustomed to remain away from the nest. From the extraordinarily few occasions on which some known male birds were seen at the nests, it seemed likely that the absences of the latter might extend to periods of days. In opposition to this conclusion, as James Fisher has pointed out to me, is the fact that if the number of nests in a control area are known and the number of gannets alighting in the control area in a given period are known, then the average time spent away from its nest by each absent gannet is also known, and that a calculation on this data shows that the average period of absence on Noss was about fifty-five minutes. Actually, the period of absence would be longer than this, as among those gannets alighting in every five-minute period would be some of the average number of thirty-two non-breeding gannets that shared the control area with the 186 breeding pairs, while one or two of those alighting would do so more than once in the five-minute period; so that seventy-five minutes would, I think, be nearer the mark—with which may be compared Fisher's figure of eighty minutes for the gannets of a control area on Ailsa Craig. These figures represent the average period of absence. They were undoubtedly greatly exceeded by those males I had under observation, and the average would be kept down by the quick return of the females. They must also have been greatly exceeded by those ringed gannets breeding on Grassholm, which were recovered at distances of up to 160 miles from that gannetry. Nor are these figures necessarily those of incubating or brooding periods—for, as we have seen, it was very often the newly alighting bird which left the nest again, without changing over with its mate.

There were no Shetland records of adult gannets feeding young ones at sea, as there would almost certainly have been, did this occur, considering the far-reaching activities of fishermen off Shetland and the unusually keen interest of Shetlanders generally in birds: so the interval before the true fledging must be presumed one of starvation. The question then arose as to whether the nestling was fed up to the hour of its departure. As already pointed out the feeding of the young was never at any time the frequent spectacle that one might have expected it to be. All that could be said was that I never observed a fully feathered young one in the act of being fed, though those with down only on the head were, and that I saw only one act of feeding after August 21st—to one of a pair of 'twins', fully feathered except for a big patch on its head—though of course there must have been other instances among the less advanced young. (It was not until the end of July that I realized that one pair in the control area, and two pairs outside it, had successfully reared twins or were at any rate feeding two young apiece.) Nor did

I ever see black young ones importune returning parents for food, as they constantly did in the black-and-white stage—which suggested, incidentally, that it was not hunger that was the stimulus leading to departure. It was fair to presume, therefore, that feeding ceased about the end of the ninth week and about ten days before the young one took off: while to this period must be added the further starvation period between take off and true fledging.

Early in October, when the oldest fledgelings had been nearly two months off the cliffs and when the youngest were just going down to the sea—the curve of a graph of increasing fledging showed that the last of the young would go down at the end of the first week of October—the bulk of the adults also left the cliffs for good, after regular attendance for six months or more.[1] The most remarkable feature of their departure was that it was *not* brought about by the fledging of their young which in some instances must, as we have seen, have antedated this by as much as two months, during which time they had been in regular attendance at the abandoned nest-drums!

Normally 99 per cent of the gannets left Shetland waters early in October, but in some autumns immense shoals of sillock, the young of the saithe, attracted a proportion of the adult gannets to winter, and in 1945–6 as many as 500 at a time were diving for saithe in Lerwick Harbour and more at other points around Shetland, and continued to do so until the middle of February, when the earliest pairs would be thinking about visiting the gannetries on Noss again. (It is interesting to note that these wintering birds did not roost on the Noss cliffs, but flew straight out to sea just before dusk, returning to the harbour at day-break.)

POSTSCRIPT

In the summer of 1947 Theo Kay conducted further investigations into the young gannet's post-fledging activities. On August 24th he took his famous yacht, the *Soldian*, around Noss. Let him continue the account:

[1] In 1947 the gannetries had been deserted by October 18th, though gannets were on the wing off Noss as early as December 19th following.

'We went first to the cliffs and found three young ones between the Cradle Holm and the Noup and within a couple of
hundred yards of the cliffs. We then motored—the wind was
very light from the north—about four miles east and zig-zagged
to about five miles south of the Noup. Roughly speaking, we
covered twenty square miles and within this area we saw twenty-
five to thirty young. *None* of these could fly. When we approached to within twenty or thirty feet they spread their wings
and flapped away from us over the surface. The flapping was a
feeble attempt to get on the wing and after six to eight flaps the
attempt was given up and either the bird turned on us, with
beak in the air, or it continued to paddle away from us. A shrill
cry was made when the bird was excitedly trying to get away
from us, shriller and not so strident as the *kirr, kirr* of the adult.
This was the behaviour in every instance. When covering this
area of water I could see that we might have gone right through
it and not seen a single young one. They are spaced widely apart,
perhaps more than half a mile on the average, and a good look-
out has to be kept to pick them out. All were paddling slowly
to the south-east and south. I am convinced that every one
was completely on its own. Not the slightest attention was
paid to them by passing adults. A feature of some interest
was that every now and then they exercised their wings as is
done at the nest. This was an aid to us in picking them up on
the water.'

Three days later Kay made a further expedition, accompanied
on this occasion by George Russell:

'To-day we counted, within an area perhaps a little smaller
than on the 24th, fifteen young ones: a difference being that six
of these were discovered roughly east of the Noup, the others
being south-east and south. (There was a breeze from the south.)
Two of those seen to-day, while at a distance from us and un-
disturbed, made deliberate attempts to get on the wing by making
about a dozen flaps over the water. The attempts did not succeed
—as was also the case with three young fulmars—but the efforts
were much better than the ones they subsequently made when
trying to escape from us. It may be surmised from this that given
a few more days of wing exercising, a further loss of fat and a

fresh wind, they would very likely be able to get on the wing, although perhaps not to fly very far.'

On September 12th Kay went out again, leaving Lerwick at 10 a.m. and returning at 7 p.m.:

'The day was favourable, as I wanted to see what effect a breeze had on the young birds; a south-west gale was forecast but did not materialize fully until my return. We passed the Bard Head a mile off, steering SE. and proceeded six miles before turning N. and NW. to the Noup. The water was very dark except for the broken tops to the seas and it was difficult to pick out dark objects. No young birds were seen in this area, nothing but an occasional adult gannet, a few fulmars and a sprinkling of puffins, adults in little groups and young birds always singly. On getting to the cliffs I found a full house of adult gannets but fewer young ones than I had expected. There were no youngsters below or near the cliffs, but I had an idea I would find some east from the Noup, owing to the wind direction, and proceeded out that way. About a mile off I came on one, and half a mile farther another, and that was the total for the day. By approaching these birds from leeward I gave them every chance to get on the wing from off the tops of the seas with the strong wind blowing, but they merely flapped to windward and collapsed exactly as they had done with a calm. Very clearly these young birds cannot fly under any weather conditions until they have been at sea for a time and are tuned up. By that time they are away from Shetland. I am absolutely convinced that the young gannets are quite on their own. A parent could never find a youngster after it had drifted all night in a heavy sea and a gale of wind.'

IV

SOME STATISTICAL ASPECTS

A major difficulty in studying the gannets on Noss was the absence of any self-contained gannetries, or even of sizable self-contained groups of pairs within a gannetry, close enough to an O.P. for accurate observation. Even my chosen gannetry covered the whole face of the cliff, except for a sheer slab here and there, and continued round a bulge on its north side into another gannetry without any break in the ranks of nesting birds. From the east or seaward end of my O.P. from 500 to 600 gannets could be counted on the cliff-face at any given time according to hour and season. The distance of the majority of their nests from the O.P. made this far too great a number for anything approaching accurate observation. I was, therefore, obliged to restrict my observational block to that smaller area of cliff visible from the west end of the O.P. Even so, some nests in the upper parts of that earlier-mentioned central recess were partly or wholly in dead ground, so that their occupants were sometimes visible and sometimes not, depending upon their precise position on or near the nest; there were no sharply delimited boundaries to any part of the block; and the lower nests were too distant. Thus, according to my exact position on the O.P., down to the very inch, and to the amount of light during the hours of 'darkness', so the number of nest-sites in my control area varied from one count to another; and, if there are gaps in the series of records in the Appendix, the reader will perhaps be charitable and remember that such factors as wind, cold, rain and fatigue often make impossible at the actual time the recording of details that may seem to present no difficulties to one sitting in an armchair. Most regrettably, from my point of view, there had been a big increase in the number of gannets on this cliff since 1937, when from the same O.P. it was estimated that only sixty-seven to sixty-nine pairs occupied that central recess, which was now boundaryless.

The maximum number of occupied nests counted in this non-rigid control area increased from 113 on April 28th, to 133 on May 10th, to 168 on May 28th, to a peak of 180–186 on June 13th and subsequently, with which may be compared the peak total of 142 nestlings on August 12th. In September, however, I must unwittingly have extended the boundaries of the control area, for I was counting over 200 occupied nests. This progressive increase was also reflected in the total number of birds counted in the control area, which rose similarly from month to month. There was, in addition, a daily muster of birds without nests varying from twelve to sixty-seven in number. These birds stood or sat about in ones or *pairs* in those parts of the colony where there were no nests and were certainly non-breeding birds and not off-duty breeding birds.

The control area thus contained a potential maximum of some 360 or 370 breeding birds plus anything up to seventy odd non-breeding birds. This potential maximum was, of course, never observed because the proportion of nests on which both birds of the pair were present at a given time never exceeded 42·7 per cent, and could be as low as 4·3 per cent, the average being 21·3 per cent. There were certain definite seasonal fluctuations in the proportion of couples present. Up to the beginning of the Hatch, covering roughly the month of May, the average percentage of couples on nests was 12·6 per cent. During June, which covered most of the Hatch, it rose to 20·5 per cent. From the peak of the Hatch to the beginning of the Fledging, July to mid-August, it rose again to 26·9 per cent, rising again during the last fortnight of August to 28·5 per cent, but falling during the first fortnight of September, by the end of which period 80 per cent of the young in the control area had fledged, to 17·9 per cent.

This progressive increase coincided with the growth of the nestling and, one presumes, the necessity of feeding it at more frequent intervals. It must be noted, however, that there was no corresponding stepping-up in the alighting-rate of birds in the control area, though there was in the number of departures. The percentage declined with the falling off in the presumed frequency of feeding as the fledging stage approached and after the fledging.

There were also irregular highs and lows associated with time and weather factors. At 11.45 a.m. on May 6th, for example, there was a high following upon a sea-fog; and at 3.15 p.m. on May 16th, another high associated with a very stiff up-draught, after a gale the previous day, which probably tended to keep many partners of sitting gannets longer on the ledges than they would normally have stayed, though the numbers of those alighting was normal and of those departing only slightly below normal. Similarly, there were lows at 3.40 p.m. on July 17th, when fog was right in to the Noup; at 3.15 p.m. on the 21st, when it was calm and sunny with some swell after fog and heavy swell during the night; and at noon on August 4th on a calm sunny day following a gale, with an exceptional low of 4.3 per cent that same evening at 7.19 p.m. with a strong breeze. While the average percentage of couples present was normally high throughout the season between the hours of 10.30 a.m. and 6.30 p.m., and normally low from 6.30 p.m. to 10.30 a.m., one could never definitely forecast a low for the latter period, if weather conditions were normal.

We must now consider the daily and seasonal tempo of activity at a gannetry. As often as possible I noted the numbers of gannets alighting in and departing from the control area in a five-minute period. James Fisher and H. G. Vevers had previously adopted a somewhat similar method both on Ailsa Craig and Noss, but had rejected it as unsatisfactory for their particular purpose of estimating total populations. As, however, this was not my primary purpose—which was to obtain comparative data as to the diurnal activity in a gannetry throughout the breeding season—and in view of the long period over which my statistics were to be conducted, I had no hesitation about continuing with mine.

During the period May 10th to September 15th the average percentage of nests in the control area on which gannets were observed to alight in a five-minute period was 10.7 per cent, and from which they departed 8.3 per cent.[1] The rate of alighting and

---

[1] The discrepancy between average percentages for alighting and departures is due to the fact that the bulk of the departures took place during one period in the early hours of the morning, when few counts were made.

departing showed no major seasonal fluctuations, except during the Hatch, when there was a 25 per cent drop, but was affected by time and weather factors. At 1.45 p.m. on May 28th, for example, only 5·3 per cent of the nests were receiving alighting birds and only 2·4 per cent losing departing birds—the cause, thick mist filling the abyss of the Wick. There were similar lows on May 30th and June 24th with thick fog; on July 2nd, when it was hazy with a considerable swell running after a gale; and also on August 7th, associated with a high percentage of couples present.

If the seasonal alighting-rate was relatively stable this was not, however, the case with the twenty-four-hour rate, for there was a daily rhythm, which was maintained, with exceptions, throughout the season. Between the hours of 2.30 p.m. and 5 p.m. the average number of birds alighting in a five-minute period varied only from 10·1 to 15·3 throughout the season, but between 3.30 a.m. and 5·15 a.m. it might vary from 4·5 to 22. Normally, the maximum activity was recorded between the hours of 4.30 a.m. and 7 a.m., according to the hour of sunrise; then fell, during the forenoon, rising at midday for that afternoon high—which, however, seldom approached the peak of the early morning hours. After 7.30 p.m. it began to fall steeply to zero or near-zero activity between the hours of 9.30 p.m. and 2.30 a.m. or 5 a.m., according to the season.

The rate of departure followed an almost similar course to that of the alighting, with the same fall during the Hatch, but a notable rise during the first fortnight of the Fledging. There was that same diurnal stable period between 2.30 p.m. and 5 p.m., but once the early morning rush was ended the hourly fluctuation was less than in the case of the numbers alighting. The only occasions on which the number of departures markedly exceeded that of those alighting were in the early morning. At 3.37 a.m. on August 18th, for example, eighteen gannets departed to eight alighting. This reversion was due, of course, to the fact that this was the hour at which those non-sitting birds that had spent the night on the cliffs were leaving the ledges, before the main arrival of those gannets coming in either to join or to relieve their mates, after a night at sea. Forty minutes later the figures were reversed, with thirty-seven birds alighting against twenty-five departing. Similarly, at 4.5 a.m. on June 13th, when the sun was just up, the numbers of those departing was only four compared with sixteen alighting. In this instance the roosting non-sitters had already left the ledges.

I found one insuperable obstacle to taking a census of all the gannets on Noss. The obstacle was not primarily the physical one of actually counting the number of nests or the number of birds sitting on apparent nests—though distances from the landward side might be as great as 300 yards, and several hundred feet from an unsteady boat on the seaward side—but the expanse of cliffs to be covered: an expanse so vast, their stratification so inconvenient, and the gannetries so continuous, that I found it impossible to count the latter in sections. It was thus impossible, whichever way one traversed, whether up and down or across and back, to remember which rows or blocks of birds one had already counted, and to be certain that one did not count them again or miss them altogether.

This was my experience in 1946 and, in my opinion, the numbers of gannets on Noss have now passed beyond the point where it is possible to assess them more accurately than to the nearest thousand: for owing to the peculiar stratification and formation of the cliffs the photographic method seems out of the question. All that can now be hoped for is evidence of *relative* increase or decrease and evidence of extension of the gannetries; and I was able to note one previously unnoted extension of four pairs, three of which reared young, well down the south face of the west cliff of Puffin Geo, nearly a hundred yards from the nearest gannetry at the south corner of Rumble Wick—though as all four had well defined nest-drums they must have been there for some years.

As my attempts to count all the nests in the gannetries were inconclusive I will only suggest that, according to my counts, there may have been the following number of pairs in 1946:

North Noup	South Noup	Rumble Wick	Total Pairs
1000–1250	600–950	1000–1575	2600–3775

There still remains to be considered another difficulty confronting the census-taker. The fact that a gannetry of 180 breeding pairs may include at one time any number from twelve to sixty-seven apparently non-breeding birds may not perhaps influence a census in which an attempt is made to count nest-drums, though we have seen that a small percentage of pairs sat on nests that could not be recognized as such at any distance, while a few non-breeding birds might sit for long periods on bare rock. In my particular gannetry these non-breeding birds were a continual and exasperating source of statistical confusion, for in watching birds alighting there was not time to observe whether all alighted beside nests or not. It was possible, however, that they were not so numerous in other gannetries occupying a more central position on the cliff-face with fewer convenient empty platforms.

In April one or two not fully mature birds, with a little black edging to their secondaries, were to be seen in the endless stream of gannets circling off the Rumble Wick cliffs, and in the first days of May a pied bird, with back more black than white, but an unblemished though very pale head, might be present on a ledge in the control block. There were at least five immature birds on the block south of mine: none had nests, but two, one with many black feathers on its back, appeared to be paired. The numbers of these immature birds circling the Wick, especially of those dark birds fledged the previous year, increased considerably at the end of May. One or two of the latter were in completely black plumage, except for buffish-white heads spotted with black and a white V on the tail. In the middle of June two still younger birds appeared in the Wick. These were brownish-grey, with whitish beaks and greyish-white speckled bellies. Throughout June and July these two drab-headed youngsters, which with their white tail Vs much resembled brent geese, would fly round the Wick hour after hour: but about the middle of August they disappeared—for by the end of July there were very few noticeably black-plumaged birds about, and only one or two stayed until the first days of September.

In addition to these non-breeding birds scattered about individual gannetries there was on Noss a very big colony of non-

breeding gannets of which no mention had been made by previous observers, probably because it was not in permanent daily
session. It was on May 13th that I noticed that four long rows
of gannets were sitting on a protuberant turf and rock ramp two-
thirds of the way down the grassy south-east siding of the Noup
and immediately above the sheer base of the cliff. At that time
I took them for breeding birds. Four days later, on an afternoon
with a stiff southerly up-draught, I noticed that groups of thirty
were gathering on the turfy platforms near the summit of the
south corner of the Noup. Then on the 30th, when the Noup was
wreathed in mist, more than a hundred were gathered on the
reefs at its southern base. On June 2nd a cloud of more than 300
sailed off the east face of the Noup when we chugged past in the
Soldian, and the next afternoon I discovered that all the birds
sitting on the ramp were non-breeding, and that there was not a
nest anywhere on this face. Of 186 present, fifty-eight were in
recognizably immature plumage. On June 24th there were 250
on top of the Noup, and by the afternoon of July 10th there were
no fewer than 605 on the ramp, of whom 235 were in recognizable immature plumage—recognizable as immature, that is, with
wings closed—with a further 120 flying about off the cliff. There
must have been many more immature among them, could their
wings have been seen, for it was the wings that retained the black
feathers of immaturity longer than any other part of the plumage. In this respect I noticed that some adult breeding birds on
the cliffs had white mirrors on their black primaries, though
these were absent in others.[1]

Some of the apparently adult-plumaged birds in this non-
breeding colony on the Noup were to be observed idly pulling
up grasses and campion and strewing it around them, and a proportion of them were associating in *pairs*, sitting and standing
about, shaking nest-stuff, quarrelling, and *urrah*ing. Being in
pairs these could not therefore have been off-duty breeding birds,
as has been suggested of similar congregations at other British
gannetries. According to the weather, so those non-breeding
birds collected on the ramp and other parts of the Noup; just
as with mist wreathing the top third of the Noup, a big swell

[1] I may have mistaken this for the bastard wing.

running into the Wick, and a stiff south wind causing a strong up-draught, some would gather on Puffin Holm, on which they alighted with great difficulty, hanging on the up-draught. Here, as many as thirty-five—one or two among them, both in pied and white plumage, with pure white heads—would sit within thirty feet of me, busy making themselves nests, attempting to mate, cossetting, and *urrah*ing: just like breeding birds. On one occasion, when the up-draught was the strongest experienced, rendering any approach to the cliff-edge dangerous, and littering the hill above Puffin Holm with white feathers from the gannetries, seven of these non-breeding gannets were sitting on the seaward end of my O.P. One, sleeping with head in scapulars, did not observe its fellows' departure when I stepped over the dyke, and I was able to sit down at my leisure beside it and take hold of it by its tail, when it reacted rather sleepily, gave a wild *urrah*, with a horrific look at the intruder, and whirled off into the gale.

The 600 present on the ramp on July 10th marked the peak of non-breeding aggregation. Thereafter there was a big clearance of dark-plumaged gannets from Noss waters and never more than 100 were to be found on the ramp for the remainder of July and August, with very few blackish birds among them: while in the first days of September their numbers fell to forty or fifty, with the same number circling off the Noup, and perhaps only one blackish bird among them.

At a rough estimate, therefore, there were on Noss in 1946 some 5,000–7,500 breeding gannets; plus some 700 non-breeding birds on the east face of the Noup; plus, say, 5 per cent non-breeding birds in the gannetries—bringing the total of non-breeders up to a minimum of 1,000 and the total population to between 6,000 and 8,500 individual gannets.

Part V

FRAGMENTARY AND INCIDENTAL STUDIES

I

A SOVIET OF KITTIWAKES

Noss Sound! April 18th.

For the past three hours there has been a continuous traffic of snowy-breasted kittiwakes passing south through the Sound, eddying to and fro with angular flight. As each wayward flight comes into my field of view round the Cols Ness grey wings are lost against grey sea and the flock appears as a dancing pattern of white projectiles, until its members eddy down over the calmer waters of the Sound. Through it they pass in absolute silence at an average rate of fifty flights, or 1,000 birds, an hour.

On May 8th the rate had risen to 3,000 an hour: but thereafter I never recorded one in excess of 500 or less than 300 an hour, and no flight ever comprised more than fifty-five individuals.

Henceforward, this passage was a dominant feature of Noss throughout the spring and summer, beginning not later than 8.30 a.m. and continuing until 9.30 p.m. Whence came these kittiwakes and whither were they bound? For a day or two these queries puzzled me. Then I discovered that their destination was the large freshwater Loch of Grimsetter eighty feet above the sea. Into the great square chasm of the Millburn geo and up the trickle of the Mill burn they streamed in purposeful silence to bathe in the loch, which the bonxies also frequented for this purpose. When they had bathed then they shoaled down the burn again at wondrous speed with the wind behind them. Strange was their wild wave-cresting flight over the green braes of the deserted township—effortless, imponderable, buoyant, a mere wafting of disembodiment. Then all those that had fore-gathered at the loch, five hundred perhaps, would mill around at the entrance to the geo, before disintegrating and setting out for the cliffs of Noss, *not* back the way they had come through the Sound, but directly across the sea to the island's south coast.

When, subsequently, I began work on Noss itself I traced the origins of this bathing passage all the way down the north side of the island from the Noup. Religiously following every indentation of the coast, no flight ever anticipated the ultimate turn Grimsetter-wards at the northern entrance of the Sound, and I never saw any pass down the south coast. Presuming that no individual bathed more than once during the day it will be seen that in a twelve-hour period of activity up to 36,000 kittiwakes passed through the Sound.

It was commonly believed unusual for kittiwakes to bathe in freshwater lochs. None had frequented the little pool of Pondsbury on Lundy: nor indeed ever visited the top of that island. In Shetland, however, the members of the Hermaness colony bathed regularly in the adjacent Loch of Cliff, while the Dunnet Head colony in Caithness also bathed in a freshwater loch.[1]

The Noss colony extended from the west face of the Cradle Holm on the south coast to the geo east of the Whiggie in the north, but its headquarters were the two faces of the Noup. I made no attempt to estimate the number of nesting pairs by direct counts, but obtained some incidental clues to this during the nest-building stage. This, it seemed, would never begin. As early as the first week of May Rumble Wick had echoed to the incessant clamour of those kittiwakes on the south face of the Noup, but day after day passed and still nothing broke the regular routine —the intermittent 'shoaling' down off the cliffs and up again of sections of colonies, the bathing passage down the north coast and through the Sound.

It was not until the afternoon of May 13 that I observed the first departure from this daily routine, when as many as a thousand at a time were shoaling off the Rumble Wick cliffs, mounting up over them on a stiff up-draught in flights of one or two hundred and sailing down westwards over the Hill of Setter. I suspected that this new move was directed by a communal impulse to begin collecting nesting-material, and sure enough the next afternoon I found that those flocks coming down over the Hill of Setter were alighting at the Voe of the Mels to collect

[1] And this was also a practice of Faroe kittiwakes, and of those on Foula off Shetland.

weed, slime and liquid mud in the Stinking Geos. I might well ask myself what stimulus or directive it was determining that on such and such a day large numbers of kittiwakes should depart spontaneously from one routine and begin another.

Though it was blowing a gale with almost continuous squalls of rain the next morning, the kittiwakes were nevertheless alighting on the cliffs with nesting material, which they either plucked from high up on the green sidings of the west Noup or for which they eddied up on the blast from Rumble Wick, veering high and low over the Hill of Setter (without interference from the bonxies), and sweeping down to the Voe of the Mels or to the Hill of Papilgeo. At these places mass flights were to be seen hovering, alighting, moving on a little, and alighting again, tearing up beakfuls of moss or grass or slime. It was significant that this the most turbulent spell of weather for three weeks did not prove a deterrent to these activities.

On the morning of the 17th I noticed that other flights were coming in from sea and working their way up the north coast Noup-wards, passing the entrance to Pundsgeo in a continuous procession at an even flow of 1,500 an hour. At the same time another procession was coming down the Head to collect beakfuls of mud from the dubs above the Whiggie burn, while in the afternoon hundreds were 'dubbing' in the corrie above the Cradle Holm, with clouds hovering above them awaiting their turn.

By the 19th, collecting had risen to a new peak of activity and method was being evolved, for the unbroken stream eddying down the south side of the island, to collect stuff from the leats of the old dam outside the hill dyke, then passed on north across the island's narrow waist and joined those other flights working back up the north coast to the Noup.

It was ten days before this that some more adventurous spirits of the daily bathing passage had begun to anticipate the Grimsetter turn through the Sound and to cross the island at its waist; and a fortnight later as many, or more, were streaming back from bathing north through the Sound as up the south coast. This short cut across the waist of the island was further popularized by the 'dubbing' procedure and on June 14th I noticed that most of the bathing flights were following this route to Grimsetter, though it entailed the possibility of having to run the gauntlet of the arctic skuas' vicious attacks.

Meanwhile, on the morning of May 22nd, I found that the northern stream of 'dubbers' was passing down over the corrie of Pundsgeo in a continuous cloud at the rate of 9,000 an hour. The next afternoon a joint stream, composed of birds returning up the north coast and others returning through the corrie, was passing Noup-wards at the rate of 10,000 an hour. Not for a second was there any visual break in the stream of birds rounding the point of Pundsgeo, and at times it was not possible to count them more accurately than in tens. The majority passed straight across the inward curving mouth of the geo and followed it out again, until some bird or flight better acquainted with the coast-line broke the continuity and led a new stream across the mouth of the geo again. At the same time an outward-bound stream, wafting up over the north side of the Noup, was coming down over the corrie at the rate of 11,500 an hour, while yet another was passing down over the Hill of Setter to the rocks and sidings of the Voe of the Mels at the rate of 18,000 an hour. I could not remember ever watching a more impressive spectacle.

Here, then, were four streams of kittiwakes 'dubbing' at the rate of some 40,000 an hour, besides others at work on various sidings and the brow-edge of the Cradle Holm.

Though the first individuals were on the wing off Rumble Wick as early as 1.30 a.m., and the first flights of a hundred or so would be coming up into the Wick from the Cradle Holm and mounting up their customary chimney at its north end as early as 2.23 a.m. to begin the day's 'dubbing', this was not prosecuted in full earnest until about 10 a.m. Between 4.30 p.m. and 6.15 p.m. the streams of collectors gradually petered out.

On the morning and afternoon of the 25th, when I observed the first pair of kittiwakes mating on the cliffs and possibly the first eggs were laid, 30,000 'dubbers' an hour were at work, but by the 27th 'dubbing' was on the decline and hundreds of kitti-wakes passed the morning basking in the sun on the extensive sloping rock-face of Muckle Hell at the southern entrance to the Sound.

June 1st saw the end of this three-week period of nest building and by the 10th, when incubation was in full swing, very few couples were to be seen at the nesting cliffs; but all day one heard the joyful clamour of the off-duty sunbathers on the rocks. From time to time five hundred or a thousand or two thousand would rise in a cloud: some to settle again, others to shoal off cliff-wards, *via* the Sound or the Nesti Voe or across the sea to the Feadda Ness, while others passed on to bathe at Grimsetter. The nucleus of sunbathers, however, never seemed to diminish, for it was continually augmented either by those returning from Grimsetter or by those arriving from Noss. From 8 a.m. until 9.30 p.m., weather permitting, off-duty kittiwakes might be seen lazing on these rocks, while the last flock of bathers did not return through the Sound or up the south coast until 10.30 p.m. or 11 p.m. in the Simmer Dim, though by this hour there would be very few on the wing off the breeding cliffs. Theirs were the last cries one heard at Gungstie on a sunny night and the first in the morning, and a gay sound it was, that *eek-kek-gewer, eek-kek-gewer.*

Early in July, on the first perfect night of the summer, I experienced one of my most dramatic hours on Noss. Its drama was perhaps heightened by the mysterious and ethereal nature of the Simmer Dim. At bright midnight, when there was still a pearly red glow in the north sky, I was both thrilled and mystified to observe flights of up to fifty birds intermittently circling out from the south face of the Noup in a crazy milling saraband. It was impossible to identify them from Rumble Wick, but I was sure that I was watching the nocturnal flighting of fork-tailed petrels breeding on the grassy east face of the Noup. To obtain a better view of them I climbed up the Head, reaching the summit at 1 a.m. By this hour upwards of a hundred birds were continually milling out from the lower parts of the Noup, to perform their intricate and crazy measure in an uncanny and absolute silence. From time to time a dead-white gannet 'swam' among them. While some of the dancers were continually returning to the cliffs, others milled higher and higher and ultimately made away to sea northwards. By 2 a.m., when the dance ended, I had finally determined, to my bitter disappointment though considerable interest, that its silent performers were kittiwakes—though it was extremely difficult to pick up their black wing-tips in the 'dim' and distinguish them from fulmars —and that the display was a preliminary to the cocks setting out for the fishing grounds. I found subsequently that they might begin flighting as early as 7.30 p.m., but I was never again fortunate enough to watch a dance of such continuity or with so many performers.

As clues to the number of breeding pairs of kittiwakes on Noss we have noted, for what they are worth, that in a twelve-hour day a maximum of 36,000 passed through the Sound to bathe in the Loch of Grimsetter and that between 30,000 and 40,000 left the breeding cliffs to collect nesting material every hour—an arbitrary period representing the time taken by one bird of a pair to collect material. There was in addition a third clue. Early in July one season Theo Kay had counted the kittiwakes returning to Noss from their Atlantic fishing grounds and had found that they passed at the rate of 1,830 an hour. Though individuals might be seen going to and fro the cliffs and their bathing or fishing grounds for twenty-one hours of the twenty-four at this season—the first young hatched about June 20th and fledged about July 19th—their period of full activity was not more than sixteen hours. For a sixteen-hour day, therefore, the number of fishers returning to Noss would have amounted at this rate to some 29,000.

II

THE AMOROUS TYSTIE

A week after our arrival in Shetland, when the sea was moderating to an oily calm after days of gales, I was lying one morning high up on the sidings of the Mills of the Ord. On the sea, between the Ord and the Bard Head, I could count some forty tysties—dark nigger-brown little birds with coral-red legs and webbed feet stretched out behind short tails. Every few minutes the majority of the forty would swim together, coalescing into one big pack, numbering at most seventeen individuals, and two smaller packs of eight apiece, while the remainder kept apart in ones and twos, paying no attention to the activities of those in the packs, though within sight and sound of them.

The tystie's social display was one aspect of bird-life I had especially wished to study in Shetland, for previous observers had described this as play. Recalling my experiences with other auks and with sea-duck, however, I expected to find this display to be in fact part-sexual, part-aggressive. So it was with keen interest I watched events on the sea below, and it soon became evident that the primary cause of excitement among the little flocks continually coalescing and disintegrating was twofold: the males' tense interest in the females and rivalry between the males themselves. The latter made themselves conspicuous by their constant rearing up in the water with beaks depressed to breasts. Their apparent objective was their desire to mount upon the females' tails, but this they never achieved, because the females responded (or objected) by spinning around to face them—thus initiating that continuous twirling around of the individuals of the display pack previously interpreted as play. This twirling around and its accompanying high-pitched piping attracted other tysties in the vicinity, and when more than two were gathered together then the commotion among rival males began, just as it did among the drakes in the great winter rafts of scoter duck or in spring among shelduck or piping parties of oystercatchers.

The male tysties would jump out of the water and fight—which I could not remember seeing the other auks do—and dive to evade the assaults of their rivals. They would chase one another with breasts reared high out of the water, would raise their wings, dove-like, and move over the sea thus (hence perhaps another origin of the name *dovekie*), or push their heads through the water, submerged except for wings and backs. Then a part or the whole of the pack would submerge instantaneously and pursue one another under water in great excitement, swimming with beating wings, the white plumes of which rendered them conspicuous without the aid of polaroid glasses. At other times a whole or a part of the pack would move forward over the sea in a series of short flights, which would terminate suddenly in spontaneous submergence. And then the display pack would gradually disintegrate, until perhaps only a couple of pairs were left, and the females would turn back their heads and sleep—until awoken again by a renewal of the males' attentions. But in all these antics I could detect no play pattern: these were the familiar responses to sexual and aggressive stimuli.

The previous September I had seen strings of as many as twenty-seven tysties, mainly young birds in pale grey and white plumage off Bressay, but now in April this characteristic formation was only to be observed on those rare occasions when the ones and twos keeping station all round the coast were attracted to coalesce by the activities of a couple in the vicinity. But it was no less rare to see two birds of a pair together. Day after day the two might be seen keeping distance from thirty to fifty yards apart off the same stretch of coast, as presumably they had begun to do intermittently in February or March, but never were they to be seen together. Every few seconds they would dip their bills up to the hilt in the water, bringing them up with a splutter and a shake, and from time to time they would dive for a period of thirty-five or forty seconds. Undoubtedly they were keeping station off that stretch of cliff on which they would ultimately land towards the end of April to visit prospective nesting-holes, but what puzzled me was why, once the pairs had taken up their positions off these territories, male and female could not swim together, as pairs of any other species would do.

A few days after I got into Noss, I was able to see more of both courtship and territory visiting when, on making my way down the north coast from the Noup on April 26th and arriving at Pundsgeo at 7.20 a.m., I found five or six tysties swimming at the entrance to the geo and was delighted to see, for the first time, a further five or six standing in a group on the yellow-lichened rocks, very smart in their black and white plumage, their wet puce-coloured legs and webbed feet gleaming as if newly painted. Elsewhere—and there were some scores along this northern reach of coast—pairs and single birds were sitting or standing on the wave-polished rocks immediately above the sea, which was breaking on the cliffs this tempestuous morning; or were to be located in dark niches deep down in geos by their incessant penny-whistle piping, a drawn-out *sphee-ee-ee*, resembling the creaking of a rusty-hinged signboard. This thin sad piping was continually crescending to an excited twittering when a male, amorously inclined, elevated his head, depressed his bill, and stalked slowly around his mate, shifting from one foot to the other like a puffin. From time to time one would walk up a sloping ledge, lifting its wings high over its back, revealing their pale undersides, or would whirr down to the clear green flood of water foaming up the geo and join those of its fellows bobbing about on the smooth grey-green swell outside, uttering the while that mournful bat-piping, their stiletto-like bills wide open to reveal scarlet interiors.

I was particularly anxious to spend more time watching those tysties 'sitting-up' on the rocks and in the geos, but subsequent study showed that these visits to what were presumably the environs of nesting territories were restricted to the early hours of the morning, though pairs and solitary birds were to be seen hanging about offshore right round the island at all hours of the day. At 7 a.m. on the 29th, however—a calm summer's morning with some swell—I could count sixty-eight tysties between Papilgeo and the Scarfi reef east of Pundsgeo, twenty-one of which were sitting-up in ones, twos or threes. Those afloat—the biggest pack contained nineteen birds—were conducting themselves in the now familiar manner. They would make little flights just above the water or swim beneath it; three or four would dip bills in the water together and then dive with a splutter of wings; and the males would rear up, piping excitedly, the females evading them by diving and swimming just beneath the surface, when their paddles stretched out behind retained their rosy hue, though their plumage suffered a change to mole-grey and their beating wings appeared as white moons.

Those sitting up on the slime-green rocks, piping incessantly, allowed me to approach to within twelve feet of them, but did little of interest, and by 8.50 a.m. nearly all those ashore had flown down to the sea and the pack offshore had disintegrated. One could not even be certain of finding them sitting up in the early morning. When I arrived at Pundsgeo at 4.45 a.m. on May 1st, for instance, I found twenty-seven tysties afloat at the entrance to the geo, dipping bills, chasing one another and diving; and though at 6 a.m. a piping dozen were swimming up the geo as far as the boulder-beach at its head, none landed, and only two pairs flew down from hidden niches. It was not until the end of this week that here and there a solitary bird might be seen sitting up in the afternoon or evening.

The days passed and to the casual observer no apparent change was noticeable in their behaviour. At 11.15 a.m. on May 17th I heard the spun-glass threads of tystie music from the concealed depths of Pundsgeo, and some pairs flew down from the boulder beach at its head and out past eleven others swimming underwater all at once: now over dark rocks, now through the palest green waters of a sunlit sandy pool. Round and round they swam, white-lobed wings (primaries being closed) clipping at two beats a second, rosy shanks stretched out behind hoary bodies. The males were in continual zig-zagging pursuit of females and rival males, both above and below water, and an amorous male would dive right under a female: while mated pairs would twirl around one another for minutes intermittently, as the male swam, with 'mincing' mandibles, on his mate's tail. Sometimes a solitary bird, sometimes a pair would fly up to sit on a low rock: but by 12.40 p.m. the pack had disappeared, leaving one pair sitting up.

A month later the same procedure was still to be observed, and at 8.30 p.m. on June 14th I watched twenty-five in the geo of the Point of Hovie, where a bull seal was barking to his cow, while nesting shags also barked and brayed from the broad ledges that ran round the sides of the geo. Many of the tysties were in pairs and three were heavily spattered with white matter, which indicated that they had been incubating: but this fact in no way diminished the ardour of the rearing males, who breasted the water in pursuit of the females at astonishing speed, with little tails jutting up perpendicularly, like a plane's tail-fin, and scarlet paddles (clearly seen beneath the water) stroking alternately and so swiftly that their effect was that of a propellor. At intervals they would circle around one another in intense excitement with wings half-raised, or shoot at rivals with menacing beaks, gaping scarlet.

With the major portion of my time devoted to the gannets and skuas it was clear that I should not be able to make anything of the tysties' breeding habits, nesting as they did in cracks in the geo walls and in the boulder beaches above high-water mark. When one or two came out of the Pundsgeo beach on the evening of the 24th, however, I climbed down to investigate, but found nothing except old nests and chicks of herring-gulls, and had to face the flame-throwers of two fulmars, who stored more oil than I allowed for. The tysties evidently nested at no great depth under the boulders, for when I advanced to the edge of a geo several would pop out from the beach and fly down to the water and then up perhaps to one of the ledges in the walls of the geo.

They continued to occupy these sitting-up platforms and also to court and fight on the water until the end of the third week in August. As late as 10 p.m. one could hear the brittle glass threads of 'creaking' tysties in Pundsgeo and find them sitting up in groups of from one to four, revealed in the twilight only by the white flashes of their wings against the dark rocks. As they shifted their positions with much shuffling of wings one would hear, too, the excited lisping notes of the males, before they settled down to roost.

Actually the first intimation I had that young had hatched was at noon on August 5th, when an adult on the water of the Hovie geo had a six-inch ribbon-like butterfish dangling from its bill; and five evenings later I saw one enter a crevice under a big boulder with one of these thin red weed-like objects and come out again very quickly without it. On subsequent days I saw others bring small crabs and little tarnished-silver and orange-brown wrasse, which they continually dipped in the water: but only one of them would enter its nesting hole in the boulder beach while I was present at the top of the geo, emerging again in two seconds.

It was the 25th before I saw the first fledgeling tystie, accompanied by an adult, on the Nesti Voe; but once they fledged family ties seemed to be broken, the young scattered from nesting waters, and by September strings of as many as twenty, mainly or all young, were to be seen off Bressay.

III

THE TRIALS OF AN EIDER DUCK

Some two hundred pairs of eider ducks kept station off the north and south coasts of Noss. Many immature ducks and drakes accompanied them, and some of these also appeared to be paired off. There were, in my experience, phenomenal numbers of young drakes off Noss, and a fleet of seventy eiders might include as many as twenty of these. In April I noted that one at least of them could coo perfectly.

It was not until the morning of May 19th that the first duck came ashore, visiting the Maiden's Paps, and the next afternoon a drake flew down from the Head over the Paps at very great speed and was followed half an hour later by a duck, also at speed. By the early morning of the 21st as many as twenty ducks and drakes might be seen flying off the Head in a flock, and on the morning of the 25th I flushed the first duck off her four beautiful stone-green eggs laid in a circlet of dark-grey white-tipped down in the corrie behind the Maiden's Paps. Immediately I retreated to the Paps she returned to her nest.

That afternoon, when I was watching bonxie pair 160 on the western slopes of the Hill of Setter, a duck and a drake waddled over the skyline, with much tossing of heads, followed at a little distance by a second drake and then by two more ducks. The first duck kept a score or two yards in advance of her drake, as they waddled right through the incubating bonxies, which at this stage seldom took any notice of them nor of those other ducks that hurtled swiftly down over the bonxie grounds, though once I saw a bonxie chasing a drake round the Hill of Pundsgeo lazily and without malice.

Every now and again the duck sat down to rest, the drake following her example, and one such rest lasted for twenty minutes, before she was on the move again. Every time she moved on the drake tossed his head and immediately got up to follow her, maintaining throughout his correct distance behind her. After fifty minutes of this leisurely progress, which included five more shorter rests, I could stand the cold and cramp in my hand and neck no longer and, getting up, saw the other drake and one of the ducks sitting together. On my rising the two pairs waddled off down the hill together, finally taking flight: but they were loath to leave the hill and alighted again—though one of the drakes ultimately flew down to the sea—and on my return from Rumble Wick an hour and a quarter later one pair was still sitting on the hill. The next morning a party of three drakes and two ducks were flying round the Head as early as 3.15 a.m.

By the 28th one of the ducks I had watched nest-prospecting on the Hill of Setter was incubating two eggs only nine feet from bonxie 160, who was also sitting on eggs, and at noon another with two eggs had her drake sitting beside her. Most of those ducks with only two eggs had no down or very little in their nests, the eggs being almost covered instead with shredded reindeer-moss. The extraordinary thing was that the eiders nested all among the bonxies on moor and hill, and I found a third duck sitting on five eggs only six feet from bonxie 114 in the corrie of the Maiden's Paps. A tight sitter, she would allow me to approach right up to the nest, without stirring, throughout her period of incubation.

Two eggs completed eider 160's clutch and by June 3rd they lay in a great heap of down. Bonxie 160's elder chick chipped its shell that day and the eider, on returning to her nest, running and falling, running and falling, was mobbed all the way by the pair of bonxies, though once she had settled on her eggs she was left in peace. Four days later, however, her eggs had been destroyed and the down scattered. When I ringed the bonxie's younger chick on the 12th I found it sitting only one yard away from a second duck nesting twenty yards from the bonxie's mound. At my approach the eider moved off her nest and, trailing her wings on the ground, pecked about distractedly among the down scattered from the other nest. Many nests and eggs were now being destroyed by some agency, probably bonxies—

for it was a familiar sight to see a pair of bonxies pecking holes in a clutch of eider's eggs and drinking their contents. I never searched for any eiders' nests, but in the course of my rounds on the skua grounds I came across more than forty in the tussock-grass and heather on the bonxie grounds, under peat-banks and in old peat-cuttings, and in clumps of thrift-roots and turfy hollows in the rock at the extreme points of holms, which, as in the case of oystercatchers, were much favoured, being immediately above the sea. I never found a nest with more than five eggs, though clutches of up to eight eggs have been recorded in Shetland. The eggs varied in colour from the customary dull duck-green, through pale fawn, to pale, almost ivory, stone.

By the middle of June a morning flight of what were presumably incubating ducks was a regular feature of island life. As early as 2.15 a.m. or 2.30 a.m., when a pale fire was reddening the east, many ducks were to be seen flighting singly or in twos and threes off hill and moor, and passing down to the Voe of the Mels with their customary low, direct and speedy flight, infrequently accompanied by a drake—for the latter were to be seen flying about the moor or waddling around on the hill in company with as many as six ducks as late as June 18th, and a unique feature of Bressay at this season was that of the drake eiders swimming on the freshwater lochs with their ducks. Those ducks which had been incubating for three weeks or so appeared, however, to sit tight at the early morning hours, while others would be coming up to lay, for some of those I flushed had no eggs, though a little down.

It was at noon on June 18th that I noticed for the first time a party of eight ducks walking up from the low cliff at the sea's edge on to the east end of the North Croo. On subsequent afternoons and evenings flocks of up to thirty ducks might be seen gathered together on the green edge of the Croo or flighting around the moor. After resting awhile on the seaward edge of the Croo they would get up in parties of six or eight and waddle, with frequent rests, hundreds of yards up on to the Hill of Pundsgeo, tossing their heads incessantly to the accompaniment of a conversational *kok-kok-kok*. After having advanced some way, a few would fly round the moor in circles, but others would continue on foot. For twenty minutes on one occasion I watched one duck prying her head into one peat-crevice and overhang after another, but never finding one to suit her before, to my exasperation, she was put to flight by a pair of bonxies. These activities bore every sign of being for the purpose of nest-site selection by prospective layers, yet the evening parade on the Croo continued in gradually lessening numbers until the first week of August, when the flock of ducks on the sea off the Croo was already one hundred and fifty strong. Moreover the last of the drakes going into 'eclipse' plumage had left the ducks in the Noss voes in the middle of July, to join the great raft of five hundred of their fellows daily afloat between the Bard and the Voe of Mels, while the last of the ducklings had gone down to the sea by the middle of August.

It was on the evening of June 24th that the first family of five ducklings had appeared on the waters of Papilgeo. Some evenings later a curious incident occurred when at 9.45 p.m. a duck and three ducklings, accompanied at a little distance by two rather bigger ducklings, surfed on to a reef platform below the cliffs at the entrance to a geo, and the ducklings (the larger pair still keeping their distance) began to feed on the green slime, sometimes running here and there after small game cast up by the surf. After feeding for a quarter of an hour, however, all left for a geo farther east up the coast, still keeping the same formation!

It was a marvel to me that the ducks succeeded in bringing off any ducklings, let alone full broods, for once the young bonxies hatched it was hardly possible for an eider to leave her nest and not find her eggs holed and sucked by bonxies on her return, and there must have been further losses among the few ducklings that hatched, during the course of their long journey down to the sea on the bright summer nights. Nor were the ducklings safe when they had reached the sea, for herring-gulls would pick them off the water and batter them insensate on the reefs, while the communities of ducks, though approaching such a marauder hesitantly, with much condemnatory tossing of heads, would take no further action. Actually I was never able to count more than forty ducklings in all in Noss waters.

THE MYSTERY OF THE YOUNG PUFFIN

The behaviour of puffins on Noss was very strange. None had been seen in Shetland waters prior to our arrival, and none were seen throughout April until the evening of the 25th, when single puffins were appearing off the cliffs and alighting for brief periods on the brow-edge of the Cradle Holm and on ledges of the cliff-face beneath. On these a score of little red-footed and white-bellied sea-parrots might be seen lined up in a row, occasionally shifting from one foot to the other: while one pair nebbed bills for several seconds and others scuttled in and out of burrows after moments of tense deliberation. (Ten years' landing dates in the Orkneys ranged from April 16th to 22nd, from five to fourteen days after their initial appearance in onshore waters.)

Apparently they stayed in this first night, for at 4.40 a.m. the next morning there were hundreds on the cliffs, on the sea, and flighting hither and thither. A new warp had been woven into the aerial pattern over Rumble Wick, the well-remembered circling small black arcs of these little sea-swifts. Some were standing outside burrows in the turfy brow-edges of holms or on the green cliff sanctuaries of fulmars: others were ranked up on cliff ledges for, like the Lundy razorbills, some of the Noss puffins nested in crevices in the bare cliff-face and under talus and boulders where not a green thing grew, from Papilgeo in the north round to the Hovie geo in the south. From time to time a soft sepulchral caw might be heard and, on alighting from sea, one might make over to neb bills with another, whereupon a third would join in and all three would neb together in perfect accord.

On the 27th, however, there was not a puffin to be seen on the island, and for a couple of weeks thereafter I saw none or only occasional ones and twos scuttling in and out of their burrows between four o'clock in the evening and seven o'clock in the morning. Not until the morning of May 9th were they to be seen in numbers, and these had all disappeared by noon; and it was the evening of the 18th before I again saw numbers assembling, preparatory to a full house the next day—though incubation must have begun between May 9th and 18th.

Thus far they were obeying the recognized laws of British-breeding puffins, whose custom it was to visit the breeding grounds initially at intervals of a week or so; and though Noss puffins had returned a month later than those on Lundy, their first eggs must have been laid less than a week after the first on Lundy. But once incubation had begun on that island a feature of its bird-life was the massing of puffins in the morning and early afternoon on their nesting sidings—except for ten days at the peak of the incubatory period—and an intense social activity among their assembled thousands.

There was no such assembling on Noss. At intervals of a week or ten days a full house might be seen, and even then possibly only on one side of the island; but for the rest of the time a puffin was not a common object on the island to the casual observer, and that social activity which had made them such a fascinating and interesting study on Lundy was totally lacking. All I ever saw as I went my round would be one or two whirring up to the holms and occasionally alighting, and one or two others emerging from burrows, first appearing at the entrance in characteristic crouched position, with cautious head outstretched for some seconds before venturing forth, then scuttling out in a flash. Admittedly my observations were comparatively casual, but I seldom saw nesting stuff brought up, and all the puffins were extremely nervous, in marked contrast to their notable confidence on Lundy. Even when large numbers were present, and some were collecting grasses, they did not do anything with the latter. An hour's watching might result in my recording only two pairs nebbing and one cock indulging in a prolonged head tossing, which, however, might not lead to anything. When incubation was at its peak, there was never a sight or sound of them, except when the swaabies on the Cradle Holm set up their bass clamour and three or four puffins would

A greyish-black squab

All soft curves and no rigidity

Clumps of thrift-roots were much favoured by Eider Ducks

Tysties, standing in a group on the yellow-lichened rocks, very smart in
black and white

scuttle out of their holes. It was hard to credit that more than ten thousand pairs of puffins were breeding on the island, and had I first visited Noss instead of Lundy I might well have supposed that the puffin's behaviour was so uninteresting that a visit to the latter island would have been a waste of time.

Although I already recognized that the incubatory and fledging periods of sea-birds were subject to considerable variation, I had not realized before how great might be regional variations in behaviour. So far as I could judge, the difference in the behaviour of the puffins on Noss and those on Lundy was fundamentally a difference of temperament: of timidity as against boldness. For this difference there were, superficially, good reasons. On Lundy the adult puffins had little to fear except an occasional stoop from a peregrine. They could stay above ground as long as they wished without persecution, and the mere fact of being outside their burrows in large numbers led naturally to the fullest expression of their social impulses. On Noss, however, those puffins nesting on the south side of the island had to reckon with the three hundred swaabies nesting on the Cradle Holm and the scores of herring-gulls and lesser black-backs nesting on the adjacent sidings. On the north side there were no swaabies, but there was always the bonxie. True, I never saw a bonxie, or for that matter a swaabie, attack a puffin, but clouds of puffins would sail off the holms and sidings whenever a bonxie flapped past, and one or two puffin skeletons were found on the bonxie grounds. The atmosphere above ground, even if not actually dangerous, was not of a nature to encourage prolonged social activity. Certain it is, that if I had gone to Noss to study puffins I should have had a very lean time and written off the species as one whose display and social activity was mainly marine and subterranean.[1]

To the casual observer only two dates of the puffins' breeding cycle were obvious: those of their arrival at their breeding grounds and of the hatching of their young—presuming, that

[1] R. F. Moore points out that there were fifty or sixty pairs of greater black-backed gulls and some three hundred pairs of lesser black-backed gulls on Lundy which, even if not actively victimizing the puffins, must have constituted as great a threat to their confidence as those on Noss; and that, therefore, there must be some more fundamental reason for this variability in puffin behaviour.

was, that the carrying of fish by adults began within twenty-four hours of the chick's hatching. The first puffin with fish—transparent whitish fry less than an inch in length—was observed at noon on June 21st, a week later, correctly, than on Lundy. Now, according to R. M. Lockley, the only observer except myself who had studied puffins intensively, the nestling of three pairs examined on the island of Skokholm was deserted about the fortieth day by its parents, remaining alone and unfed in the burrow for a further seven to ten days. (*British Birds* xxvii.) These figures were based on the fact that matchsticks placed in the mouths of burrows were not displaced between the fortieth and forty-seventh or fifty-first day. But these figures were not reconcilable with my experiences on Lundy, where I had the misfortune to lose all my known eggs and chicks, and was thus only able to judge progress by external events. These were that the peak of fish-carrying had passed by the twelfth day, that the last puffin with fish was seen on the thirty-first day, and that the last landing of the mass of the puffins took place on the forty-sixth day.[1] With respect to these figures it must be remembered that they covered the entire colony of puffins, and that duration periods for individuals must necessarily have been shorter. It may be gainsaid that I may have missed one or two puffins bringing up fish before or after the bulk of them began or finished on Lundy; but the fact remains that the mass of them did not bring up fish after a maximum of thirty days and that the mass of them left the island forty-five days after fish-carrying had begun.

As no further light had been thrown on these two sets of figures since my Lundy study I was particularly anxious to check them on Noss, though it must be confessed that I was much more interested in observing the actual manner of the fledgelings' departure, now that I had seen that of the other auks. I could not spare the time from my major studies to observe when fishing finished though, according to the Lundy figures the mass of puffins should have finished about July 22nd and according to the Skokholm figures about July 31st. Actually, on this latter date, when there were full houses all round the island, only three

[1] It is not known on what date the young fledged.

birds out of some thousands were observed with fish at three different times—1.35 p.m., 5.50 p.m., and 6.15 p.m. to 7 p.m. Presuming that a period of from seven to ten days elapsed between the cessation of feeding and desertion, then I might expect the old birds to begin deserting their young about July 29th and August 7th,

We have seen that puffins were only rarely to be observed on Noss during the period of incubation. As soon as hatching began, however, they were seen to stand about the holms and sidings in numbers, mainly in the evening. The biggest colony was situated on a typical boulder-strewn Lundy siding above the cliff-face on the north side of the Noup. At 9.30 p.m. on July 12th there was a full house present in this amphitheatre and, for the first time on Noss, I witnessed the familiar mass circling over the slope: but by 10.5 p.m., when dusk was falling, nearly all the puffins had disappeared. There was again a full house here at 7.45 p.m. on the 15th, most disappearing by 10.15 p.m., and again at 7.25 on the 19th and every night thereafter, the mass of birds always leaving by 10.15 p.m.

On the 31st a new stage was reached when a full house was present as early as 1.35 p.m., though only one bird was bringing up fish at this hour and two between 6.15 p.m. and 7 p.m. There was again a full house at 6.30 p.m. on August 4th, when hundreds were flighting over the siding, and by 8.15 p.m. a thousand were flighting at one time when disturbed. By August 10th it was evident either that the figures for both the Lundy and Skokholm puffins were at fault or subject to variation, *or* that the adults did not in fact desert their young after ceasing to bring up fish to them: for it was now at least ten days since the mass of the birds had finished fishing and fifty days or more since fishing had begun, while on August 6th ten fledgelings had been observed many miles north and east of Noss; yet the adults were present in maximum numbers at 6.50 p.m. all round the island on the night of the 10th, and at 7.30 p.m. there was a full house in the amphitheatre, where some birds were rapping bills and gaping threateningly and one had a beakful of fish. At 7.50 p.m. I noticed that a herring-gull was standing on a rock at the bottom of the siding, waiting, one would have said, remembering their habits with guillemots and razorbill fledgelings, for the young puffins to come out of their burrows, and I was tremendously excited. And sure enough to my astonishment at 8.5 p.m., when the sun was setting and only a few hundred old birds were left on the siding, a fully feathered young puffin appeared at the entrance to its burrow under a big boulder. Moving around on a periphery of a few inches it fanned its wings vigorously, while two adults peered over the top of the boulder at it. In general form it resembled the adult, but its smoke-flecked cheeks and black beak, forehead and crown, gave it a strange 'oiled' appearance. Two minutes later it entered its burrow again.

At 8.13 p.m. a second young one appeared beside one parent, fanning its wings so vigorously that they were as blurred as a travelling bee's, and at 8.20 p.m. a third.

At 8.25 p.m. the first young one came right out of its burrow, followed by one parent, and the latter went out to sea—returning five minutes later, when a fourth young one appeared. But the latter was the last to appear and by 8.45 p.m., when the light was failing, only six adults remained on the siding. Why, then, had the young ones not gone down to the sea? For according to Lockley this they ought to have done 'straight after dusk'.

At 2.15 p.m. on August 12th the amphitheatre was deserted except for a pair of herring-gulls and two puffins, probably a pair, flying around with three-inch fish, while three more scuttled out of burrows. Half an hour later I noticed that hundreds were swimming in from sea, and at 7.10 p.m., when the amphitheatre was already in the shadow thrown by the Noup's gigantic north face, while the sun shone brilliantly on the remainder of the island, there was the customary full house —though its numbers had now passed their peak—with the usual herring-gull in position. Five minutes later a new, fifth young puffin appeared for a brief interval at the entrance of its burrow with two parents and nebbed with one of them, with a curious bumpy cooing note. The parents then nebbed while a third adult looked on. Yet Lockley had found that, 'Like the young shearwater, the young puffin remains alone fasting in the burrow for several days. During this period, day and night, it sits close to the mouth of the burrow as if too timid to venture out.'

An occasional *hoor-aa* was to be heard from other adults underground and from time to time a pair would go tumbling down the siding in grappling combat. At 7.30 p.m. a sixth young one was wing-flapping outside its burrow for a short time. Again two parents, one of which was 'oiled', were in attendance. Forty minutes later this young one appeared again, ten minutes after a mass flighting of adults over the siding, and at 8.20 p.m. a seventh, whose parents had disappeared some time previously, came out of its burrow but entered it again immediately. It was followed five minutes later by an eighth, which was accompanied by one parent.

At 8.55 p.m. when the light was failing, no adult or young puffins were visible on the siding, the gull had abandoned its vigil half an hour earlier, and I was tormented with clouds of midges, but determined to see the matter through to the end.

The next two and a half hours was an intolerable ordeal of torture by midges, as I was unable to shift my position, while a full moon remained exasperatingly in a heavy bank of cloud beyond the Noup. The only incidents were those of a golden plover making a landfall on the Head and an adult puffin leaving the siding at 9.55 p.m.

At 11.30 p.m. when the midges had almost finished with me and my eyes were sore from peering hour after hour into the twilight over the siding—for the moon was still in the cloud-bank and now moving behind the Noup—I felt pretty certain that the fifth young puffin was moving about at the entrance to its burrow. Though nothing transpired this encouraged me to continue a vigil which had now lasted four and a half hours. At 11.45 p.m. an adult groaned and ten minutes after midnight another flighted over the siding, while what appeared to be a bat twisted along the brow-edge where I was lying; but after five and a half hours I confessed myself beaten and left at 12.25 a.m., when a guillemot was still calling vainly to its young one to join it on the sea.

If my long vigil had not achieved any positive results, there were some negative points to be considered. What had happened to the four young puffins which had appeared outside their burrows on the night of the 10th? There had not been a sign of them, nor had any adults visited their burrows. There was no proof that they had gone down to the sea later that night or in the early hours of the morning, but where were they? And how was it that though a thousand adults were to be seen on the wing over the siding, with hundreds more on the ground, at a given time, I had in two nights seen only eight young puffins? I was driven to the conclusion that for days past the latter had in fact been going down to the sea in the early hours of the morning, their parents visiting them, though not with fish, up to the night of their departure; while the eight that I had seen were among the few that had not yet left for the sea. As in the case of the gannet it was not the old puffins that deserted their young, but the latter that deserted their parents.

I was not able to fit in an early morning visit to the puffinry, but at 7.40 p.m. on the 16th I found that there had been a large-scale exodus of adults. Only 350 were present on the siding—though one here and there might still be seen tearing up grasses with great vigour—and no young ones appeared up to the time of my departure at 8.25 p.m., though the gull was again in attendance. I was interested to observe pairs of adults present at the burrows of the first and fifth young ones. Had the latter still been in the burrows it was unthinkable that they should not have come outside, as on earlier nights. Though it was still light when I left, all but five of the adults had disappeared.

This was my last night at the puffinry, and though a very few puffins were to be seen around the island, mainly at small colonies, until August 26th they seldom came ashore, and the precise details of the young puffin's fledging remained a matter for speculation, with the probability that it was subject to regional variation. The data for all stages of the puffin's reproductive cycle on all three islands is unsatisfactory and inconclusive. Fresh data is required, preferably from a new locality.

V

NIGHTS WITH NORTHERN GUILLEMOTS

Noss guillemots differed from those of more southerly British stations, such as Lundy and the Farne Islands, in belonging to the Northern race with markedly darker plumage, and also in the high proportion of bridled variants among them. Of 4,224 recorded on Noss in twenty-five counts of ten colonies between April 27th and June 21st, 978 or 23·1 per cent were bridled, average colony counts ranging from 18·4 per cent to 32·0 per cent. Other counts during the past twelve years had found the proportion of bridled birds to range from 23·6 per cent to 29·1 per cent, while a small count of 230 guillemots in 1890 gave 13·4 per cent and another of fifteen birds in 1867 gave 6·6 per cent. Counts in 1946 of 1,064 birds on the west cliff of the Cradle Holm gave 23·3 per cent compared to 12·9 per cent in 1890.

Like kittiwakes and puffins they returned to their breeding cliffs on Noss considerably later than they did to Lundy or the Farnes, and it was reported that they did not pay their initial visit to the island until the end of February. It was April 28th before I first noted a full house on the cliffs—as late as 7.15 p.m.—and again on the 29th and 30th. After this there was the customary week when only a few hundreds were present until May 7th and 8th, and a second week of small numbers up to the 16th. Subsequently, considerable numbers were always present, reaching a peak on June 2nd, when most appeared to be sitting on eggs, which were first evident on May 22nd. Their colonies extended from the Fugla Skerry on the north coast to the Hovie geo on the south.

On June 21st I observed the first adults bringing up fish to the nesting ledges, and a tremendous *arrg, arrg* of jubilation from a row of fifteen guillemots on one ledge in my gannetry would herald the arrival of one of their fellows with a disproportionately undersized tinfoil fish, and seriously disrupt my concentration on counting gannets! None, however, of those bringing up fish appeared to have young, and though by the 25th they were being much persecuted by arctic skuas, it was not until the end of the month that I could make out any young on the ledges, and July 2nd before I began to hear their faint twittering *quew-ee, quew-ee.*

Occasional strings of adults, up to twenty-five strong, had first been noticeable returning from their northern fishing-grounds, often at a considerable height and sometimes spearheaded by a puffin, in the opening days of June when incubation was approaching its peak. The earliest fishers would arrive at Noss at 4 a.m., when those roosting or incubating had been sleeping for some three hours, the first of the latter leaving the cliffs twenty minutes later. By July many strings and small disintegrated clouds of fishers would still be coming into the island as late as 9 p.m., and at midday they would be approaching the north Noup at the rate of 2,000 an hour. In the middle of the month this figure had risen to 4,300 an hour, with which we may compare Theo Kay's estimate that guillemots from Noss passed out to the Atlantic fishing grounds at the rate of 3,830 an hour, or 64,000 in a seventeen-hour day.

There was one aspect of life in a guillemot colony I had always wished to see again since certain memorable nights on Lundy— the fledging of the young guillemots—and at 7.50 p.m. on the calm dull evening of July 12th I perceived that which I had sought on previous evenings: a young guillemot standing alone in a cell in the honeycombed sandstone of Puffin geo *without* its parents. I knew then that the fledging was about to begin. For an hour after this, however, there was neither check nor abatement in the customary surge and fall of raucous uproar from the thousands of guillemots on the Noup; but at 8.45 p.m. I detected a change in the cadence of the uproar and, casting around for the meaning of this, saw that a great stream of guillemots was pressing into Rumble Wick in a turmoil of excitement, every individual uttering an incessant and explosive *airr-rr-gg, airr-rr-gg.* The calling-down of the young had begun and these

Fulmar!

Puffin slope

were their last nights on the cliffs. Once again, after the lapse of seven years, I heard that haunting *queewee, queewee, queewee* that one heard only from those big chick guillemots ready to go down to the sea; and with the light growing dim at 9 p.m. the calling of the adults on the water became continuous. Half an hour later the wheezing pipe of young razorbills was also to be heard. (There were probably fewer than 1,000 pairs of razorbills on Noss, between the Hovie geo and Pundsgeo. I first noticed them sitting up on April 25th, recording eggs on June 3rd and young on July 12th: but the adults were extremely nervous and wary, tending to leave the cliffs, and often their eggs, as soon as I appeared.)

By 10 p.m. it was becoming dusk, but strings of guillemots, all carrying fish, were still coming in high from the north, and at 10.30 p.m. when it was so dusk as to be difficult to take notes, many adults were still calling from the water and their young were still noisy on the cliffs. The latter, however, were mainly the younger chicks, with their distinctive piping *coo-ee*: the main hour of departure for the older ones had passed and the lone chick had disappeared from its cell.

Three nights later, when strings of fishers were coming in to the island at the rate of 4,500 an hour, I could hear other adults calling off Pundsgeo at 7.30 p.m., and an hour later one or two chicks were swimming with their parents off the south face of the Noup, where the tumult was almost overwhelming in its volume. On a broad reef at the base of the cliff twenty-four swaabies and thirty-five herring-gulls stood waiting. The up-draught was too strong in Rumble Wick, however, for me to watch profitably, so I moved down to the shelter of Puffin Geo, where I found fifteen adults on the water below the cliffs and a chick swimming away with one parent, who fought savagely with other adults, before the two of them ultimately swam out of the geo and away to sea. Two more chicks, diving as they went, got away with one parent apiece at 8.45 p.m. and 8.50 p.m., and at 9.10 p.m. a chick and its parent alighted on the water together. Meanwhile single adults were continually flying down from the ledges and then flighting up again and banging against the cliffs. By 9.30 p.m. however, excitement was on the wane in this geo and only one chick could be seen standing without its parents.

Though the light was dim by 10.15 p.m.—the sky being overcast in the south and west—several adults and some young continued to call off the Noup until my departure at 11 p.m., when the tumult was subsiding.

By the 17th the *queewee, queewee* of half a dozen older chicks standing alone was to be heard above the ceaseless twittering *cooee* of the younger ones as early as 4.10 p.m., when two or three adults were already calling from the water in Puffin Geo—and this despite a blazing sun there, the remainder of the island being entombed in fog. Five minutes later a chick appeared on the water with one parent, but they made no attempt to go away to sea, swimming about the base of the cliffs instead, with the customary bevy of curious adults crowding round to examine the fledgeling. They were still in the geo half an hour after this, and as no more chicks had come down and none were calling, their descent may have been accidental—though by this time a herring-gull had taken up its stand in the geo and a dozen swaabies were waiting below the Noup.

At the end of the first week of fledging there was an appreciable decrease in the numbers of adults in Puffin Geo and also on the north face of the Noup, and on the 19th half a dozen adults were calling from the cauldron of surf seething at the base of the cliffs at the entrance to Puffin Geo as early as 2.45 p.m., when a similar number of chicks were standing alone on the ledges. But activity in the townships was still at a peak and at 6.30 p.m. as many as eighty strings of homing fishers were in view off the north coast at one time. At 7.15 p.m., however, all was quiet in the north coast geos and it was 8.15 p.m. before the older chicks began to call in Puffin Geo and the first two adults appeared on the water. Five minutes later, when many single adults were dropping from the cliffs and plunging into the boiling green and white surf at their base, the herring-gull alighted on its favourite ledge. At 8.40 p.m. I caught a glimpse of one chick dropping into the cauldron and racing at incredible speed over the surge, lifting itself with raised wing-arms well out of the water, to its parent waiting on the edge of the surf; and away to sea they went straightway in noisy triumph—in contrast to that earlier afternoon pair. The gull did not see this fledgeling and left ten minutes later in disgust. Judging by the inactivity of those of its fellows below the Noup very few young guillemots were leaving their ledges on this stormy foggy night.

For some days we had been waiting for wind and swell to abate in order to take the yacht *Soldian* into Rumble Wick and moor her under the great townships of guillemots on the south face of the Noup. Theo Kay had indeed lain there all night on the 10th, but though five young ones had come down from the ledges before 10 p.m. none had parents waiting for them on the water and all were gobbled up by gulls: so they were probably accidental tumblers. On the evening of the 21st, however, I saw the *Soldian* round the Bard Head in a sudden deluge of westerly rain and at 6 p.m. she sailed into the Nesti Voe to take me aboard.

By 6.30 p.m., when we were off the Cradle Holm, one or two young guillemots were already on the sea and masses of adults were calling off the south face of the Noup. We lay off the north face first, and before we realized what was happening there was a plop in the water right alongside the yacht and a fledgeling bobbed up. It must have come down from a great height, for though we were more than fifty yards from the cliffs it appeared to drop vertically into the sea. Only when one was in a boat immediately below the overhang of the Noup did one begin to appreciate its towering height and gigantic proportions.

The numbers of young coming down from the cliffs began to accelerate at 7.45 p.m., and at 8.30 p.m. we moved round to the south face in Rumble Wick, where from the beginning of the fledging there had always been the maximum of tumult and where, at a guess, ten thousand guillemots might be seen on the ledges at any one time. An hour later the operation was at its peak on a now comparatively calm evening with slight misty rain and a gently rocking swell, after the succession of stormy nights. During the past two hours we had seen about one hundred and ninety young guillemots come down from the cliffs. Initially, quite a number had come down without parents, either to find the latter on the sea at the base of the cliffs, or to swim around the yacht calling incessantly: but when the rate of descent quickened the great majority were escorted down by one parent and a few by both parents.

Between 9.30 p.m. and 10.10 p.m., when a further one hundred and sixty came down from the south face at the rate of four every minute, the *tempo* of the operation, its excitement and complexity, the ceaseless tumult, surpassed all telling; and the figure of one hundred and sixty was a minimum estimate, for there were periods during this forty minutes when fledgelings were coming down all along the face of the Noup more quickly than I could record them. They tumbled off those long ledges, hundreds of feet from end to end, immediately above the sea. They dropped from higher ledges, plopping into the sea all around the yacht. They floated down from the topmost shelves and platforms three or four hundred feet above us, with the young one in the lead and the parent a foot or two above it, either braking hard, with wings and webbed feet spread wide, when close above the mast, or passing high above it to alight with a plop or a soft splash.

One in every ten or twelve fledgelings was escorted by both parents, on either side and a little above it. Ninety-nine out of every hundred alighted within fifty yards of the cliffs, but at least one fledgeling with two parents made a splendid flight, alighting some three hundred yards out from the cliffs,[1] and there were a few other flights approaching this distance, including those of one or two razorbills, of whom five or six with one parent apiece came down close by the yacht. It was very difficult to pinpoint one fledgeling out of hundreds actually leaving its ledge on these tremendous cliffs towering vertically above the yacht to a height where their remote tops were wreathed in mist: but some of those on lower ledges could be seen, as well remembered on Lundy, peeping over the edge for long periods, then being brooded in the parent's little tent of sheltering wings, and then bowing forward again to peer over, before the little fellow ultimately did (or did not) take the plunge with a little leap out into space—and quite a number of those that came down were small black-headed chicks only about ten days old,

[1] Two hundred yards according to Theo Kay.

The Guillemot townships and Kittiwake ledges, Rumble Wick

A Bridled Guillemot

and distinct from their grey-headed and white-cheeked elder brothers. The desperate adventurer was followed immediately by its parent who, however would keep above it throughout its swift fluttering flight down, on wing-coverts only, at an incline of about 22½ degrees out of the vertical.[1] The fledgelings appeared to have a certain steerage control, for not one hit the yacht, though scores alighted within a few feet or yards of it. Alighting on one side of the yacht, they might dive and surface on its other side, and one diving directly down under the yacht was not seen to surface again. They came up perfectly dry from their initial and often prolonged submersion, but continual diving soon wetted them, settling them down by the stern. One or two of those who came down without parents from a great height did not submerge on alighting, but swam around us with breasts raised high out of the water. In this attitude their white bellies gleamed dazzlingly white, possibly significantly so, in the grey evening light—too significantly, for the majority or all of these orphans were snapped up by the waiting gulls.

Never ceasing for a second was the harsh *arrg, arrg* of those parents following their young down on the wing, crazy with excitement, and often our first warning of a pair coming down was the raucous alarum of a parent whose chick was heading straight for the mast. Continuous was the *queewee, queewee* of those solitary fledgelings advertising their presence on the water while looking for their parents, and one young razorbill cried his sad *psee-ee-ee* vainly around the yacht for a long while. Meantime the villainous swaabies took a dreadful toll of those fledgelings swimming out to sea, mainly of those unescorted by parents, picking them off the water and bolting them whole, though nearby adult guillemots would shoot through the water threateningly at a swooping swaabie, cawing furiously. A curious incident occurred when a gannet picked up one fledgeling and refused to surrender it to a swaabie also seizing it, obstinately pressing his head down in to the water and threshing his wings. Six bonxies took their toll from a reef platform at the south corner of the Noup, on to which many fledgelings fell from ledges above. Though unharmed by their fall·the majority

---

[1] Forty-five to fifty degrees according to Theo Kay.

of the latter soon fell victims to bonxies or gulls. An accidentally fallen young gannet also stood forlornly on this shelf at the edge of the surf, ultimately tucking its white head back into its scapulars and seeking peace in sleep. I had seen it fall from the Noup that afternoon, when it lay apparently stunned, though later recovering.

At a guess perhaps three-quarters of the chicks that fledged this night got safely away to sea with their parents, though it had to be remembered that this was only a very small percentage of the potential, for egg losses in a community of guillemots were commonly very heavy, and it was doubtful whether 10 per cent of those nesting actually in gannetries even hatched chicks.

The multitudes of guillemots continually crossing and crisscrossing the Wick at all heights above the mast, the tumultuous din, the knowledge that we were witnesses of a spectacle possibly never before observed by man on so vast a scale, the minute to minute expectation of yet another pair or trio dropping down to the mast, together made these three hours the most amazing of a naturalist's life.[1] The passing of a rorqual whale, cartwheeling close by the Noup with, very curiously, a shark-boat chugging Bard-wards only a couple of hundred yards farther out, went almost unheeded.

At 10.10 p.m. when the light was very dim, we reluctantly hauled up our light anchor and stood away for home, though there was still no slackening in the rate of descent and no appreciable diminution could be observed in the numbers of guillemots in the serried rows and massed townships on the face of the cliff above. All the way down the north coast as far as the Whiggie geo there were fledgelings on the water and adults calling, before we ultimately passed into a strange quiet, and a smooth passage home to Noss Sound, with only silent flights of kittiwakes returning from bathing and puffins running over the sea before us, threshing the water with their wings. It was 10.45 p.m. when I was put ashore in the dinghy at Gungstie and the

---

[1] In his recent book, *The Atlantic Islands*, Kenneth Williamson refers, however, to the 'drive' of those young guillemots down on the water by the men of Faeroe during 'Operation Fledge'.

yacht, with its cabin brightly lit in the near-darkness, stood out to sea again for Score Head and Bressay Sound.

So great were the numbers of guillemots on the Noup's south face that I was still unable to detect any decrease three days later: but though many adults were flying at cliff-top height carrying big fish, there were probably few chicks left at the end of this second week of the fledging. By the 26th some adults were actually calling on the sea as early as noon, when one fledgeling was already down, but though many adults and chicks were calling in thick fog that night at 10 p.m. and continued to do so from far out to sea until 11.15 p.m., there was no longer the tremendous turmoil that had characterized previous nights.

By the end of the third week of the fledging the adults were to be counted only in hundreds and some of those long ledges on the south face of the Noup were now empty or had only a couple of occupants apiece, and on August 4th, after three days of cold gales and heavy rains, there was hardly one guillemot remaining of all the thousands that had formerly peopled the north Noup. There were still several hundred in the north-coast colonies, however, for, as on Lundy, the smaller colonies farthest removed from headquarters on the Noup lagged considerably behind the latter in their breeding time-table. At 7.15 p.m. that night the only adult guillemot still present in my gannetry was sitting half-heartedly on a cracked egg, while a big chick was running up and down an otherwise empty ledge and one or two adults and young were calling from the Wick below. Two of the former were calling as early as 11.15 a.m. on the 7th and the last young ones called and fledged at 9.16 p.m. on the 12th. Solitary old birds, however, continued to call vainly from the sea, both north and south of the Noup, until August 22nd.

VI

VALE

Less than a month after midsummer day the Simmer Dim was darkening though, on climbing up from the Cradle Holm deep in shadow to the heights above Rumble Wick an hour before midnight, the broad band of fiery crimson in the north-east would be so bright that my eyes could hardly bear to watch its swift transition through primrose yellow to palest duck-egg green. Half an hour later, when the young guillemots were still going down to the sea from their cliff-ledges, bright streaks of gold fire from a long narrow window of yellow lamp-glow in the north-east illuminated the pages of my notebook as if it had been moonlight; but north and west the long black fingers of those innumerable nesses and skerries of Shetland stretched, eternal, into the grey reflecting mirrors of voes and sounds studded with green and red pin-lights and lit intermittently by the winking lanterns of lighthouses. From the hidden dusk of the sea came the rhythmic thudding of a fishing smack's engines. The deep-toned thunder of the three hundred great black-backed gulls on the wing above the concealed Holm was menacing in its suddenness, matching the sullen pounding of the swell deep down in the geos.

By the middle of August daylight was only just coming into the sky when I stepped out of Gungstie at 3 a.m. and a bright fishing moon would be shimmering on the sea. There was the damp fishy smell of curing piltocks in the fresh morning air and the cold oily rush of a flowing sea. It was silent morning now, except for the throbbing of a haddock-boat's engines, until the shrill piping of an oystercatcher wakened the gulls and their everlasting gibbon-howling began. By 7 p.m. the sun was already sliding north behind the Ander and I could write in my *Journal*: 'On a bright *wintry* eve with showers the Sound is full of shags and once again fleets of them, a hundred and fifty strong, are fishing in the Nesti Voe. Once again starlings murmur from the chimney stacks and their autumnal song is heard: it sounds mellower than, and lacks the harsh grating notes of, the spring song.'

Autumn was touching the flowers too. Leaves and flowers of roseroot were fire-tinted; angelica towered from the sidings; the green circumference of the Cradle Holm's russet core was white with mayweed; the delicate pink streamers of ragged-robin had taken the place of the vernal squill on the sidings.

Autumn was in the sea. Many of the herrings now being landed at Lerwick from the fleet of swift ninety-foot Shetland motor-boats and big Lowestoft drifters were spent from spawning, and a portent of the season was the putting into Lerwick harbour, on a day here and there, of big 1,000-ton deep-sea trawlers from Hull and Grimsby, *en route* to the Icelandic and Bear Isle cod-banks.

On August 26th I spent the night alone in Gungstie for the last time, with the moaning of the ewes for their weaned lambs ever in my ears. For two days and a night there was continuous drenching rain, while from the Maiden's Paps upwards all Noss was entombed in thick southerly fog. These depressing weather conditions did not, however, prevent me from working seven hours at a stretch measuring out the bonxie territories, pacing-out yards up and down hill, through flooded bog and tussock to tussock—as soaking and as exhausting a business as I hoped never to do again. August was often accounted the slackest month in the naturalist's year, but this had not been the case on Noss. During the first three weeks of the month I had worked harder, perhaps, than at any time since May, for in addition to routine work the mapping out of skua territories had involved taking some four hundred measurements, entailing about twenty miles of pacing on ground so broken and boggy that my two feet were never on the same level for two strides together.

On the evening of the 26th there fluttered south through the corrie of Pundsgeo a magnificent moth with a three-inch spread of wings, the hinder pair of which were almost as long as the fore-pair. Its general colouring appeared to be dark-blue, bordered and in-circled with greyish-white, but I could not assign it to any known British species.

On Bressay the fog coincided not only with the first big hold-up of passage migrants of the year, but also with that of considerable numbers of red-admiral and painted-lady butterflies, which danced in fives and sixes along the Cruester road and feasted with moss-carder bees on the Michaelmas daisies in the garden at Heogan.

Thus far no mention has been made of any migratory movements through Noss, partly because these would have been incidental to my work on the island and partly because there were almost none. Their absence was due, so far as the spring passage was concerned, to the prevalence of westerly and northerly winds, and in respect of the autumn passage to, I suspect, the presence a dozen miles north of Noss of the big island of Whalsay and the easterly stretching archipelago and light-stack of the Out Skerries, which would tend to 'cover' Noss from those migrants coming down from north and east. In any case I left Shetland too early to see the best of the autumn passage.

Such sparse migration as there was on Noss calls for no detailed comments, for it embodied no outstanding exceptions from the general pattern of East Coast migration, except that it was less in evidence than in any previous year or place in my experience and, when there was a big hold-up of small passerines on Bressay, during that end-August fog, there were no notabilities among them. On Noss the only at all noteworthy occurrences were that of a cock snow bunting in full breeding plumage, which frequented the Head for a couple of days during the first week in May and was the first of its kind I had ever seen in breeding plumage on migration; a cock blackcap in the first week of June, which struck a strangely incongruous note in frequenting the dyke on the north side of the Head above the Whiggie geo; my first cock blue-headed wagtail, which appeared on the green above Rumble Wick in the middle of June; the few house-martins and swifts which spent hours hawking insects along the Rumble Wick cliffs and over the Noup in June, July and August; and a small north to south passage of solitary merlins speeding across the island in the middle of August.

As the evening of that last solitary day on Noss drew on, my impatient spirit summoned me to the door of Gungstie again and again to see if my ferryman was coming round the corner of that deceptive hill below Houllmastouri, on which it was so difficult to pick up a figure against the hillside. How deep and vivid a green was the Ander, its top wreathed in mist. Not much burning harvest-bake here, after more than twenty inches of rain during the spring and summer! My dogs, bored, waited for the signal to go down the steps to the creek. The inevitable white whaler went out past the Bard. Two hours earlier the herring fleet had passed in succession close by the Bard on their usual east by north route to the night's fishing grounds. Now that the terns and common gulls had given up their territories on the Big Ness and nearly all the oystercatchers had left Noss, it was pretty quiet round Gungstie, except for the maaing of the ewes, but from time to time I heard the *phwee-phwee-phwee* of migrant curlews and the thin whistling of fledgeling herring-gulls, while shags dived and slapper-pattered in the Sound, as of old, and the *chug-chug-chug* of the whaler came to me like the swift thudding of my heart. And then at last, when brewing my third cup of coffee, I saw through the gathering gloom of mist-shrouded dusk the stalwart oilskin-clad figure of my deliverer striding along the Ander shore with his three dogs; and so home through a November fog to the lights along the waterfront and the deserted townships.

By the second week in September the Island was very quiet —no gulls on the pastures, no oystercatchers anywhere, starlings in large bands, all the cliff-birds gone except the gannets and an occasional fulmar, shag, flock of rock-doves, or gulls coming over from Bressay in the evening to their roosting cliffs. Here and there a summer's day: Noss very pleasant in the warm evening sun, and picturesque the scene of lambs being loaded into the *fourern*, ferried across the shag-droven Sound, and pitched out on the rocky cove on the Bressay shore. My thoughts went back to those few precious May days, and Laurence and I sitting in the summer sun outside Gungstie. I forgot how cold the wind had been.

On September 15th I went into Noss for the last time. It was a wild day, following a westerly gale during the night and several days of strong winds and torrential rains. No longer were bonxies pirating in Rumble Wick. Only the splendid gannets cast their shadows on the dazzling yellow-grey face of the sunlit Noup, towering above a double rainbow laid almost flat on the sea across the Wick. Another four or five weeks and they too would have deserted Noss. Less than a month after their departure the first of the homing fulmars would already be prospecting nesting sites for a new season; for they visited their Shetland stations as early as November 2nd!

That afternoon I looked my last on the island from the Ander road, when flights of herring-gulls were already veering and tacking Noss-wards from the Bressay cornfields. Very green in the sun were the Big Ness and the Hill of Papilgeo, and there were vivid green patches at Setter, on the Maiden's Paps and on the upper part of the Head. Though a bonxie 'floated' over Setter, the island's winter inhabitants were taking possession—a family of ravens crossing the waist of the island; cormorants, with white-bellied young, standing on the Turr Ness side by side with swaabies; a hundred curlew lined up on the Big Ness.

By the 17th the wind, accompanied by torrential squalls of rain, had blown from strong to gale force night and day, without ceasing for a minute, for seven days, and the swell running into Bressay Sound was so mountainous that the Hoversta ferrymen were in two minds whether or not to attempt the morning passage to Lerwick, while we were even more uncertain whether to attempt the plane journey to Inverness the next day.

Despite the chop and swell, however, gannets were plunging vertically into the harbour waters, and rows of young tysties, a few terns and drake eiders, and a solitary bonxie were also to be seen in the Sound. With the herring season at an end and the fish factory closed the mass of gulls had gone from Heogan and only the one-legged herring-gull was constant. All oyster-catchers had left Shetland. Wheatears from Greenland and Scandinavia whirled about the dykes.

When the *St. Clair* braved her homeward passage to Aberdeen that stormy night and backed out from the pier to turn in mid-Sound (God pity the sheep and cattle crowded below deck!), the harbour was as empty of shipping as in those far-off, no less tempestuous days of April. Only the yacht *Soldian* lay at her moorings outside the small-boat harbour to recall the crowded hours of summer. The Lerwick lifeboat and the Shetland herring-boats had been hauled up for overhaul and painting. The English drifters had followed the herrings south to Northumberland and East Anglia. Whalers and shark boats had returned to Norway. From the Hill of Cruester I could make out only two boats tied up along the waterfront—the Shetland motor-steamer, the *Earl*—which had battered her way into the Sound that morning from the North Isles of Shetland four hours behind schedule, and a timber boat unloading cargo at one of the wharves. Off Heogan the Sound was empty except for the three immemorial coal-hulks anchored in midstream.

With these impressions of Shetland, her people, and her birds the *Journal* closes, but all three live on in these memories of a Shetlander in exile:

> *Kin doo mind da myrds o tirriks*
> *Flicthin up wi sic a shirrik,*
> *Aboot da Holms o Sefster*
> *Dat boanie simmer day;*
> *An da peerie tirriks skjoagin*
> *Athin toogs an denkies oagin*
> *An da pinks gjain 'snik' atween wir taes,*
> *Dat day, noo, kin doo mind?*
>
> *Kin doo mind da dunters hurrin,*
> *Lik da twinin o a pirrin,*
> *Ta dir deuks among da drooie lines*
> *Juist ooie baas o doon;*
> *And below dem: what a gairden!*
> *Green silk ripplin: waar laeves wavin,*
> *Gadderin, spreddin, risin, fadin,*
> *Ta da singin o da Soond;*

Mukkle slippery, frilly tangles
Ringed wi peerie rooderie spangles,
Fat yoags clesped i dir curly taes,
Sae lilac an sae broon;
Da starfish' rosie fingirs
Ta dir bledds sae clossly clingin,
I dir boasies boanie skadmen's heads
White, purple, pink an roond?

O! An kin doo mind da skeetiks,
Da moots o fleetin skeetiks,
Sping-spangin troo da trowie treeds,
Da silliks glowerin green;
Da saandie loos an shaalders,
Crimson, black, an grey an silver,
Sik a rinnin, peeplin, pipelin,
Dat day, noo, kin doo mind?

Da sluebs lik sweemin glessis,
Thoosins shoalin by da nessis,
Sae saft an weet an sliddery
Troo wir fingirs trailin on;
Da Holms lyin dere afore wis,
Foamin pink wi flooers ta loor wis,
Tang fannin roond dir rooderie rocks,
I'm sure doo needsmst mind!

Minds doo no da puffin neesiks
Boolin glissnin blue an sleekit,
Da maakril skuttrin i da tap,
Da maas aa gaaldrin doon,
Da mukkle dosin selkie,
Lyin stritched apo da skerry,
His flipper wavin wantin lik,
Dat day, noo, dus doo mind?

An wir aald laekin foweraern,
Wir freend in fun an farin,

266

She looked sae sprush an spritely,
Dat day below da Holms,
As jink as onny lassie,
Wi hir pent sae fresh an glossy,
Waatery wubs aa mirlin roond hir boo,
Spun quently bee da sun?

Minds doo curled i da stammreen,
Da chattrin waater lapprin,
Just trow da boards fornenst dee lug,
Is faider sailed wis hame,
An fur aa we wir black faantin,
Niver aatim wir we aantin,
Dat foo wir we wi unkins,
Dat day, noo, kin doo mind?

267

Part VI

A SHORT HISTORY OF NOSS BIRDS

STRIKING A BALANCE

In the preceding chapters we have learnt something of the breeding history of nine species of sea-fowl nesting on Noss. In all, thirty species of birds nested on the island in 1946, against thirty-nine known to have nested in its recorded history.

The cliffs and sidings, predominantly in the upper half of the island, were the breeding grounds of the true rock-birds: gannets, guillemots, razorbills, puffins, kittiwakes and fulmars—though one or two pairs of the latter nested along the brow-edge in the lower half of the island and some scores of puffins in dry boulder-beaches at the heads of geos. In addition there were something over one hundred pairs of shags between the geo of the Point of Hovie on the south coast and Papilgeo on the north coast; a dozen pairs, perhaps, of rock-pigeons, notably in the Cradle Holm geo and along the low cliffs of the North Croo; and a pair of peregrine falcons on the south face of the Noup. These Noss falcons had been famous as the finest in the North, always excepting those of the Fair Isle, for more than three hundred years, and from time to time two pairs had bred on the Noup. As is the custom of peregrines, however, they have not nested on Noss every year, as many as three pairs occasionally nesting on Bressay.

Also in the coastal sector were eight pairs of hooded crows nesting in the cliff-face of holms; not less than sixty-five pairs of tysties, nesting in the boulder-beaches; the single colony of eight pairs of arctic terns, nesting on the rocks below the Big Ness, in company with thirteen pairs of common gulls; several hundred pairs of herring-gulls nesting in the cliff-face where, as on the west Noup and the Cradle Holm, there was abundant vegetation, but mainly on the yard-wide strip of turf, loam and rubble that topped the cliff inside the dyke around the upper half of the Island. They also nested on geo boulder-beaches, on grassy holms, on rocky skerries (on which they built enormous pile-nests of dead grasses and mosses), and on the green of the coastal strip round the island from Booth's Voe in the north to the Big Ness in the south. In the three latter habitats were also to be found ten colonies, comprising about one hundred pairs, of lesser black-backed gulls, located on the slopes above the Point of Hovie and the Cradle Holm in the south and from Booth's Voe to east of the Whiggie geo in the north. With the exception, however, of an odd pair among the lesser black-backs on the northern skerries and at Setter, all the greater black-backs were concentrated in a single colony of some one hundred and forty or fifty pairs on the Cradle Holm.

Nesting both in the coastal sector and also the interior of the island were perhaps a dozen pairs of Shetland starlings: some in dykes, some in the geos and cliff-face in company with the true rock-birds; not less than twenty-three pairs of rock pipits: mainly in the cliffs, but in one or two instances right out in the middle of the moor; twenty pairs of Shetland wrens: some in the sidings at the heads of geos and others (together with half a dozen pairs of twites) in dykes from the summit of the Noup down to Gungstie; thirty-one pairs of oystercatchers, favouring especially the holms, and nesting as high up the coastal strip as the south corner of Rumble Wick; and two pairs of ringed plover on the sandy, shaly, flagstone waste of the North Croo.

Finally, in the interior of the island were a single pair of house sparrows at Gungstie and, sparsely distributed all over the island, fifteen or twenty pairs of wheatears; while outside the hill-dyke were ten or fifteen pairs of skylarks, nesting as high as the Hill of Setter; nine pairs of lapwings distributed from the north end of the hill-dyke, where the golden plover formerly nested, to the Setter *crö*; half a dozen pairs of Faeroe snipe below and above the Maiden's Paps; and eider-duck, arctic skuas and the bonxie, the dominant bird of the interior.

There were certain birds nesting on Bressay in 1946 that did not nest on Noss. There were no records indeed of mallard, teal, redshank, cormorant, storm petrel or corn-bunting ever having

Northern Guillemots

Kittiwake

One or two Puffins would be whirring up to the holms

nested on Noss, though the latter was reported as seen in 1914. The arctic tern was, of course, the predominant tern in Shetland, but there was a colony of *common* terns at Hoversta on Bressay, and a single pair of these had nested among the Noss arctic terns in 1915. The numbers of the latter had fluctuated between six and twenty pairs during the past fifty years, not nesting at all in 1922, and nesting on the Bressay shore of the Sound in 1938. The merganser had nested at least once on Noss; the raven frequently on the Noup, though not apparently since 1933—a pair of jackdaws may (doubtfully) have nested on the cliffs in 1934; the blackbird at Gungstie during the 'thirties; the meadow pipit in most years apparently; and one or two pairs of the golden plover regularly or intermittently up to the 'thirties.

Then there were three species—sea eagle, curlew, and whimbrel—that no longer nested on either Bressay or Noss. A pair of eagles had used alternate eyries on the Noup and the Bard, mainly on the Noup, up to 1895; while one or two pairs of whimbrel had continued to nest on Noss up to 1922, the single pair of curlew nesting for the last time shortly before this.

We must now consider the obverse of this summary. Up to the year 1898 the seafowl breeding on the Noss cliffs and holms were auks and kittiwakes, while the hinterland was dominated by arctic skuas and gulls with, among the larger birds, hundreds of eider ducks and a few whimbrel, curlew, golden plover, oystercatchers and snipe. In that year, however, or a little previously, a new era opened on the island with the nesting of the first pair of fulmars on the Noup, twenty years after their initial colonization of Shetland, on Foula, and ten years before any report of their breeding on Bressay. I could not find time to take any Noss census, but my general impression was that in 1946 there were certainly more than one thousand, but less than ten thousand, breeding and non-breeding pairs, sitting about the cliffs and sidings, from the west geo of Mansie's Berg on the north coast right round to the geo of the Point of Hovie in the south.

On Bressay, where their increase appeared to have been both more rapid and more numerous, they nested all round the coast, wherever anything in the nature of a cliff was available, except on the western shore between Ham and Heogan, and probably exceeded ten thousand pairs.

Little more than a decade after the first report of their nesting on Noss, and when they were increasing at a great pace, a more radical change was effected in the balance of species on the island by the nesting in 1910 of two pairs of bonxies on the high flat of the Hill of Setter. In this respect it may be noted, without any special significance being attached to it, that a couple of bonxies had been shot on the island in the spring of 1888, and that two years later two eggs were taken from bonxies on Foula and placed under gulls on Noss.

Up to the middle of the nineteenth century the bonxie had only survived in Shetland thanks to the protection it received in its traditional breeding grounds on Foula and in Unst, and as early as 1774 there were stated to be only six pairs on Foula and three in Unst. By 1860, however, there were fifty or sixty pairs at Hermaness in Unst. Thereafter, the majority of the pairs apparently alternated between Unst and Foula, and by 1891 there were one hundred pairs on Foula though only nine on Unst. Their subsequent increase both on Foula and Hermaness was rapid and was responsible no doubt for the establishment of new colonies on Noss and in several other parts of Shetland (and also Orkney), including Bressay, where one pair nested on the heights of the moors south and east of the Sand Vatn in 1913 and 1914. To all appearances the latter habitat would seem an ideal bonxie ground, with its large loch and commanding heights, yet the colony seems never to have exceeded twenty pairs—which was its approximate strength in 1946. Similarly, though a few scattered pairs of arctic skuas have also nested between Grimsetter Loch and the Sand Vatn since the earliest times, their numbers never appear to have exceeded ten pairs. Probably in both cases the primary attraction of Noss has always been the potential food supply afforded by the enormous numbers of seafowl nesting on the cliffs.

By a remarkable coincidence the arrival of the bonxie on Noss coincided with that of the third new colonist—the gannet, which was first reported prospecting the island in 1911 or 1912, one pair subsequently breeding on the south Noup in 1914, the first to do so in Shetland, three years before colonization also began on Hermaness. Nothing definite can be deduced as to the possible origins of these pioneer gannets.

During the next decade or so no material changes were recorded on Noss, other than the continued increase of fulmars. Only one pair of bonxies had nested in the years 1913 and 1914, being robbed of their eggs in both years; and up to 1920 no more than ten pairs of gannets were nesting. In 1922, when two pairs of whimbrel brought off young, there were still only eight or twelve pairs of bonxies and twenty or thirty pairs of gannets, which were now colonizing the north face of the Noup. But the whimbrel had nested on the west slopes of the Hill of Setter (at present occupied by a colony of lesser black-backed gulls) and the curlew in a clump of *juncus* on the Head, where by this time even twelve pairs of bonxies would have constituted a sufficiently formidable invasion to discourage the further breeding of these species.

The arctic skua had been recorded breeding on Noss as early as 1700, and by 1831 it was said to be more numerous on Noss than anywhere else in Shetland—with which we may compare the statements that in 1774 'thousands' nested on Foula, and that after protection was given on Noss in 1865 more than three times as many were nesting two years later; while in 1890 the 200–300 on Hermaness were said to be somewhat exceeded by the colony on Noss. There may, doubtfully, have been a maximum of two hundred pairs on the island at one time—the number estimated in 1914. The beginning of a progressive decrease in their numbers was noted in 1923, the first year that the bonxies (now fourteen pairs) nested on an outlying part of their breeding grounds on the Hill of Pundsgeo.[1] In 1929 the bonxies (now about thirty pairs strong) invaded their main breeding grounds, north and west of the Paps; and it was probably shortly after this that the golden plover deserted Noss. The numbers of

[1] According to one authority there were only forty or fifty pairs in 1922. The fact is that most of the estimates, whether of skuas or gannets or any other species, conflict to a remarkable degree; and the difficulties I myself experienced in counting skuas and gannets during my five-months' study suggests that counts based on a few hours', or even days', observation must be considered generally unreliable.

the arctic skuas were then about sixty pairs, and thereafter there was a sharp decline in their numbers to forty-eight or fifty pairs in 1934 and an absolute low of twenty-five pairs in 1939. This decrease coincided with the now rapid increase in the numbers of bonxies from fifty pairs in 1932 to sixty-eight or seventy pairs in 1934, eighty pairs in 1938, and ninety or one hundred pairs in 1939.

It must not necessarily be presumed, however, that the little skua's decrease was brought about by the bonxie's increase, for the species is one that has always fluctuated in numbers and alternated in locality in Shetland, and there has been in fact, as we have seen, an increase in their numbers during the war. Presuming the estimate for 1939 to be approximately accurate, their increase between 1939 and 1946 has been of the order of 48 per cent, compared to one of less than 20 per cent in the case of the bonxie. In 1946 seventy-seven pairs of bonxies nested on or above the Maiden's Paps and thirty-six pairs below them in what was formerly the main stronghold of the arctic skuas, which nested all over the moor north of Setter, with a pair or two above the Cradle Holm. As, however, there were still only eighty pairs of bonxies in all as late as 1938, when the arctic skua was approaching its absolute low, it is possible that only about twenty-five pairs of bonxies were then nesting on the grounds below the Paps. On the other hand the map of the skua breeding grounds affords clear evidence that by 1946 the arctic skuas, despite their increase, were being compressed into a single area north of a line from the Voe of the Mels to the Corrie of Pundsgeo, and that the bonxies were driving wedges into this remaining area and forcing the little skua back on to the unsuitable nesting ground of the bare-herbaged North Croo. Though there were losses among eggs and nestlings of bonxies in territories adjacent to skua colonies these were not significantly greater than the norm.

By 1946, therefore, a situation had been reached whereby the bonxie, now in its thirty-seventh year on Noss, dominated the interior of the island outside the hill-dyke, having concluded the expulsion of the herring-gulls (begun in 1924) and of lesser black-backed gulls into the coastal surround. In 1890 the latter were reported as breeding on the Cradle Holm and the west moor, while herring-gulls nested on the Head and the Hill of Setter. By 1923, however, the lesser black-backs had been driven from their old grounds; but at this time they were actually increasing in numbers and responded to this expulsion by establishing new colonies, and continued to increase, despite the bonxies killing 'great numbers' of both adults and young, until 1929 when, though still the most numerous of all the gulls, a decrease in their numbers was noticed. Similarly, the original colony of some thirty or forty pairs of common gulls had been driven from the North Croo and were now restricted to the Big Ness (which a dozen pairs had first colonized in 1924), with an additional couple of pairs among the lesser black-backs on the skerries east of Booth's Voe. Their decrease could probably be ascribed to the deployment of the latter.

The great black-backed gull (and also the herring-gull) was first recorded nesting on the Cradle Holm as far back as 1774, and in great numbers there in 1809; but it is stated that owing to the activities of egg hunters it ceased to do so subsequently, leaving the Holm to be occupied by herring-gulls and eider ducks. In 1867, however, three years after the permanent removal of the cradle, it re-established itself, forty pairs nesting, and by 1898 one hundred pairs were recorded as nesting. (According to another authority, however, it was never totally banished from the Holm, from ten to thirty pairs being in occupation up to the time the cradle was removed). By 1914 it was variously estimated that two hundred or five hundred pairs were in occupation and 'more than this' in 1922, with an *increase* continuing until 1930! As a 'good many' were nesting on the mainland of the island in 1926, it is possible that their numbers may have been increasing at this time, but any estimate in excess of two hundred pairs must be considered very questionable. As it is extremely difficult to take a census of them on account of the dense herbage in which they nest, and the further fact that it is not practicable to take in the whole top of the Holm from a single viewpoint, it is possible that, in fact, there has been little or no decrease to my estimate, based on several counts, of between one hundred and thirty-seven and one hundred and fifty nesting pairs.

We have seen that by the nineteen-thirties the bonxie was rapidly assuming a dominant position in the interior of the island, and at this time also the status of the auks and kittiwakes on the cliffs was being affected by the spread of the gannet and possibly by that of the fulmar. From a total of twenty or thirty pairs in 1922 the gannet had multiplied to about two hundred pairs by 1930, to about eight hundred by 1934 and to an estimated 1,830 pairs by 1939—together with around a thousand pairs of fulmars. The increase of both species continued to be phenomenal, and by 1946 it was no longer possible to compute their numbers accurately, my rough estimate for the gannets being some six or eight thousand individuals. For at least twenty years the gannets had been, as we have seen, peacefully, but none the less ruthlessly, expelling the guillemots and to a lesser extent the kittiwakes from their immemorial breeding ledges on the Noup and in Rumble Wick, though tens of thousands of both species still remained. In addition to actual loss of territory those guillemots still nesting within gannetries suffered heavy losses in eggs in the commotion caused by the alighting and departing of gannets, and enormous losses in fledgelings from the depradations of swaabies, herring-gulls and to a lesser extent of bonxies. Their victimization by the arctic skua can be dismissed as of no significance, as can the piracy of the bonxie on the gannet. Similarly, in addition to actual loss of territory, the kittiwakes suffered a very heavy mortality, both of adults and young, from the attacks of bonxies.

From these various causes it seems possible that, even if there were no further increase in the numbers of gannets and bonxies, the vast majority of guillemots and kittiwakes must finally be driven from the Noss cliffs. At the present time Noss is the only guillemot ground on the east coast of Shetland, except for a very small colony on the island of Mousa to the south, while there is only one other colony of kittiwakes. Their expulsion might possibly be accelerated by the increase to saturation point of the fulmar, whose eggs and young are immune on Noss—though the latter's nesting habitat encroaches more on those of cliff-breeding herring-gulls, puffins and razorbills, the latter already very few in numbers and possibly decreasing during the past ten years. No doubt a certain toll is levied on both adult and young puffins by gulls and bonxies, but they should be able to maintain their numbers, though lack of suitable terrain might prevent any increase, since many are already nesting in abnormal cliff sites. The tystie and the shag, one presumes, are unaffected by any of the above factors, though the breeding numbers of the latter must be greatly lessened by the heavy winter shooting off Noss and Bressay.

Striking a balance, we find that since 1896 Noss has lost the sea eagle, whimbrel, curlew, golden plover, and possibly raven, blackbird and meadow pipit as permanent breeding species, but has gained the fulmar, bonxie and gannet, while the lapwing, which was first reported as establishing a small breeding colony in 1866 and appears to have bred intermittently since then, is now nesting in greater numbers than previously recorded.

Herring-gulls and lesser black-backs and the arctic skua are at present increasing. Guillemots, razorbills, kittiwakes, common gulls and possibly the greater black-back, eider duck, probably ringed plover, and the house sparrow are all decreasing. The decline of the house sparrow (and also that of the blackbird) from what is variously described as 'scores' or 'a few pairs' during the Jamiesons' time to a single pair in 1946, must be attributed to the absence of permanent human residents on the island during the past seven years, with the complementary absence of the feeding of grain to domestic fowl—though it must be noted that the sparrow almost disappeared from Bressay in the late 'twenties, possibly from the same disease that decimated the sparrows on Yell at this time. It is likely to join the extinct species in the immediate future, and the island will become the preserve predominantly of fulmars, gannets, gulls, bonxies, puffins, shags and the few smaller species: the future status of the arctic skua being doubtful.

It has been suggested that the numbers of the bonxie should be controlled, as it is alleged to be a menace to sheep. Actually, Theo Kay has sifted all evidence to the effect that the bonxie has ever attacked sheep in Shetland, and found it not proven, while its reputation on Noss has already been dealt with. Suppose, however, that its breeding was controlled on the island from now on, as a measure of protection to the other nesting species, and that its numbers were reduced by, say, half at the outset. In this event it would be a fair, though uncertain, presumption that the arctic skuas and the eider duck—which was much reduced in numbers by soldiers stationed on Bressay during the war—would increase and that the mortality among kittiwakes would be much reduced. In this respect, however, it must be remembered that both gulls and arctic skuas take eiders' eggs, and that throughout the 'twenties and 'thirties, during the years of the bonxie's steepest increase, the eiders were also increasing and nesting in great numbers on Noss. There is no reason to suppose, however, that golden plover, curlew and whimbrel, would return to breed, for the golden plover nests but sparingly on Bressay, where the curlew ceased to breed about the time the bonxie colonized that island, while the whimbrel was probably always an intermittent breeder on Noss, only single pairs being recorded as far back as 1879 and 1887, and no prospecting pairs visiting the island since 1928. Moreover, the presence of the bonxie must necessarily make any territorial expansion of herring-gulls and lesser black-backs be at the expense of other species in the coastal surround; while the gulls are themselves responsible for losses among the eggs and young of the arctic skuas and other species. To a very small extent the bonxie's expansion is itself limited by the circumjacent colonies of gulls, which destroy nestlings of isolated pairs of bonxies.[1] Even in the event of such control, the kittiwakes and guillemots would still have to combat the territorial encroachment of gannets and the attacks of swaabies and herring-gulls.

To all intents and purposes, therefore, the control of the bonxie might benefit only the arctic skua and the eider duck, and would undoubtedly result in an increase of the extremely harmful herring-gull. No question could arise, of course, of controlling the gannet, though for the purposes of argument we may note that this would enable the guillemots and kittiwakes to stand any drain caused by the bonxies and swaabies, and to multiply. Were the swaabies controlled, then their place would be taken

[1] In 1947 Laurence Sutherland saw a peregrine lifting a bonxie nestling from one of the scattered pairs in colony 8 on the Head—the first such record.

by the other large gulls. Since, therefore, the arctic skua is very well established in Shetland, whereas the total number of bonxies in the British Isles may not exceed one thousand pairs, I am of the opinion that the *status quo* should be maintained on Noss for a further five years at any rate. At the conclusion of that period it should be possible, with this 1946 survey at hand for comparison, to gain a much clearer impression of what equilibrium is being maintained among these various species. By that time, too, we should be in possession of some figures as to the percentage of fledgeling bonxies, ringed in 1946, returning to their birthplace, and thus be in a position to estimate the species' probable annual rate of increase.[1]

Work begun
April 1946

Concluded
June 1948

---

[1] Since the above was written, the Zetland County Council have revoked the protection order on the bonxie in all colonies south of Hermaness.

In 1948 I was able to revisit Noss during the first fortnight of June, after an absence of twenty months, and realized how fortunate I had been in 1946, when I did not lose a single clutch of eggs by human agency. In 1948 any serious work on the skuas would have been impossible, for not only had the bonxies lost two or three score eggs by the middle of June, but several arctic skuas' nests had also been robbed. The little skua does not stand up to such treatment with the same resilience as the bonxie. Only eighteen pairs were to be seen regularly on the breeding grounds, and only eleven of these had eggs. Lift the protection on one species and you lift it on all, when the protected area is an island. Noss is no longer a sanctuary.

I was amused to find that most of my pegs were still standing; but, under the circumstances, it was pathetic rather than gratifying to find that twenty-eight out of the thirty-one pairs of arctic skuas present on the Island were paired off in identical combinations of colour phases to those of 1946 and were nesting in the vicinity of their customary mounds. Of three new combinations one was that 1946 unmated bird, which had now acquired a mate. There were no new pairs and seven of the old pairs were never seen. Four of the latter had belonged to Colony I, which the bonxies had now surrounded. One pair of the latter, indeed, occupied pair 2's mound—one of the missing pairs—and I am inclined to think that this may originally have belonged to a pair of bonxies, for it was much bigger and more developed than any other of the arctic skuas' mounds.

Nowhere could I detect a ringed skua. In this respect a later date for my visit would have been preferable—but was not practicable—for immature birds, presumably in their first or second summers, had visited Noss towards the end of June in 1946, and again in August that year.

My ringed bonxies I did not expect to return to Noss for some years. I paid special attention, however, to those bonxies on the gathering hill, which was on the 1946 site, but there were no ringed birds among them or anywhere else on the island. In the time at my disposal it was not possible to form any accurate opinion of the numbers of the bonxies, but nowhere had there been any outward extension of their breeding area, except round the Pundsgeo colony of arctic skuas. On the contrary there were only three pairs instead of eight in that flanking Colony II above the Setter *crö*, and there were also fewer pairs on the Head. On the other hand there were more pairs in Colony Id and a remarkable increase in Colony V on the gathering hill, where no fewer than a dozen pairs were nesting all round the 'lek'. Once again it was most interesting to find that six of these clutches of presumably aged birds—one had an almost white head—contained eggs deficient in pigmentation and with abnormally rough shells, varying in colour from an almost pure 'dunnock' blue to greyish white.

A still more interesting discovery was that pair 116 in Colony XI had a clutch of *three* eggs. Their territory was only 200 yards from that of pair 80, which had laid three eggs in 1946. There was nothing abnormal about the eggs, and they were sufficiently alike to suggest that they were the output of a single female. To my astonishment, however, I found that *three* bonxies were to be seen in regular occupation of the territorial mound, where they consorted in perfect amity, and all three would mob my companion, R. A. Richardson, and myself at our approach. When the first egg hatched, one bird—always the same pale bird—might be seen sitting on the nest, while a second bird fed the chick and the third stood by looking on! In respect to my suggestions in Part II, as to the origins of the occupants of the gathering hill, it is interesting to note that we never visited pair 116's territory without finding all three birds present.[1]

The only other feature of note, so far as the bonxies were concerned, was the extraordinary number of addled eggs, due perhaps to the disturbance they had suffered this season. Very few pairs had hatched both their eggs, and we found no chicks more than a week old, whereas in 1946 the eldest were more than a month old at this date.

[1] Two of the three eggs hatched successfully.

As in the case of the bonxie, it was not possible to determine any considerable territorial extensions to the gannetries, though a colony of non-breeding birds had stripped a ramp of its vegetation high up on the South Noup, and this earthy block will probably be colonized in due course. On the other hand I was surprised to find only one pair of gannets in Puffin Geo, all alone among the guillemots, in place of the four pairs in 1946. In the control gannetry there was an additional nest and a nest-less pair on my top ledge, and pair 6's old niche was again occupied. Large numbers of non-breeding birds were occupying their customary ramp on the east face of the Noup, and an amusing interlude was provided by an immature gannet, which had come down on the green steep of the Head inside the dyke and, unable to get air-borne, assaulted me savagely, bounding towards me with flapping wings and lunging beak, to the accompaniment of a raucous quacking.

Of incidentals Shetland produced its usual crop of surprises. Theo Kay greeted me with a remarkable hybrid gull, which he had obtained near Lerwick in January. In general it resembled a glaucous gull, but its size and wing-spread were those of a great black-back, its mantle was a darker grey than that of a herring gull, and its primaries, though similarly patterned to those of a black-back, were pale black. It was presumably a hybrid between glaucous and black-back, and a black smudge near the red gonys showed it to be almost fully mature.

In the evening there was an immature Iceland gull in the harbour and, a day or two later, an immature glaucous on Noss. It was typical of Shetland that in little more than a fortnight I should see eight species of gulls, and there was an unusual incident when a swaabie dropped onto a guillemot, high over Rumble Wick, and seized it in its beak, though the latter was able to free itself after a minute or so and whirr away down to the sea and back to the cliffs, apparently none the worse. Although I had seen swaabies picking little auks and fledgeling guillemots off the sea, I had never previously seen one taking prey on the wing.

Guillemots, incidentally, had now established three small colonies on the Bressay cliffs; and, during 1947, two pairs of red grouse, which are sparsely distributed in various districts of Shetland, had also taken up residence on Bressay; while in 1948 a pair of merlins and possibly a single pair of curlew also nested. Finally, among the Noss terns we noticed at least two pairs of common terns. This led us to examine very closely the colony of common terns at Hoversta, now more than seventy-five pairs strong, as that 'castanet' mobbing note typical of the arctic tern led us to suspect that some of the latter were also nesting in this colony. This we found to be the case, but we also found that in many instances the commonly accepted diagnostics of bill and leg colour, dusky breast and length of tail were not sufficient to differentiate common from arctic through binoculars, and it would not surprise me to learn that there were hybrids among them.

APPENDIX A

SHETLAND NAMES OF BIRDS MENTIONED IN TEXT

Raven	Corbie
Hooded Crow	Craa
Twite	Lintie
Corn Bunting	Shurl (Docken Sparrow: Bressay)
Snow Bunting	Snaa Fool
Skylark	Laverock
Meadow Pipit	Hill Teetick (Banks Teetick: Bressay)
Rock Pipit	Teetick
Wheatear	Staneshakker
Wren	Stinkie (not Bressay)
Heron	Haigrie
Mallard	Stock Duck
Long-tailed Duck	Kaaloo
Eider Duck	Dunter
Red-breasted Merganser	Herald Duck
Cormorant	Loerin (Skarf: Bressay)
Shag	Skarf
Gannet	Solan Goose
Fulmar	Maalie
Red-throated Diver	Rain Goose
Whimbrel	Tang Whaup
Curlew	Whaup
Purple Sandpiper	Ebb Sleeper (Ebb Cock: Bressay)
Oystercatcher	Shalder
Ringed Plover	Sandy Loo
Common Tern	Tirrick
Arctic Tern	Tirrick
Common Gull	Peerie Maa
Herring Gull	Maa
Herring Gull (immature)	Scorie
Great Black-backed Gull	Swaabie
Glaucous Gull	Iceland Scorie
Great Skua	Bonxie
Arctic Skua	Scootie Aalin
Razorbill	Sea Craa
Guillemot	Loom (Longi: Bressay)
Black Guillemot	Tystie
Puffin	Tammie Norie (Bressay)

286

PLACE NAMES OF SHETLAND

NOSS

Noss	The Nose or Rocky Point
The Noup	The Overhanging Cliff
Geo of the Cuddacks	The Geo of the Cow-dykes
Scarfi Taing	The Cormorant's Point.
Geordie's Holes	Geordie = Gord = Garor (a fence or farm: hence a farmer's name).
Taing of Flitsand (*Tangi Flit*)	The Tongue or Point of the Strip of Sand.
Gungstie (*Gunnar-* or *Gunnhildar-Stadir*)	Gunnar's or Gunnhildar's dwelling or farm.
Cols Ness (*Kolls*)	The Round-topped Ness.
Nesti Voe (*Nes-te*)	The Voe of the Ness with the Rocky Toe.
Turr Ness (*Turs*)	The Ness of the Cairn.
Whilloquey	The Creek of the Cattle-fold.
Faedri Geo (*Fede-ris*)	The Geo of the Little Hill of Pasture.
The Voe of the Mels	The Voe of the Sandy Lands.
Mansie's Berg	Magnus's Rocky Headland.
Papilgeo (*Papilsgjo*)	The Irish Priest's Geo.
North Croo (*Kru*)	North Sheep-fold.
Clingri Geo (*Klingregjo*)	The Geo with the Round Hole.
Fugla Skerry	The Bird's Skerry.
Pundsgeo	The Geo of the Fold.
Scarfi Skerry (*Skarf-I*)	The Skerry of the Cormorants.
The Cletters (*De Kletters*)	The Low Rocky Shore.
Whiggie Geo (*Viga*)	The Geo of the Stream.
Heogatoug (*Hjogatug*)	The High Headland.
Hellia Cluve (*Helja-Klov*)	The Flat Rock with the Narrow Cleft.
Tarristie	The Beach of the Tang.
Setter (*Seter*)	The Homestead or Summer Pasture.
Hovie (*Hov*)	The Point of the Arable Land.
Feadda Ness (*Fede*)	The Ness of the Pasture.
Rumble Wick (*Onghul*)	The Bay of the Fish-Hook (poss: the Stony Bay: *Ronawul Wik*).
The Face of Keen	The Steep Face of Cliff.
Owsen's Pund	The Oxen Fold.
Peerie Pund	The Little Fold.
Selkie Hole	The Seal's Hole.
Mukkle Baa	The Big Sunken Rock.

Hooker's Stane	The Fisherman's Rock.
Buskie Baa	The Lumpy Sunken Rock.
Mail Gate	The Sandy Road.
Sneck o' Mukkle Dandy (Sandy?) Lea	The Cleft in the Big Sandy(?) Slope.

BRESSAY

Bressay (*Brus(a)-øy*)	The Isle of Brusi.
Roonack (*Ronek*)	The Geo of the Narrow Channel.
Ander Hill	The Penthouse Hill (Andrew's Hill?).
Rules Ness	The Foals' Ness.
Loder Head	The Head of the Storm Noise.
Burgi Geo	The Geo of the Broch.
Houllmastouri (*Holm-Stori*)	The Steep Holm(?).
Ullins Water (*Ulens*)	Olinn's Water.
Virdick (*Virdek*)	The Hill of the Beacon-Cairn.
Ward Hill (*Wart*)	The Hill of the Beacon-Cairn.
Hamar	The Projecting Rock.
Longa Skerry	The Long Skerry (poss: The Guillemot's Skerry).
Sildries	The Hill of the Herring(?).
Grimsetter	Grimr's Homestead.
Muckle Hell (*Mukkle Hella*)	The Great Rock.
Seligeo (*Selgjo*)	The Geo of the Seal.
Sand Vatn	The Sandy Water.
Bard Head	The Overhanging Cliff.
The Mills of the Ord (*Uro*)	The Mills of the Fallen Talus.
Kirkabister (*Kirkjubol-stadir*)	The Church-, Farm-, or Dwelling-Place.
Ham	The Haven or Township.
Cullingsburgh (*Culbinsbrough* = Kolbeinsborg)	Irish Priestly Centre.
Hoversta (*Hafr-Stadir*)	Hafr (the He-Goat's) Homestead.
Gorie (*Garor*)	A Farm or Enclosure.
Cruester Hill (*Krukster*)	Krokr's Hill *or* The Setter by the Sheepfold.
Heogan (*Hjogen*)	The Burial Place.
Beosetter (*Bjoster*)	The Cattle Pasture.
Gunnista	*See* Gungstie.
Baa Berg	The Sunken Rock of the Breakers (cf. Skerry = a dry rock.).
Score Head (*Skor*)	The Cleft Head.
Moornaquien (*Murnahwen*)	The Bog of the Mill-Stream.
Wadbister (*Vatnbolstadir*)	The Farm of the Loch.

Appendix C

STATISTICAL DETAILS OF THE NOSS COLONY OF GREAT SKUAS

Number of Breeding Pairs[1]	113.
Number of Non-breeding Individuals	50 plus.
Average distance between Territorial Mounds	58 yards (Min.: 15 yards; Max.: 130 yards).
Number of Eggs	219–223 (99 clutches of 2, including 2 double clutches; 4 clutches of 1 or 2; 10 clutches of 1; 1 clutch of 3; 1 clutch of 4).
Average Distance of Nest from Mound	18 yards (Min.: on Mound; Max.: 44 yards).
Colour Percentages of Eggs	70 per cent brown or olive or olive-brown; 25 per cent stone or cream ground; 5 per cent grey or green.[2]
Laying Interval	48 hours (28 observations).
Peak Laying Date	May 22nd—23rd (Extremes: April 30th—June 20th[3]=99 observations: 29 known, 70 deduced).
Peak Mobbing Date	May 24th—27th (April 28th—June 9th; some to June 20th).
Number of Nestlings	155 (56 pairs and 43 singles).
Average Period from Fracturing to Chipping	34 hours (Min.: 19 hours; Max.: 73 hours = 22 observations).
Average Period from Chipping to Hatching	21 hours (Min.: 10 hours; Max.: 67 hours = 44 observations).
Average Period from Fracturing to Hatching	52 hours (Min.: 36 hours; Max.: 85 hours = 23 observations).
Average Incubatory Period	29·6 days (Min.: 28 days; Max.: 32 days = 37 observations).

[1] Including a clutch of 4 eggs as 1 pair. There may possibly in addition have been one or two pairs that lost their clutches before I pegged out their territories, and abandoned these without laying again.

[2] In detail (with numbers of like-coloured clutches in brackets): brown 9 (1), golden-brown 47 (15), yellow-brown 7 (2), cream-brown 4 (0), stone-brown 18 (2), maroon 5 (0), stone 10 (0), golden-stone 5 (1), cream-stone 9 (1), cream 4 (0), olive-cream 4 (1), golden-olive-brown 7 (2), golden-olive 5 (0), olive-brown 20 (4), olive 30 (7), olive-stone 8 (2), green-stone 2 (0), grey-stone 8 (0), grey-green 1 (0), olive-green 2 (1).

[3] One clutch June 27th—29th; one found July 26th.

Peak Hatching Date	June 19th—27th (Extremes: May 28th—July 15th=149 observations).
Number of Fledgelings	114 (34 pairs and 50 singles).
Fledging Period	46·1 days (Min.: 42 days; Max.: 56 days=77 observations).
Fledging Dates	July 13th—August 20th.
Number of Fledgelings leaving Island	Less than 111.
Leaving Dates	Mid-August—late-September.
Period between Fledging and Leaving	circa. 24 days (approx. Min.: 18 days; Max.: 39 days).

APPENDIX D

BREEDING STATISTICS OF ELEVEN COLONIES OF GREAT SKUAS

Map Number of Colony	Number of Pairs	Average Distance in yards between Territorial Mounds	Average Distance in yards of Nest from Mound	Average Date of Laying	Number of Eggs per Pair	Period of Days within which whole Colony laid	Percentage Hatching	Percentage Fledging	Number of Young reared per Pair
I.	36[8]	52	13	May 17 (April 30–June 11)	1·9	43	79	54	1·03
A	13	52	11	May 15 (April 30–May 26)[3]	1·9	27	92	48	1·12
B	8	61	12	May 23 (May 13–June 3)	1·9	22	67	67	1·25
C	6	53	17	May 28 (May 14–June 11)	1·7	29	90	60	1·17
D	6	37	14	May 16 (May 5–24)	2·3[2]	20	57	36	0·83
II.	8	46	21	May 27 (May 13–June 15)	1·7	34	71	64	1·12
III.	11	54	16	May 15 (May 2–31)	2·3[1]	30	44	44	1·00
IV.	3	70	30	May 18 (May 8–31)	2·3[1]	24	57	57	1·33
V.	7	55	17	June 4 (May 20–June 20)	1·7	32	58	33	0·57
VI.	4	87	17	May 22 (May 17–25)	2·0	9	100	87	1·75
VII.	5	83	15	May 19 (May 13–25)	2·0	13	60	40	0·80
VIII.	6	93	18[7]	May 24 (May 13–June 1)	1·8	20	73	36	0·67
IX.	11	56	14	May 19 (May 6–30)	1·9	25	86	57	1·09
X.	7	49	8	May 21 (May 11–June 1)[5]	1·7	22	83	83	1·43
XI.	11	81	16	May 23 (May 16–June 3)	2·0[6]	19	68	45	0·91
XII[4].	7	169	16	May 28 (May 17–June 15)	1·9	30	54	38	0·71
Norm.		58	18	May 22–23 (April 30–June 20)	1·9	22	70	51	0·98

[1] Including second clutch.
[2] Including one clutch of 4 eggs.
[3] Excluding one clutch June 27th.
[4] Seven Isolated pairs (including 3 in Colonies).
[5] Excluding a clutch in July.
[6] Including one clutch of 3 eggs.
[7] No proper *made* mounds.
[8] Including three outlying pairs not included in sub-colonies A—D.

STATISTICAL DETAILS OF THE NOSS COLONY OF ARCTIC SKUAS

Number of Breeding Pairs	31.
Number of Non-breeding Pairs	6½.[1]
Total Number of Individuals	75.
Percentages of Colour-Phases	Dusky or Brown 69·3 per cent; (Yellow- necked Brown phase 10·7 per cent). White 30·7 per cent
Percentages of Colour-Phases by Pairs	White x White 18·9 per cent; Dark x Dark 56·9 per cent; Dark x White 24·3 per cent.

Percentages of Colour-Phases by Sexes

	Male per cent	Female per cent
Dusky	69	31
Brown	47	53
Yellow-Neck	25	75
White	43	57

Date of Return to Territories	April 28th—c. May 20th: Breeding Pairs; May 24th—June 24th: Non-Breeding Pairs.
Average Distance between Territorial Mounds	77 yards (Min.: 30 yards; Max.: 110 yards).
Number of Eggs	57—61 (25 clutches of 2, including 1 double clutch; 3 clutches of 1; 4 clutches of 1—2).
Average Distance of Nest from Mound[2]	11 yards (Min.: on Mound; Max.: 25 yards).
Colour Percentages of Eggs	65 per cent olive; 35 per cent olive-brown, olive-yellow, stone-green, shades of brown.[3]
Laying Interval	24—48 hours (2 pairs 72 hours).
Peak Laying Date	May 28th—June 2nd (Extremes: May 20th—June 12th[4])=28 observations: 7 known, 21 deduced.

[1] One un-mated bird.

[2] Or most frequently observed standing-place.

[3] In Detail (with numbers of like-coloured clutches in brackets): cream-brown 1 (0), golden-brown 2 (0), brown 1 (0), olive-brown 5 (2), olive 33 (14), olive-green 2 (1), stone-green 1 (0), stone 1 (0), olive-stone 4 (1), olive-yellow 3 (0).

[4] Second Clutch June 19th—20th.

Number of Nestlings	46—48 (18 pairs; 10 singles).
Average Period from Fracturing to Chipping	44 hours (Min.: 17 hours; Max.: 72 hours[5] = 22 observations).
Average Period from Chipping to Hatching	28 hours (Min.: 7 hours; Max.: 68 hours = 26 observations).
Average Period from Fracturing to Hatching	65 hours (Min.: 19 hours; Max.: 120 hours[6] = 30 observations).
Average Incubatory Period	25—26 days (16 observations).
Peak Hatching Date	June 21st—July 1st (Extremes: June 15-16th—July 6-7th[7] = 37 observations).
Number of Fledgelings	29 (6 pairs; 17 singles).
Fledging Period	29—30 days (Min.: 27 days, Max.: 33 days = 22 observations).
Fledging Dates	July 21st—30th (Extremes: July 15th August 7th).
Number of Fledgelings leaving Island	24—28.
Period between Fledging and leaving Island	c. 28 days (Extremes: c. 21—33 days).
Leaving Dates	August 17th—September 2-4th.

[5] One record 145 hours.
[6] One record 171 hours.
[7] Second brood July 14th.

Appendix F

BREEDING STATISTICS OF THREE COLONIES OF ARCTIC SKUAS

Map Number of Colony	Number of Pairs	Percentage of Pairs Breeding	Average distance in yards between Territorial Mounds	Colour-Phase percentage					Average Date of Laying	Number of Eggs per Breeding Pair	Percentage Hatching	Percentage Fledging	Percentage of White Fledgelings	Number of Young Fledged per Breeding Pair
				Sooty	Brown	Yellow-Neck	White	White x White Pairs						
I.	10	70	60	20	50	10	20	0	May 31	2·3[4]	81	56	11	1·0
II.	14	93	70	18	43	7	32	21	June 6	1·9	84	56	21	1·0
III.	6	100	107	25	8	25	42	17	May 27	1·7	80	40	0	0·7
IV.[1]	7½	62	342[2]	20	27	7	46	37	May 30[3]	1·6	25	25	0	0·4
Norm.		82·4	77	58·6		10·7	30·7	18·9	May 30	1·9	79·6	49·1	13·7	0·9

[1] 7½ Isolated Pairs.
[2] Nearest Bonxie 162 yards (Min. and Max. distances of nearest Bonxie mound 70—360 yards).
[3] Three Pairs only.   [4] One double clutch.

294

APPENDIX G

STATISTICAL DETAILS OF A NOSS GANNETRY

Date	Hour	No. of Occupied Nests counted	Percentage of Nests on which both Birds of Pair present at one time	No. of Gannets alighting in Gannetry in 5-minute period	Percentage of Nests on which Gannets alight in 5-minute period	No. of Gannets departing from Gannetry in 5-minute period	Percentage of Nests from which Gannets depart in 5-minute period	No. of Nestlings counted	No. of Nests from which Fledged Young have departed	Weather
April:										
28	19.40	113	11·5	?	?	?	?			Light NE. breeze, sunny.
29	10.00	105	4·7	?	?	?	?			Calm, some swell, sunny.
May:										
6	11.45	114	19·0	?	?	?	?			Mist early.
7	12.40	90	11·2	?	?	?	?			Fair, distant haze.
10	15.45	133	7·5	14	10·5	9	6·8			Stiff updraught, clear visibility.
13	13.00	116	11·9	15	12·9	16	13·8			Fresh NE., sun and squalls.
16	15.15	126	28·5	13	10·3	8	6·3			Very stiff updraught, bright.
22	14.15	103	14·3	16	15·5	8	7·7			Mist on Noup, big swell.
24	21.45	114	12·2	0	0·0	0	0·0			Calm and fine.
26	23.05	75	6·0	0	0·0	0	0·0	1?		Dusk, fog at sea.

STATISTICAL DETAILS OF A NOSS GANNETRY—*cont.*

Date	Hour	No. of Occupied Nests counted	Percentage of Nests on which both Birds of Pair present at one time	No. of Gannets alighting in Gannetry in 5-minute period	Percentage of Nests on which Gannets alight in 5-minute period	No. of Gannets departing from Gannetry in 5-minute period	Percentage of Nests from which Gannets depart in 5-minute period	No. of Nestlings counted	No. of Nests from which Fledged Young have departed	Weather
May										
28	13.45	168	18·1	9	5·3	4	2·4	4?		Thick mist filling Wick.
30	11.28	154	21·4	4	2·6	5	3·2	12?		Thick mist filling Wick.
31	15.05	135	?·?	21	15·5	11	8·2			Mist at sea.
						Hatch Begins				
June:										
3	13.50	157	22·7	19	12·1	16	10·2			Light breeze, sunny.
9	16.57	135	22·3	20	14·7	13	9·6			Calm, sun and cloud.
13	4.05	180	22·3	16	8·8	4	2·2	25+		Sun just up: shining on Gannetry,
14	7.42	165	18·2	14	9·0	13	8·4	29+		On-cliff breeze.
20	16.00	130	20·4	?	?	?	?	65+		Fair, after 48 hours' rain.
24	11.23	155	10·9	5	3·2	1	0·6			{Fresh breeze, fog at sea.
24	21.30	160	26·0	6	3·7	8	5·0	79+		{Dead calm.
25	16.38	157	21·6	16	10·1	10	6·3			Sun already off cliffs.
						Peak of Hatch				
July:										
1	14.36	174	38·2	25	14·4	20	11·5	120+		Moderate W. gale.
2	9.05	185	37·8	15	8·1	8	4·3			Fresh breeze, considerable swell, some haze.

Date	Time									Weather
4	24.00	86	37.2	0	0.0	0	0.0			Calm and fine.
6	18.42	139	31.7	16	11.5	7	5.0			NE. breeze, occasional sun.
10	12.17	144	37.1	18	12.5	15	10.4			Dull, W. breeze.
12	13.09	151	26.6	19	12.6	15	9.9			Fine and warm.
17	15.40	170	21.2	26	15.3	20	11.7	117+		Updraught, mist on Noup.
21	15.15	178	15.5	25	14.0	15	8.4	116+		Calm, sunny, some swell.
26	12.00	?	34.2[1]	21	?	20	?	132		Light breeze, sunny.
31	13.13	177	35.4	16	9.0	13	7.3	137		Fresh N. breeze.
August:										
4 {	12.04	?	16.3[1]	19	?	9	?	130		Calm and sunny.
{	19.19	183	4.3	18	9.8	11	6.0			Fresh breeze, dull.
7	11.20	182	38.9	12	6.6	11	6.0	128		Light breeze, sun.
8	5.15	186	8.9	41	22.0	34	18.3			Calm.
12	11.46	179	21.2	29	16.1	24	13.4	142		Fine, light breeze.
Fledging Begins										
17	11.23	?	42.9[1]	23	?	30	?	130	5+	Sunny.
18	3.37	156	9.5	8	4.5	18	10.2	112	20+	Daylight, calm.
21	11.12	180	36.5	35	19.4	24	13.3	116	27	Summery.
25	13.05	180	23.2	25	13.9	26	14.0	99	44	Mist off Noup.
Peak of Fledging										
September										
1	15.10	202	14.8	23	11.3	16	7.9	58	86	E. breeze, intermittent fog on Noup.
7	10.30	204	18.0	?	?	?	?	32	111	Summery, fog-swell.
9	10.10	180	19.5	13	7.2	8	4.4	29	114	Dull and sun.
15	11.15	222	19.6	16	7.2	17	7.6	24	119	Strong W. wind and rain-squalls.

[1] Based on independent counts of numbers of pairs and single birds present.

Monthly Average,	No. of Occupied Nests counted	Percentage of Nests on which both Birds of Pair present at one time	No. of Gannets alighting in Gannetry in 5-minute period	Percentage of Nests on which Gannets alight in 5-minute period	No. of Gannets departing from Gannetry in 5-minute period	Percentage of Nests from which Gannets depart in 5-minute period
Apl. 28–May 26	104	12·6	10	12·3[1]	7	8·6[1]
May 28–June 25	154	20·5	13	8·5[1]	8½	5·6[1]
July 1–Aug. 12	164	26·9	20	12·6[1]	14	9·4[1]
Aug. 17–Aug. 25	172	28·5	20	10·6[1]	20	9·5[1]
Sept. 1–Sept. 15	202	17·9				
Apl. 28–Sept 15	159	21·3	17	10·9[1]	13	8·3[1]

[1] During hours of Activity only.

298

INDEX

299